American Book Company

THE STANDARDS EXPERTS

Physical Science
Georgia EOCT

M000267572

Dear Student,

Welcome to American Book Company! This book has been made just for you! Every book will give you the practice and skills review you need for 100 percent of the standards on your test. Our writers covered each standard as clearly and simply as possible, so the book is easy to understand.

Start by taking the diagnostic test. When you finish, turn in the book with your answers marked and follow your teacher's instructions. Once your test is graded, you will have your own personalized path of learning to prepare you for the test.

You can use the book in two different ways at this point. You can work through all of the material in the book to master all of the tested standards. Or, if you do not have much time, you can only work on the parts where you made the most mistakes. Two additional full length tests are available within the book for skills mastery.

We look forward to hearing of your success when you see your test results!

Sincerely,

Frank J Pintozzi

Dr. Frank Pintozzi
Executive Vice President
American Book Company
www.americanbookcompany.com
888-264-5877

American Book Company
The Standards Experts

PASSING THE
Georgia EOC Test
in

Physical Science
Adheres to Georgia GPS Standards

Liz Thompson

American Book Company
PO Box 2638
Woodstock, GA 30188-1383
Toll Free: 1 (888) 264-5877 Phone: (770) 928-2834
Fax: (770) 928-7483 Toll Free Fax 1 (866) 827-3240
Web site: www.americanbookcompany.com

ACKNOWLEDGEMENTS

The authors would like to gratefully acknowledge the formatting and technical contributions of Becky Wright.

We also want to thank Mary Stoddard for her expertise in developing the graphics for this book.

A special thanks to Marsha Torrens for her editing assistance.

This product/publication includes images from CorelDRAW 9 and 11 which are protected by the copyright laws of the United States, Canada, and elsewhere. Used under license.

TABLE OF CONTENTS

Preface

Passing the Georgia End of Course Exam in Physical Science will help students who are learning or reviewing material for the Georgia test that is now required for each gateway or benchmark course. **The materials in this book are based on the Georgia Performance Standards as published by the Georgia Department of Education.**

This book contains several sections. These sections are as follows: 1) General information about the book; 2) A Diagnostic Test and Evaluation Chart; 3) Chapters that teach the concepts and skills that improve readiness for the end of course exam in Physical Science; 4) Two Practice/Post Tests. Answers to the tests and exercises are in a separate manual. The answer manual also contains a Chart of Standards for teachers to make a more precise diagnosis of student needs and assignments.

We welcome comments and suggestions about the book. Please contact us a

American Book Company
PO Box 2638
Woodstock, GA 30188-1383

Toll Free: 1 (888) 264-5877
Phone: (770) 928-2834
Fax: (770) 928-7483
Web site: www.americanbookcompany.com

About the Author

Liz A. Thompson holds a B.S. in Chemistry and an M.S. in Analytical Chemistry, both from the Georgia Institute of Technology. Research conducted as both an undergraduate and graduate student focused on the creation and fabrication of sensors based on conducting polymers and biomolecules. Post graduate experience includes work in radioanalytical chemistry. Her publications include several articles in respected scientific journals, as well as partial authorship of the textbook *Radioanalytical Chemistry* (2007). At every educational level, Mrs. Thompson has enjoyed teaching, tutoring and mentoring students in the study of science.

PREPARING FOR THE GEORGIA EOCT TESTS

Introduction

If you are a student in a Georgia school district, the End of Course Test (EOCT) program requires you to take a test at the end of each content area course. Physical Science is one of these content areas. The EOCT will count for 15% of the student's grade in this course.

This book will help students prepare for the Georgia Physical Science EOCT. The following section will provide general information about the physical science test.

How long do I have to take the exam?

The test is given in two 45 – 60 minute sessions.

What materials will I be allowed to use during the exam?

You may not use a calculator for the physical science test. You will be provided with an equation reference sheet and a periodic table of the elements.

How is the exam organized?

There are 40 multiple choice questions in each section of the test, for a total of 80 questions.

The questions for the test will be linked to the Georgia Performance Standards (GPS) for Physical Science released by the Department of Education. The GPS are divided into two broad categories; these are Characteristics of Science (SCSh) and the Physical Science Content (SPS) Standards. The nine SCSh standards address the learning, reasoning and application skills necessary to study science. The ten SPS standards constitute the factual basis of physical science.

Each question on the Diagnostic Test, Practice Test 1 and Practice Test 2 in this book is correlated to one of these standards; the specific standard is noted to the right of each question on each of the three tests.

Diagnostic Test

Directions:

Today you will be taking the Physical Science End of Course Test. There are 80 questions, divided into two sections. Read each question carefully and then choose the *best* answer.

Be sure that the question number on the answer sheet matches the number on the test. Then mark your answer by filling in the circle on your answer sheet. Do not write your answer in the test booklet. If you do not know the answer to a question, skip it and go on. You may return to it later if time permits.

If you need to change an answer on your answer sheet, be sure to erase your first mark completely. Do not make any stray marks on the answer sheet.

Georgia Physical Science Reference Sheet

Motion and Force

$v = \dfrac{d}{t}$ v = speed or velocity $\left(\frac{m}{s}\right)$ d = distance (meter, m) t = time (second, s)

$a = \dfrac{\Delta v}{\Delta t} = \dfrac{v_f - v_i}{t_f - t_i}$ a = acceleration v = velocity t = time f = final i = initial

weight = mg m = mass (kilogram, kg) g = gravitational acceleration $(9.8 \frac{m}{s^2})$

$F = ma$ F = force (newton, N) m = mass (kilogram, kg) a = acceleration $\left(\frac{m}{s^2}\right)$

Electricity

$V = IR$ V = potential (volt, V) I = current (ampere, A) R = resistance (ohm, Ω)

Gas Laws

$P_1V_1 = P_2V_2$ P = pressure (atm) V = volume (liter, L)

$\dfrac{V_1}{T_1} = \dfrac{V_2}{T_2}$ V = volume (liter, L) T = temperature (kelvin, K)

Energy, Work, Power, and Efficiency

$KE = \frac{1}{2}mv^2$ KE = kinetic energy (joule, J) m = mass (kg) v = velocity $\left(\frac{m}{s}\right)$

$PE = mgh$ PE = potential energy (J) m = mass g = gravitational acceleration h = height (m)

$W = Fd$ W = work (joule, J) F = force (newton, N) d = distance (meter, m)

$MA = \dfrac{F_r}{F_e}$ MA = mechanical advantage F_r = resistance force F_e = effort force

$P = \dfrac{W}{t}$ P = power (watt, W) W = work (joule, J) t = time (second, s)

Efficiency = $\dfrac{\text{Work output}}{\text{Work input}} \times 100\%$

Waves

$v = f\lambda$ v = velocity $\left(\frac{m}{s}\right)$ f = frequency (hertz, Hz) λ = wavelength (meter, m)

$f = \dfrac{1}{T}$ f = frequency (hertz, Hz) T = period (second, s)

Go On

THE PERIODIC TABLE OF THE ELEMENTS

Key:

Atomic Number →	36
Symbol →	Kr
Name →	Krypton
Atomic Mass →	83.80

Noble Gases — 18 VIIIA

1 IA	2 IIA	3 IIIB	4 IVB	5 VB	6 VIB	7 VIIB	8 VIIIB	9 VIIIB	10 VIIIB	11 IB	12 IIB	13 IIIA	14 IVA	15 VA	16 VIA	17 VIIA	18 VIIIA
1 H Hydrogen 1.007g																	2 He Helium 4.0026
3 Li Lithium 6.941g	4 Be Beryllium 9.01218											5 B Boron 10.81	6 C Carbon 12.011	7 N Nitrogen 14.0067	8 O Oxygen 15.9994	9 F Fluorine 18.998403	10 Ne Neon 20.179
11 Na Sodium 22.9898	12 Mg Magnesium 24.305											13 Al Aluminum 26.98154	14 Si Silicon 28.0855	15 P Phosphorus 30.97376	16 S Sulfur 32.06	17 Cl Chlorine 35.453	18 Ar Argon 39.948
19 K Potassium 39.0983	20 Ca Calcium 40.08	21 Sc Scandium 44.9559	22 Ti Titanium 47.90	23 V Vanadium 50.9415	24 Cr Chromium 51.996	25 Mn Manganese 54.9381	26 Fe Iron 55.847	27 Co Cobalt 58.9332	28 Ni Nickel 58.69	29 Cu Copper 63.546	30 Zn Zinc 65.38	31 Ga Gallium 69.723	32 Ge Germanium 72.61	33 As Arsenic 74.9216	34 Se Selenium 78.96	35 Br Bromine 79.904	36 Kr Krypton 83.80
37 Rb Rubidium 85.4678	38 Sr Strontium 87.62	39 Y Yttrium 88.9059	40 Zr Zirconium 91.22	41 Nb Niobium 92.9064	42 Mo Molybdenum 95.94	43 Tc Technetium 97.91	44 Ru Ruthenium 101.07	45 Rh Rhodium 102.9055	46 Pd Palladium 106.4	47 Ag Silver 107.868	48 Cd Cadmium 112.41	49 In Indium 114.82	50 Sn Tin 118.71	51 Sb Antimony 121.75	52 Te Tellurium 127.60	53 I Iodine 126.9045	54 Xe Xenon 131.30
55 Cs Cesium 132.9054	56 Ba Barium 137.33	57 La Lanthanum 138.9055	72 Hf Hafnium 178.49	73 Ta Tantalum 180.9479	74 W Tungsten 183.84	75 Re Rhenium 186.2	76 Os Osmium 190.2	77 Ir Iridium 192.22	78 Pt Platinum 195.09	79 Au Gold 196.9665	80 Hg Mercury 200.59	81 Tl Thallium 204.383	82 Pb Lead 207.2	83 Bi Bismuth 208.9808	84 Po Polonium 208.98244	85 At Astatine 209.98704	86 Rn Radon 222.02
87 Fr Francium 223.01976	88 Ra Radium 226.0254	89 Ac Actinium 227.02779	104 Rf Rutherfordium 261.1	105 Db Dubnium 262.11	106 Sg Seaborgium 263.12	107 Bh Bohrium 262.12	108 Hs Hassium 264.13	109 Mt Meitnerium 266.14	110 Ds Darmstadtium 271	111 Rg Roentgenium 272	112	113	114	115	116	117	118

Lanthanide Series:

57 La Lanthanum 138.9055	58 Ce Cerium 140.12	59 Pr Praseodymium 140.9077	60 Nd Neodymium 144.24	61 Pm Promethium 144.91279	62 Sm Samarium 150.4	63 Eu Europium 151.96	64 Gd Gadolinium 157.25	65 Tb Terbium 158.9254	66 Dy Dysprosium 162.50	67 Ho Holmium 164.9304	68 Er Erbium 167.26	69 Tm Thulium 168.9342	70 Yb Ytterbium 173.04	71 Lu Lutetium 174.967

Actinide Series:

89 Ac Actinium 227.02779	90 Th Thorium 232.0381	91 Pa Protactinium 231.0359	92 U Uranium 238.029	93 Np Neptunium 234.0482	94 Pu Plutonium 244.06424	95 Am Americium 243.06139	96 Cm Curium 247.07035	97 Bk Berkelium 247.07030	98 Cf Californium 251.0796	99 Es Einsteinium 252.08	100 Fm Fermium 257.09515	101 Md Mendelevium 258.1	102 No Nobelium 259.100	103 Lr Lawrencium 262.11

STOP

Section I

1 The following diagram shows _{SPS8e, SCSh3a} two sets of hedge clippers. Which statement correctly describes the difference between them?

 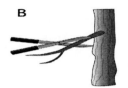

A It will take less effort to chop at the branch with Clipper A than with Clipper B.

B It will take less effort to chop at the branch with Clipper B than with Clipper A.

C Both require the same amount of effort.

D We need more information to decide which clipper requires more effort.

2 Mr. Ray tells his physical science class that Sir Isaac Newton _{SPS9d, SCSh3a, 4c} first discovered that light is refracted by a prism. Newton also discovered that the separated light could be recombined into a beam of white light. Mr. Ray asks the class to divide into four groups and design an experimental set-up to duplicate Newton's results. The groups came up with the following ideas. Which experimental design will prove that light can be separated and recombined into a beam of white light?

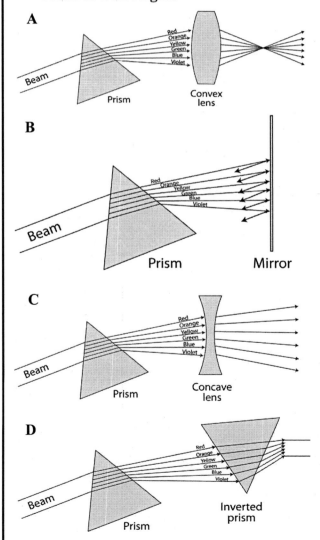

Go On

3 Select the equipment that would be used to measure the mass of sample of sodium chloride. *SCSh2a*

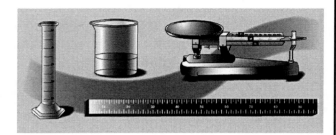

A   beam balance

B   graduated cylinder

C   beaker

D   meter stick

4 Consider the two lab setups shown below. Which of the following answer choices correctly describes the lab setups? *SCSh2a, 2b*

A   There are no lab safety rules to follow when using Bunsen burners and test tubes.

B   The student in lab scene B is correctly following lab safety rules.

C   The students in lab scene A and lab scene B are both correctly following lab safety rules.

D   The student in lab scene A is correctly following lab safety rules.

5 Fig. 1 shows a graduated cylinder that contained 25 ml of water. The mass of the cylinder and water was 68.0 g. Fig. 2 shows the same cylinder after a small stone was lowered into the cylinder. The water level rose to the 30.0 ml mark, and the mass of the cylinder, water and stone increased to 78.0 g. Select the density of the small stone. *SPS2a, SCSh5e*

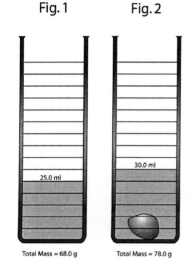

Fig. 1   Fig. 2

30.0 ml

25.0 ml

Total Mass = 68.0 g   Total Mass = 78.0 g

A   2.00 g/ml

B   10.0 g

C   0.50 ml/g

D   5.00 ml

6 Which of the following objects could an electromagnet be used to lift? *SPS10c*

A   garbage bags

B   mail

C   old cars

D   old fiberglass boats

Go On

Answer questions 7 – 8 based on the summary of the following experiment.

Temperature (°C)	Time (minutes)
10	33
20	16
30	8
40	4
50	2

A group of students investigated how temperature affects the rate of chemical reactions. They used hydrogen peroxide, which breaks down into oxygen and water, for their experiment. The students measured how long it took to obtain 50 mL of oxygen gas from a given volume of hydrogen peroxide heated to different temperatures. Their data are shown in the table above.

7 Based on the students' data, select the correct conclusion about the rate of chemical reactions.   SCSh3e

  A Reaction rates increase as time increases.

  B Reaction rates decrease as time decreases.

  C Reaction rates increase as temperature increases.

  D Reaction rates decrease as temperature increases.

8 Select the best way for the students to reduce the experimental error in their investigation.   SCSh5a

  A test more than one variable at a time

  B perform repeated trials

  C change their answers if they do not match their hypothesis.

  D perform the experiment only one time

9 The following figure describes the molecular motion of a sample of matter. Which of the following can you conclude is *not* the identity of the sample?   SPS5a, 5b

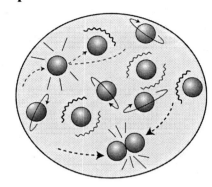

  A hydrogen gas

  B iron ore

  C superheated steam

  D liquid nitrogen

10 Mara has a glass beaker of water with a thermometer in it. The thermometer reads 17° C at time t=0 min. At time t=40 min; the thermometer reads 25°C. Which statement correctly describes this scenario?   SPS7a, b

  A The temperature of the water increased because it transferred thermal energy to the surrounding air.

  B The temperature of the water increased because the surrounding air transferred thermal energy to the water.

  C The temperature of the water increased because the water and air were in equilibrium.

  D The temperature of the water increased because glass is a thermal insulator.

Go On

Use the data table to answer questions 11 and 12.

Measurer	Length (m)	Method
Julie	1.67	Tape measure
Tiffany	1.68	Meter stick
Scott	1.67	Tape measure
Andrew	1.8	Caliper

11 Four friends independently mea- SCSh5b sured the length of a lever's resistance arm. Julie and Scott chose to use a 4-meter long tape measure. They were both able to complete the measurement without moving the tape measure. Tiffany chose a meter stick, which she had to move once to complete the measurement. Andrew chose to use a 3-centimeter caliper, which he had to move 60 times before he completed the measurement. Their measurements are shown in the data table. Which method is the BEST, and why?

A Andrew's method is the best, because the caliper is a very precise measurement tool.

B Julie and Scott's method is best because it produced the most consistent results.

C Tiffany's method is best, because her data closely matched Julie and Scott's data.

D Julie's method is best because she completed the measurement more quickly than Scott.

12 Julie put a bookbag on the resis- SPS8e tance arm of the lever. What would you do to decrease the work input needed to lift the bookbag with the lever?

A Move the fulcrum closer to the bookbag.

B Move the fulcrum farther away from the bookbag.

C Remove books from the bookbag.

D Both A and C will decrease the work input.

13 Chuck Yeager was the first person SPS9f to travel faster than the speed of sound, in 1947. When his X–1 aircraft broke the sound barrier, a sonic boom was heard. An observer on the ground saw Yeager pass overhead after the barrier was broken. When would the observer hear the plane?

A before the plane passes overhead

B as the plane passes overhead

C after the plane passes overhead

D not at all, since the sound barrier has been broken

14 In which of the following media SPS9e will sound waves travel fastest?

A space

B hot, humid air

C red Georgia clay

D loose beach sand

Go On

15 Select the BEST reason for scientists to replace an existing theory with a new theory.　　SCSh7c

A Several senior scientists announced their support of the new theory.

B A group of important religious leaders announced its support of the new theory.

C Several senior politicians announced that the new theory would boost the economy.

D A research team announced that observations were better explained by the new theory.

16 Select the product of radioactive decay that has the greatest ability to penetrate matter.　　SPS3a

A alpha particles

B beta particles

C gamma rays

D neutrons

17 A skier traveling at 30.0 m/s falls and comes to rest 10.0 seconds later. What is her average acceleration?　　SPS8a

A 300 m/s^2

B 3.00 m/s^2

C -3.00 m/s^2

D -300 m/s^2

18 Which of these substances has the highest specific heat?　　SPS7c

A water

B ice

C steam

D lead

19 Which group has eight valence electrons in its elemental form?　　SPS4a

A noble gases

B alkaline earth metals

C halogens

D alkali metals

20 Select the situation that will result in the greatest gravitational force between two bodies.　　SPS8c

A large combined mass and small distance apart

B large combined mass and great distance apart

C small combined mass and great distance apart

D small combined mass and small distance apart

21 The flow of electricity through a light bulb filament can be compared to the flow of water down a waterfall. In such a comparison, select the property of the waterfall that would be analogous to the voltage across the light bulb.　　SPS10b

A water depth

B water temperature

C rate of flow of water

D height of the waterfall

22 A washing machine is plugged into a wall outlet that has a voltage of 240 volts. The total resistance present in the machine's wiring is 12 ohms. What current runs through this circuit?　　SPS10b

A 252 amperes

B 200 amperes

C 20 amperes

D 12 amperes

Go On

23 Select the voltage that will result in a current of 10 amps in a circuit with a resistance of 12 ohms. — SPS10b

- **A** 1.2 volts
- **B** 2 volts
- **C** 22 volts
- **D** 120 volts

24 Select the result of an electrical current flowing through a wire. — SPS10c

- **A** emission of X-rays
- **B** emission of alpha particles
- **C** gravitational force between the wire and a nearby metal ball
- **D** electromagnetic force between the wire and a nearby compass needle

25 Select the scenario in which an airplane does have kinetic energy but does NOT have gravitational potential energy. — SPS7a, 8c

- **A** accelerating down the runway
- **B** waiting in line on the taxiway
- **C** parked at the loading gate
- **D** in flight

26 Select the method of heat transfer that causes the iron handle of an iron skillet to get hot when the skillet is heated on a stove. — SPS7b

- **A** convection
- **B** radiation
- **C** conduction
- **D** friction

27 The diagram at the right shows a ball at the top of a ramp. Select the statement that correctly describes the changes to the ball's kinetic energy (KE) and gravitation potential energy (PE) as it rolls down the ramp. — SPS7a

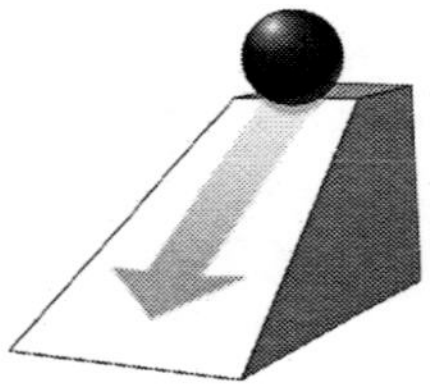

- **A** KE and PE both decrease
- **B** KE and PE both increase
- **C** KE decreases and PE increases
- **D** KE increases and PE decreases

Go On

28 The diagram of a wave indicates SPS9b two important properties of a wave: its wavelength and amplitude. Wavelength is inversely related to frequency: a longer wavelength indicates a lower frequency. Amplitude is proportional to the intensity of the energy that the wave can impart to matter: a greater amplitude indicates a greater intensity. Consider the following situation: Wave A has a wavelength 5λ and an amplitude 2γ, while Wave B has a wavelength 3λ and an amplitude 4γ. Which statement BEST describes these two waves?

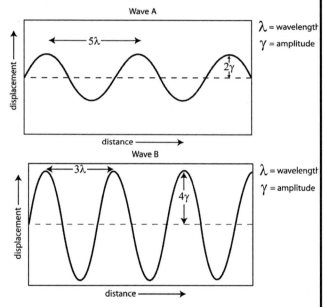

A Wave A has a lower frequency and greater intensity than Wave B.

B Wave A has a higher frequency and greater intensity than Wave B.

C Wave A has a higher frequency and lower intensity than Wave B.

D Wave A has a lower frequency and lower intensity than Wave B.

29 Electromagnetic radiation SPS9b, 9c moves from the Sun to the Earth continuously. The wavelengths emitted include infrared, ultraviolet and visible light. Which of these arrives first if all are emitted from the Sun at the same time?

A infrared

B ultraviolet

C visible

D All will arrive at the same time.

30 How are different isotopes of a SPS1a given element characterized?

A same number of protons and same number of neutrons

B same number of protons but different number of neutrons

C different number of protons but same number of neutrons

D different number of protons and different number of neutrons

Go On

31 Use the diagram below to describe where the MOST reactive metals are located. *SPS4a, 4b*

PERIODIC TABLE OF THE ELEMENTS

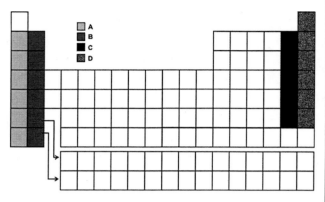

A   light gray section A

B   dark gray section B

C   black section C

D   textured section D

32 Using the diagram below, determine the number of neutrons that MOST copper atoms contain. *SPS1a*

29
Cu
Copper
63.546
2,8,18,1

A   29

B   35

C   64

D   93

33 Magnesium (Mg) looses two electrons to form a magnesium ion. Chlorine (C1) gains one electron to form a chloride ion. Select the correct formula for magnesium chloride. *SPS2b*

A $MgC1$

B Mg_2C1

C $MgC1_2$

D Mg_2C1_2

34 NaCl and H_2O are two compounds that bond differently. One forms an ionic bond, and one forms a covalent bond. Which of the following correctly represents the bonding of the ionic compound? *SPS1b*

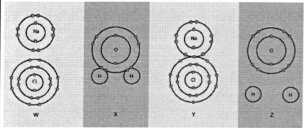

A   diagram W

B   diagram X

C   diagram Y

D   diagram Z

35 How many oxygen atoms are there in one formula unit of aluminum carbonate $[A1_2(CO_3)_3]$? *SPS1a*

A   1   C   6

B   3   D   9

10

Go On

36 Select the reason why water mole-   SPS4a
cules are polar molecules.

- **A** Hydrogen atoms are much smaller than oxygen atoms.

- **B** Water molecules have a bond angle greater than 100 degrees.

- **C** Water molecules form hydrogen bonds with other water molecules.

- **D** Oxygen nuclei attract electrons more strongly than hydrogen nuclei attract electrons.

37 Select the properties of a solu-   SPS6a, 6c
tion of salt in water that will
allow additional salt to dissolve
quickest.

- **A** high temperature and high salt concentration

- **B** high temperature and low salt concentration

- **C** low temperature and low salt concentration

- **D** low temperature and high salt concentration

38 Which of the following describes   SPS5b
the phases of matter that can be
compressed?

- **A** gas and liquid

- **B** plasma and liquid

- **C** plasma and gas

- **D** liquid, plasma and gas

39 Salt is an ionic compound, meth-   SPS6b
anol is a polar covalent com-
pound and octane — the major
component of gasoline — is a non-polar,
covalent compound. Which substance or
substances are soluble in water?

- **A** salt only

- **B** octane only

- **C** salt and methanol

- **D** octane and methanol

40 Select the balanced chemical   SPS2e
equation.

- **A** $Zn + HCl \rightarrow ZnCl_2 + H_2$

- **B** $C_2H_4 + 2O_2 \rightarrow 2CO_2 + 2H_2O$

- **C** $2Na + 2H_2O \rightarrow 2NaOH + H_2$

- **D** $2CaO + 2HCl \rightarrow CaCl_2 + H_2O$

Section II

41 As illustrated in the diagram below, Carl investigated the change of mass during a chemical reaction. He massed a balloon, two seltzer tablets and a plastic bottle that contained 50 mL of water. He recorded a total mass of 200g. Carl put the seltzer tablets inside the balloon and pulled the balloon over the neck of the bottle. He shook the balloon so the seltzer tablets fell into the water. Carl observed the tablets fizzing and the balloon expanding. Carl again massed his apparatus after the fizzing and the expansion of the balloon stopped. SPS2d

If the combined mass of the two seltzer tablets before they were dropped into the water was 5 g, select the mass of Carl's apparatus at the end of his investigation.

A 195 g

B between 195 g and 200 g

C 200 g

D more than 200 g

42 Select the type of ion produced when a strong acid is added to water. SPS4a, 6d

A hydrated

B hydride

C hydroxide

D hydronium

43 Select the particle or particles that account for more than 99.99% of the mass of atoms other than hydrogen. SPS1a

A protons only

B electrons only

C protons and neutrons

D electrons and neutrons

12

Go On

44 The diagram below shows an SPS10b
electrical circuit made up of a cell
and three loads. The voltage established
by the cell and the resistance of each
load is marked on the diagram. Select
the current flowing through the 3-ohm
load.

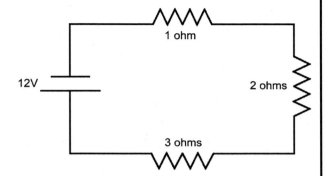

A 4 amps

B 2 amps

C 5 amps

D 0.25 amps

The chemical equation for the rusting of iron
is: $4Fe + 3O_2 \rightarrow 2Fe_2O_3$

45 Select the number of electrons SPS2e
gained or lost by every iron (O)
atom that is converted to iron (III) oxide
in that reaction.

A gain 3

B gain 2

C lose 2

D lose 3

46 Select the change that will SPS6b
DECREASE the rate at which a
solid solute dissolves in liquid solvent.

A cooling the solvent

B shaking the solvent

C adding a catalyst to the solvent

D increasing the pressure over the
solvent

47 The atomic number of beryl- SPS4a, 4b
lium is 4. Select the number of
electrons a beryllium atom will gain or
lose when it forms a beryllium ion.

A gain 2

B gain 4

C lose 2

D lose 4

48 X-rays and microwaves trav- SPS9b, 9c
eling in space have the same

A wavelength.

B frequency.

C speed.

D energy.

49 The attractive force between pro- SPS8b
tons and electrons within an atom
is called the

A gravitational force.

B nuclear force.

C frictional force.

D electric force.

50 As water changes phase from a SPS5b
liquid to a gas, what is expected
to happen?

A The distance between particles will
increase.

B The distance between particles will
decrease.

C The mass of the sample will increase.

D The mass of the sample will decrease.

Go On

51 Which of the following is NOT a strong acid? SPS6e

   A   hydrochloric acid

   B   sulfuric acid

   C   acetic acid

   D   nitric acid

52 Select the correct classification of silicon, the material used in the "chips" that power electronic devices such as computers and cell phones. SPS10a

   A   insulator

   B   conductor

   C   semiconductor

   D   superconductor

Use this data table to answer question 53.

	Initial Density (grams/cm^3)	Food Color added (mL)	Final Density (grams/cm^3)	Final Color
Sample A	1.0	1	1.1	orange
Sample B	1.0	5	1.2	orange
Sample C	1.0	7	1.2	blue

53 Reese's teacher gave her three test tubes, each containing an unknown liquid sample of a given density. Reese added orange food coloring to each test tube and then calculated the density of the sample. She placed the data she collected in the data table. She concluded that the added food color increased the density of the sample. What is another reasonable interpretation of this data? SPS2a, 2d SCSh1b

   A   Sample A is a different substance than Sample B.

   B   Sample C is a different substance than Samples A or B.

   C   All three samples contain water.

   D   None of the samples contains water.

Go On

54 Laboratory instructions indicate that 3 grams of salt should be added to 20 mL of water. The mixture should be heated to boiling and boiled until the volume is reduced by 10 mL. The beaker should then be slowly cooled. Which of the following BEST describes the effects of this activity on the salt solution? *SPS6a, 6b, 6c SCSh2b,*

A The salt will evaporate, causing the concentration of salt in the water to decrease.

B The water will evaporate, causing concentration of salt in the water to increase.

C The salt will evaporate, causing the concentration of salt in the water to increase.

D The water will evaporate, causing concentration of salt in the water to decrease.

55 The distance-time graph below describes the rate of a person skiing down a mountain. Select the skier's average speed. *SPS8a SCSh3d*

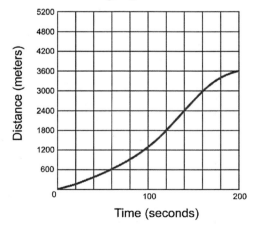

A 3,600 m/s

B 180 m/s

C 18 m/s

D 0.067 m/s

56 Describe the conversion of energy in the following process: Nuclear power reactors utilize the process of uranium fission to produce heat. *SPS3d, 7a*

A nuclear to electrical

B nuclear to thermal to electrical

C nuclear to mechanical to thermal to electrical

D nuclear to thermal to mechanical to electrical

57 What process does the following description refer to: "a wet sidewalk begins to steam in the sun after a spring shower." *SPS5b, 7d*

A melting   C evaporation

B sublimation   D fumigation

58 Marla has three balls. Ball A has a mass of 19 grams. Ball B has a mass of 1 kilogram. Ball C has a mass of 300 grams. In the absence of air resistance, which ball will fall the fastest? *SPS8a, 8c*

A Ball A

B Ball B

C Ball C

D They will all fall at the same rate.

59 Which of the following elements has the smallest total number of electrons? *SPS4a*

A nitrogen (N)   C helium (He)

B sodium (Na)   D lead (Pb)

Go On

60 An example of using a lever is   SPS8e

  A   using a big spoon to stir a pot of soup.

  B   using a fork to scramble an egg.

  C   using a ramp to push a barrel into a pickup truck.

  D   using a screwdriver to pry the lid off a can of paint.

61 At standard temperature and pressure, a 5-gram sample of powdered iron will react more quickly with dilute hydrochloric acid than a 5-gram sheet of hammered iron. Why is this?   SPS6b

  A Because the iron sheet is denser than the iron powder.

  B Because the iron powder has more surface area exposed to the acid than the iron sheet.

  C Because the iron sheet has more surface area exposed to the acid than the iron powder.

  D Because the iron sheet is less dense than the iron powder.

Consider the following reaction:

$$N_2 \text{ (g)} + 3H_2 \text{ (g)} \rightarrow 2NH_3 \text{ (g)}$$

62 Which of the following statements correctly describes the reaction?   SPS1a, 2b

  A   Two mols of N_2 react with three mols H_2 to form two mols of NH_3.

  B   One mol of N_2 reacts with three mols H_2 to form two mols of NH_3.

  C   One mol of N_2 reacts with six mols H_2 to form six mols of NH_3.

  D   Two mols of N_2 react with two mols H_2 to form eight mols of NH_3.

63 Seawater contains sodium chloride and other dissolved salts. Identify the term that correctly describes those dissolved salts.   SPS6a

  A   mixtures

  B   elements

  C   solvents

  D   solutes

64 A solution is made by dissolving 10 grams of salt in 500 mL of water. Identify the volume of the resulting solution.   SPS2a

  A   500 ml

  B   more than 500 mL but less than 510 mL

  C   510 mL

  D   more than 510 mL

65 Kyle charged a glass rod by rubbing it with a piece of cloth. Identify the statement that correctly describes how the rod became negatively charged.   SPS10a

  A   Friction stripped electrons from the rod.

  B   Protons were transferred from the rod to the cloth.

  C   Friction produced heat that in turn produced the charge.

  D   Electrons were stripped from the cloth and transferred to the rod.

Go On

66 Corundrum is a hard mineral of aluminum oxide, Al_2O_3. SCSh3e, 9a

The pure oxide is colorless, but impurities in the crystal structure of the mineral can impart different colors to it. The blue sapphire is an example of gem-quality corundrum. The red ruby is also an example of gem-quality corundrum. Which of the following statements is true about the color of sapphires and rubies?

A   Sapphires and rubies are made of different minerals.

B   Sapphires and rubies are made of the same mineral with different impurities.

C   Sapphires and rubies are made of different minerals with the same impurity.

D   Sapphires and rubies are actually colorless, but jewelers dye them.

67 What is the fastest way to separate 10 grams of sand from 50 mL of salt water? SPS6c

A   Use electrolysis to break down the water into hydrogen and oxygen.

B   Evaporate the salt water off of the sand by heating the whole sample.

C   Pour off most of the water and let the rest of the sample sit in the fume hood to dry.

D   Pour off most of the water and then filter the remaining mixture using filter paper.

68 What number should precede O_2 in the chemical equation below in order for the equation to be balanced? SPS2e

$$H_2O_2(l) \longrightarrow H_2O\,(l) + \underline{}\, O_2(g)$$

A   1/2

B   2

C   3

D   4

69 Which of the following is the BEST heat conductor? SPS7b

A   copper

B   wood

C   glass

D   silicon

70 Identify the type of current that powers a lamp plugged into an electrical outlet in a typical American home. SPS10a

A   static current

B   direct current

C   potential current

D   alternating current

Go On

71 ROYGBIV describes visible light portion of the electromagnetic spectrum, with Red light (R) at one end and Violet light (V) at the other. Which of the following statements is true? SPS9b

A Violet light has a higher frequency and shorter wavelength than red light.

B Violet light has a lower frequency and shorter wavelength than red light.

C Violet light has a higher frequency and longer wavelength than red light.

D Violet light has a lower frequency and longer wavelength than red light.

72 Identify the graph that correctly shows the effect on the current (I) flowing through a static 5-ohm resistor when the voltage (V) across the resistor is gradually increased. SPS10b

A.

B.
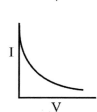

C.
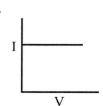

D.
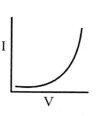

73 Identify the voltage needed to establish a current of 0.25 amps in a circuit with a total resistance of 10 ohms. SPS10b

A 10.25 volts

B 9.75 volts

C 2.5 volts

D 0.025 volts

74 The oil that is added to a car engine lubricates the engine parts. What is the result? SPS8b

A reduction in friction between metal components of the engine.

B increase in friction between metal components of the engine.

C elimination of friction of the engine.

D transformation of frictional force into chemical energy.

75 Lisa needs to move a load of bricks across the yard. The bricks weigh 650 N, which is too heavy for Lisa to carry. She decides to load the bricks into a wheelbarrow to take them across the yard. She can now lift the bricks with only 130 N of effort force. What is the mechanical advantage of the wheelbarrow? SPS8e

A 1/5

B 5

C 0.20

D 6.00

Go On

76 The following diagram depicts heat movement by   SPS7b

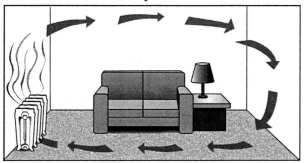

- **A** conduction.
- **B** convection.
- **C** radiation.
- **D** insulation.

77 Fusion describes the process of   SPS3b

- **A** small nuclei joining together to produce heavier nuclei.
- **B** small nuclei joining together to produce lighter nuclei.
- **C** small nuclei joining together to form a macromolecule.
- **D** large nuclei breaking apart to form lighter nuclei.

78 The wavelength of blue light is around 475 nanometers. A blue sky appears blue because it   SPS9d

- **A** absorbs light with a wavelength of 475 nm.
- **B** reflects all visible light except light with a wavelength of 475 nm.
- **C** reflects only visible light with a wavelength of 475 nm.
- **D** reflects only ultraviolet light.

79 The Doppler effect results in the listener hearing   SPS9f

- **A** increased loudness.
- **B** destructive interference.
- **C** increased pitch.
- **D** better sound quality.

80 Litmus paper is used to test for   SPS6d

- **A** metals
- **B** acidity
- **C** salt content
- **D** oxygen levels

EVALUATION CHART

GEORGIA PHYSICAL SCIENCE
DIAGNOSTIC TEST

Directions: On the following chart, circle the question numbers that you answered incorrectly, and evaluate the results. (Note that a question may be listed under more than one chapter when it addresses multiple standards.) Then turn to the appropriate topics (listed by chapters), read the explanations, and complete the exercises. Review other chapters as needed. Finally, complete the Practice Tests to prepare for the Georgia EOCT in Physical Science.

Chapters	Question Numbers
Chapter 1: A Scientific Method	1, 2, 7, 15, 53, 55, 66
Chapter 2: Laboratory Safety	3, 4, 5, 54
Chapter 3: Equipment and Measurement	2, 3, 4, 5, 8, 11
Chapter 4: Structure, Properties and Bonding of Elements	19, 30, 31, 32, 34, 35, 36, 42, 43, 47, 59, 62
Chapter 5: Nuclear Processes	16, 56, 77
Chapter 6: Chemical Equations and Reactions	33, 40, 41, 45, 53, 62, 68
Chapter 7: Matter and Energy	9, 10, 18, 26, 38, 50, 53, 57, 64, 69, 76
Chapter 8: Solutions	37, 39, 42, 46, 51, 54, 61, 63, 67, 80
Chapter 9: Forces and Motion	17, 20, 25, 49, 55, 58, 74
Chapter 10: Energy, Work, and Power	1, 10, 12, 25, 27, 56, 60, 75
Chapter 11: Waves	2, 13, 14, 28, 29, 48, 71, 78, 79
Chapter 12: Electricity and Magnetism	6, 21, 22, 23, 24, 44, 52, 65, 70, 72, 73

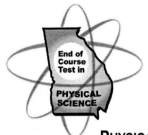

Chapter 1
A Scientific Inquiry

PHYSICAL SCIENCE STANDARDS COVERED IN THIS CHAPTER INCLUDE:

SCSh1 a – c	Students will evaluate the importance of curiosity, honesty, openness, and skepticism in science.
SCSh3 a – f	Students will identify and investigate problems scientifically.
SCSh6 a – d	Students will communicate scientific investigations and information clearly.
SCSh7 a – e	Students will analyze how scientific knowledge is developed.
SCSh8 a – f	Students will understand important features of the process of scientific inquiry.

Every day you have an opportunity to think scientifically. For instance, on a warm spring day you may step outside and notice that the sky is partly cloudy. You can even see two different kinds of clouds: billowy, cotton ball–like clouds and long, thin clouds in rows. You may say to yourself, "Those clouds are pretty," and go about your business. On the other hand, you might start asking questions about the clouds.

Figure 1.1 Kinds of Clouds

- Why are there different kinds of clouds?
- What makes one billowy and the other thin?
- Why is one type fluffy while the other is in streaky rows?

These are **questions** that deal directly with your **observation**. You probably could find the answers to these kinds of questions in an encyclopedia. You might even ask questions that require some effort on your part to answer.

- What are clouds made of?
- How does altitude or temperature affect a cloud's shape and form?
- What makes clouds appear and disappear?

In even the simple, everyday observations, there are literally hundreds of questions that can be asked. Thinking scientifically also means pursuing the answers to these questions. In doing so, you progress from merely reading about the world around you to engaging that world. This ultimately leads to a deeper understanding of your surroundings.

A functional definition of science is: the observation, identification, description and explanation of **natural phenomena**. Natural phenomena are observable facts or events in the world around us, like the clouds. Scientific processes help explain natural phenomena. Scientists believe all natural phenomena have logical, verifiable explanations — sometimes it just takes some thought, effort and time to find them!

Through the study of science, we ask questions, develop **hypotheses** (educated guesses) and design and carry out experiments to gain a better understanding of the universe. Then we must try to make sense of the experimental results through analysis. Only then can we arrive at some conclusion about our hypothesis. Take a look at the graphic below and you'll see how scientific thinking can be represented as a system.

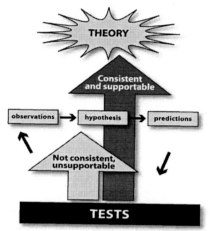

Figure 1.2 The System of Scientific Thought

To "do" science, you must have some way of thinking through the possible solutions to a problem and testing each possibility to find the best solution. There are many valid scientific processes, and an entire book could be written about how thought is translated into questions, experiments and conclusions. But since our space for this topic is limited, we'll provide you with one of the most common "scientific processes." Our scientific process will have the following steps:

Observations are made by using the **five senses** — sight, touch, smell, sound and taste — so, let's start there. Step one is to observe some aspect of the world around you.

1. Identify a problem to solve based on your observations. How can you state the problem as a question for investigation?

2. Do a little research to find out what is already known about your question.

3. State a hypothesis — that is another way of saying "an educated guess at the solution to your problem."

4. Conduct an experiment or set of experiments that aim to produce results that will support or contradict your hypothesis.

5. Collect and organize your data. What does it tell you?

6. Analyze the data and summarize the results as a conclusion in terms of the original hypothesis.

Remember, this is just one way to organize your thoughts; things don't always happen this way. Sometimes you might have a hypothesis and only later on realize a problem for which it is applicable. It's also possible that you might actually have a test and conclusion in search of a problem. Finally, your experiment may generate unexpected data, which is hard to interpret and doesn't answer your question as clearly as you were hoping. What do you do then? Well, that's up to you. There are several paths you could take. Let's look at each step more closely. After that, we will see what the options are.

1. MAKING OBSERVATIONS AND DEFINING THE PROBLEM

You may have noticed a natural phenomena many times before, like the wind blowing on your face, but never really thought much about it. Then a family vacation finds you standing on the beach, with the wind gusting so hard off the ocean that it is taking the foam from waves' tops and hurling it toward shore. Where is that wind coming from? Why is the water so rough? Is the wind stirring up the water, or is it the other way around?

Figure 1.3

On the other hand, some observations catch your attention the first time, like seeing a hot air balloon move across the sky. That should generate some questions. How does a hot air balloon fly? How do you steer it? How do you get down?

Think about those two different observations. Both are made using the five senses. How are they different? The first is an observation of a natural phenomenon — the wind. The second is an observation of a man-made object, a technological innovation — the hot air balloon. Although we can see the hot air balloon, we only see the effect of the wind on other objects and not the wind itself. At the same time, we know that the balloon is subject to gravity so the balloon is being affected by natural phenomena. So, how does a balloon rise? The hot air balloon makes use of heated gas to lift itself up enough to overcome gravity; otherwise, it wouldn't be in the air! It needs air through which to move and it needs wind to move it. Ultimately, there are many cause and effect relationships in the universe, but we need to focus our study of hot air balloons on a specific problem. Given these requirements, let's ask this question: how high can a hot air balloon go?

Asking questions helps you to define a problem. By asking questions, we can search for logical explanations for what we observe and find ways to solve problems.

2. PERFORMING RESEARCH

Research can be done on many levels — how much you need to do and where you need to look depends on the problem that you are investigating. For an explanation to a phenomenon that you feel fairly certain has already been explored, you may only have to noodle around on the Internet to find your answer. But beware! While the Internet has become a pervasively-used information resource in our society, it transmits information *of all kinds*. Some sites may contain correct information, while others are nothing more than a collection of opinions or outright falsehoods. Remember that anyone trying to sell something, whether it is a product or an item, is open to bias. Bias is the tendency to present inaccurate data or unreasonable judgement for personal gain. You must learn to judge which sites, or types of sites, contain information that you can rely on to be factual. Table 1.1 is a good start.

Table 1.1 Judging Internet Sites

Generally More Reliable	Generally Less Reliable
Sites that are updated daily	Sites that are rarely updated
News outlet sites	"Viewpoint" sites that seek to persuade
Government agency or University web sites .gov, .edu	Individual home pages .org, .com

To address a more complicated scientific question, research into journals will be necessary. This is referred to as "going to the literature" by scientists. A **journal** is a specialized publication. It differs from a magazine in a few important ways. First, the authors of journals are not paid journalists; they are scientists who want to distribute their research to other scientists. Their goal is to broaden the current body of knowledge. Second, authors who write articles for journals must follow a set of rules that define the kind of research that will be accepted, and the scientific methodology that produced it. Third, the submitted article is **peer reviewed**. That means that it is scrutinized (reviewed) by anonymous scientists in a similar field (peers). If the peer reviewers disagree with a method used or conclusion reached, they will send the article back for re-investigation or revision. The goal is to be certain that published material is as trustworthy and useful as possible.

Figure 1.4 Journal Covers

There are thousands of journals, each of which focuses on a particular subject area or specialty within an area of study. Two journals that address broad scientific issues are *Science* and *Nature*. You may have heard of these. Two journals that focus on more specialized topics are *Environmental Science and Technology* and the *Journal of Wind Engineering and Industrial Aerodynamics*. You probably have not heard of these, but they are widely read. Rest assured, there is a journal that applies to almost any scientific topic you can think of, as well as many that you did not know existed.

Let us close the topic by distinguishing what type of research can be done on the Internet versus through journal research. An Internet search will allow you to discover how a hot air balloon works, where you can go to get lessons or rides in one and where hot air balloon races and demonstrations will be held. Going to the literature will help you find out every type of meteorological research ever conducted by a weather balloon, along with statistical analysis of the data. It will enable you to find a comprehensive description of the Earth's atmosphere at every level, and thus discern the altitude to which a hot air balloon will fly. It will yield descriptions of the pollutants sampled in our atmosphere by balloons and the chemical interactions of those molecules, as well as examinations of the wide variety of implications that can be drawn from that data on issues like global warming and ozone layer depletion. A journal search will show you recorded air currents, including the jet stream, for every area of the world.

In short, well-directed research can help you find almost any answer you want — except when there aren't any answers to your question yet. Then it is time to experiment. Look over your research, take a deep breath and make a hypothesis.

3. FORMING THE HYPOTHESIS

Remember, a hypothesis is not just any guess, like guessing how many jelly beans are in a jar at a carnival. A hypothesis is an educated guess. A hypothesis is a way of forming an opinion about how or why something happens, based on patterns that you have observed over time.

The hypothesis can be developed using either inductive or deductive reasoning. **Inductive reasoning** allows you to draw on your observations of specific events to hypothesize a general trend. **Deductive reasoning** requires you to use a general truth to hypothesize particular events. Here are two examples to illustrate:

- Taylor notices that every time she throws a ball up, it comes down. She inductively reasons that next time (and perhaps every time) she throws a ball up, it will come down. She mentions her hypothesis to Cory.
- Cory uses deductive reasoning when he says, "Well, of course. That is Newton's Theory of Gravitation. Basically, it says that what goes up, must come down. So next time you throw the ball up, it will certainly come down."

Now let's go back to the hot air balloon and see how you can use your reasoning skills to form a hypothesis.

During your research, you should have accumulated some knowledge about how hot air balloons work. But unless you are fairly adventurous, you probably don't have much experience with hot air balloons. It may seem to you that you cannot use inductive reasoning to develop your hypothesis. Let's broaden the field of necessary experience. Have you ever flown on an airplane? If you have, then that is part of your body of experience with objects that fly, and you should use that experience to make a reasonable assumption.

Figure 1.5 Airplane

Figure 1.6
Hot Air Balloon

You may also develop your hypothesis deductively. It is important that your hypothesis is not immediately apparent. For instance, you might say, "All things that fly have wings." Clearly, a hot air balloon doesn't have wings, so your starting point is inaccurate. Beginning with a correct principle is vital when coming up with a hypothesis through deductive reasoning.

You may find that your hypothesis is wrong, but that is OK. You have to start somewhere! Try it now. Just remember that your hypothesis must be testable, meaning that you can design an experiment that proves or disproves its supposition. For the sake of this discussion, we'll choose the flowing hypothesis: a hot air balloon can travel higher than a commercial airplane.

4. SETTING UP THE EXPERIMENT

A **scientific experiment** should be designed to give measurable results, which either prove or disprove the hypothesis. To gather meaningful data, the experiment must be set up to examine only one condition (or **variable**) at a time.

There are three types of variables seen in an experiment:

- **independent variable** (sometimes called the **manipulated variable**) – The factors that are changed or manipulated during the experiment. They are the ones that the experiment is trying to test.

- **dependent variable** (sometimes called the **responding variable**) – This is usually the factor that the experimenter is measuring or counting. The dependent variable is the one that changes in response to the independent variable.

- **control variables** – All the other factors in the experiment. These are things that you attempt to control, and are kept constant during the course of the experiment.

How would you set up an experiment to see how high a hot air balloon could fly? Of course, you would have to purchase a balloon and all the extra equipment, learn to fly the balloon and make some very important decisions about where to fly and what to take with you. Taking all of those logistics for granted, though, you would probably start at a certain point, on a day with calm weather, and launch your balloon in such a way that it goes *up* more than it goes *over*. (Hopefully, you will have done a lot of research about wind and air currents before the launch. It may also be a good idea to take a few lessens on how to fly a hot air balloon.)

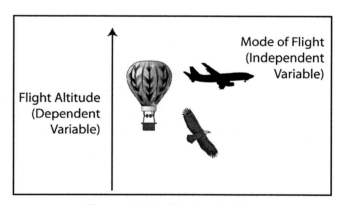

Figure 1.7 Labelling the Variables

What are the independent, dependent and control variables in this experiment? You are trying to see how high the hot air balloon can fly versus the commercial airplane, so we can call the independent variable the mode of flight. Notice that it is the independent variable because it is not dependent on anything—it is a choice you made during the hypothesis. You could have chosen a hawk instead of a commercial airplane and the experiment is still the same. The dependent variable is the variable you will actually use to compare the two modes of flight. So, altitude is the dependent variable. You want the experiment to compare the altitude of a hot air balloon and a commercial airplane and nothing else. To ensure this, you would need to conduct the experiment with all other possible variables – such as beginning location, season of the year, the time of day – kept constant so that you are not comparing two events that are not actually comparable. These are the control variables.

Scientists typically conduct many experiments at once. They do this to insure that their data is **reproducible** and consistent. They group together the things that are to be tested the same way and run the experiment. The **experimental group** is the group that will be tested, such as 10 different kinds of hot air balloons. The **control group** is the group that the experimental group will be tested against, such as 10 different kinds of commercial airplanes.

You go up, up, up, measuring your altitude at intervals. At this point you are collecting data.

5. COLLECTING AND PRESENTING DATA

Data is gathered from the observations and measurements taken during a scientific experiment. There are two types of data: qualitative and quantitative. **Qualitative data** are the observations made with your senses. This is information that cannot be assigned a numerical value. Examples of qualitative data can include shades of color, texture, taste or smell. **Quantitative data** are the measurements — anything that can be expressed as a number, or quantified. Quantitative data can include lengths, weights, time, temperature or anything else expressed as a value. Because quantitative data is a measurement, the number that is recorded is an exact and accurate quantity of a measured amount. Furthermore, quantitative data usually has a unit of some kind, like 12 meters or 5 seconds. In these cases, the unit is as important as the value.

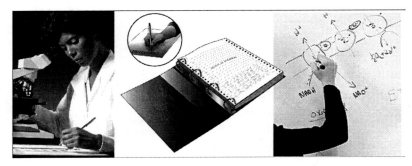

Figure 1.8 Qualitative Data

Qualitative data is **subjective,** meaning that its validity depends on the person. For instance, if you asked three people how warm it is outside, you might get three different answers, like "quite hot," "uncomfortably warm" and "very pleasant." Even if three people said "it is nice out today," you could probably find three other people who would disagree.

Figure 1.9 Quantitative Data

Quantitative data is more **objective**, meaning that it does not depend as much on the person making the measurement. For instance, if three people were asked to read a thermometer, they would all come up with similar temperatures, like 78.1°, 78.0° and 78.3° Fahrenheit. The differences in their measurements are the result of the slightly different ways that each person estimates. So, there is some subjectivity in quantitative data, but not nearly as much as that present in a qualitative observation.

All observations and measurements from the experiment must be recorded. If the data collected are organized in a logical manner, they can be more easily analyzed to determine the results of the experiment. Both qualitative and quantitative data can be organized in a data **table**. Diagrams, graphs and charts may also be used to present the data. The point is to present data in a form that makes its meaning clear. Often this means looking for **trends** or patterns in the data. Through careful evaluation, you can interpret the results of the experiment.

Up to this point, we have been considering a theoretical experiment. You will be pleased to know that it has actually been done! (Ah, now you don't have to take those hot air balloon lessons!) A *National Geographic* article contains the story. In 1961, two US Navy officers took an experimental high-altitude balloon to the outer edge of the stratosphere. The name of the balloon was the USN Stratolab V[1] and it rose to an altitude of 113,740 feet. One way to look at their flight is to view it in a **diagram**, which is a good way to show the relationship between things. The diagram in Figure 1.10 allows us to view the record altitude reached by Stratolab V and compare it to other things, like the layers of the atmosphere or the cruising altitude of a commercial plane. During their ascent, the officers recorded data on their altitude, the barometric pressure and the air temperature in a table. They also noted the time that each set of measurements was taken. This data is more specific, and should be organized in a table, as shown in Table 1.2.

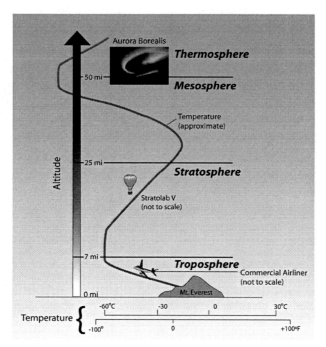

Figure 1.10 Diagram of Atmospheric Layers

Table 1.2 Stratolab Data

time	altitude (ft.)	temperature (°F)	pressure (psi)
7:08 am	0	74	14.7
7:34 am	26,000	−27	6.8
7:50 am	43,000	−73	2.4
8:10 am	53,000	−94	1.4
8:25 am	65,000	−80	0.74
9:05 am	95,000	−41	0.2
9:47 am	113,740	−29	0.09

1. See the Web site http://www.history.navy.mil/download/space-11.PDF for more on Stratolab.

Data recorded in a table can often be graphed to show the relationship between the data in a way that is easier to analyze. **Line graphs** are a great way to show how one variable how the dependent variable changes in response to the independent variable. The independent variable is plotted on the *x*-axis (horizontal axis), and the dependent variable is plotted on the *y*-axis (vertical axis). You can see this in Figure 1.11, where the change in pressure is noted at different altitudes.

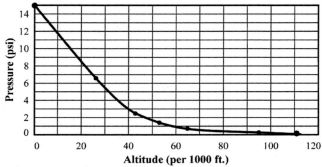

Figure 1.11 Line Graph of Stratolab Data

Line graphs are also used to compare multiple groups of data. These are called **multiple line graphs**, and could be used to compare the data from two or more balloon flights.

A **circle graph**, also known as a **pie chart**, is used to show parts of a whole. Many times, circle graphs show percentages of a whole (100%). Our hot air balloonists might use a pie chart to show the percentages of various gases that make up the atmosphere.

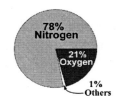

Figure 1.12 Circle Graph of Atmospheric Composition

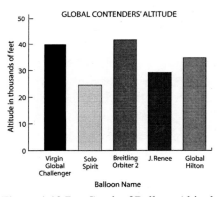

Figure 1.13 Bar Graph of Balloon Altitude

Notice that the circle graph conveys information about different things — in this case, different atmospheric gases. What if you want to compare different things that are not a part of a whole? A good way to do that is the **bar graph**. Figure 1.13 is a bar graph that indicates the maximum cruising altitude of the Global Contenders[1]. The Global Contenders were five hot air balloon teams who were competing to be the first to successfully conduct a non-stop circumnavigation of the globe in 1997. Their preparation and progress were reported on throughout the world, and examined in a Nova television special.

These are the three main types of graphs. They can be made very complicated (to show multiple pieces or groups of information) or very simple. Graphs can be a powerful tool in presenting your data, and great care should be taken in assembling them. The best graphs are lucid and clearly indicate trends. The worst graphs confuse the reader and fail to show any conclusive evidence.

Color really helps to spice up your graph, but don't go overboard. Your graph doesn't need to look like Joseph and the Amazing Technicolor Dreamcoat to get the point across!

---

1. See the NOVA Web site http://www.pbs.org/wgbh/nova/balloon/ for more on the Global Contender

6. DRAWING CONCLUSIONS

You now know a lot more about hot air ballooning history than you did when you started this chapter, but what can you get out of it? The point of every experiment is to support or disprove the initial hypothesis. Let's say that your initial hypothesis was that a hot air balloon could fly higher than an airplane. Look at the data and decide if this is true. In doing so, you are drawing a conclusion.

A **conclusion** is a judgment based on observation and experimentation. It should be a logical statement made from the results of the experiment. It is usually easier to see a conclusion when the data is well-organized, as described in the previous section.

You have to be careful about generalizing too broadly when drawing a conclusion. This often means examining your own conclusion for flaws, as well as reevaluating your original hypothesis. For instance, the diagram in Figure 1.10 indicates that the Stratolab flew much higher than a commercial airliner…but is that always the case? The bar graph of the flight altitudes of the Global Contenders indicates that they were cruising at about the same altitude as the commercial airliner, so the hypothesis may still hold. But there is an unknown here: does the commercial airliner always cruise at 30,000 feet? How high can a plane — any kind of plane — actually go?

In fact, the cruising altitudes of both the commercial airliner and the balloon are largely weather-dependent. The airline pilot wants to fly where there is the least turbulence (air disturbance), and that altitude varies depending on the air currents generated by storm systems. It cannot be too high, though, or there will not be enough air for the plane's jets to draw in to keep it aloft. The balloon pilot also wants to stay away from bad weather, but must follow air currents because he has no jet engines to propel him. So, the available data indicates that a hot air balloon can fly higher than some airplanes, under some weather conditions. That is not a very concrete conclusion, but it is something. The bottom line is that through your investigation, you realize that this scientific investigation needs some work if you are to arrive at an accurate conclusion.

At this point, you have two choices: you can go back and design a new experiment to definitively prove (or disprove) your hypothesis, or you can look over your data and use it to make a new hypothesis. Designing new experiments may mean ensuring that more variables are controlled, different variables are manipulated, or that more than one test flight is conducted. In developing a new hypothesis, you may arrive at a hypothesis that is totally different than your initial concept or you may just need to narrow the breadth of the statement. That is one of the great things about science: all information is valuable, including negative results, and can lead you in a variety of directions.

Regardless of the outcome of the results, it is important that the conclusion is well-written. Scientists exist all over the world and many do not speak English as their first language. In science, clear communication is crucial to ensure that others know exactly what you mean and are not left guessing about some aspect of your experiments or your conclusion. It is not enough to look smart by using big words and glossing over the particulars. *The point is to communicate, not to show off!*

Figure 1.14 Poor Communication Helps No One

Your conclusion may open the door to more scientific investigation. For instance, you could use your conclusion to make inferences about the results. An **inference** involves using your conclusion as a starting point in inductive reasoning. For example, if your conclusion that hot air balloons can travel higher than commercial airplanes is true and some friends of yours have a hot air balloon, then you would infer that they could travel in it to a higher altitude than a commercial airplane. Notice that the experiment hasn't been conducted and that there are a number of variables that are being ignored. Inferring from your conclusion means that you take it for granted that it is true and make generalizations from there.

Another possible use for your conclusion is in the development of a model. A **model** is mathematical description of an event. Models identify correlations and cause-and-effect relationships in the phenomena they describe. Models can be translated into computer simulations. These simulations are designed to describe the outcome of an experiment under a given set of conditions. For instance, the data in Table 1.2 could be used to develop a model. Altitude, pressure and temperature data from the experimental flight could be correlated to provide a mathematical framework. Multiple flights would generate more data and make the model more accurate. Adding more variables, like weather conditions or wind speeds, will make the model even more useful.

The result is a computer program that determines outcomes, given certain data. The model allows you to enter data like weather conditions and pressure, and then decides, based on the program parameters, what altitude your balloon can fly to. In other words, models make mathematical use of experimental data to make predictions.

GOING THE EXTRA MILE — MAKING A PREDICTION

A **prediction** is a forecast of the possible results of events. Knowledge we have gained from observation and experimentation can help us make predictions about seemingly unrelated events. Models can help, but are not always necessary. Whether or not a model is used, a great deal of extra thought must go into a prediction, for the simple reason that you are making a statement about something that you haven't tested yet. If we go back to the hot-air balloonists, we see that as the altitude increased over 110,000 feet, the pressure dropped nearly to zero. What predictions can we make? Here are three:

(a) A hot air balloon cannot fly higher because the pressure will drop to zero and the balloon will have nothing to push against.

(b) A hot air balloon cannot fly higher because the temperature will drop again to temperatures where the balloon cannot function.

(c) A hot air balloon can fly higher with a better design and more resilient materials.

Which statement do you think is correct? Based on the trend that you see in Figure 1.10, you would probably guess prediction (a) because there is more evidence for it. However, you may feel a little wary about your choice. Why? *Because you haven't tested it yet!* Ah, well that is OK! You should be wary when making predictions, but more important, you should be educated. Now, more than ever, it is important to see what research is out there. Information from other scientists can help reinforce your data, so that you can make the best prediction possible. But where to find this other information.....? That's right, back to the literature!

Section Review 1:   A Scientific Method

A. Define the following terms.

natural phenomena	control group	diagram	variable
hypotheses	qualitative data	table	independent variable
five senses	research	graph	conclusion
observations	journal	chart	inference
dependent variable	peer review	deductive reasoning	model
control variable	inductive reasoning	scientific experiment	prediction
experimental group	quantitative data	reproducible	

B. Answer the following questions.

1. Richard has a plant growth experiment to carry out. His goal is to compare the growth of one type of plant to that of another. He obtains two different species of plant from his teacher. He places them in equivalent conditions and records their growth every five days. His data is shown in the following multiple line graph.

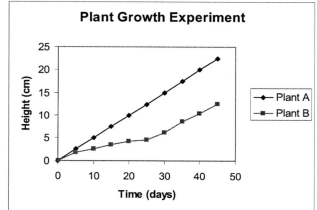

Richard is excited. His experiment is complete and he has reached a conclusion. "Plant A grows at more than twice the rate of Plant B!" he crows. He sends his data and conclusion to the Journal of Horticultural Mediocrity for peer review. You are his peer reviewer. Write a response to Richard, critiquing his experimental methods and conclusions. What would you require Richard to do, in order to have his work published?

2. What are three ways that data can be represented? Give two examples (NOT ones mentioned in this text) of the type of data suitable for each graph style.

3. What was the fundamental difference in the experiments conducted by the pilots of the Statolab V and the Global Contenders?

4. What is the difference between a prediction and a conclusion?

5. Why should an experiment test only one variable at a time?

SCIENTIFIC INVESTIGATION AND TECHNOLOGICAL DESIGN

In the last section we examined a scientific methodology. Through hypothetical observations and research we developed a hypothesis and then set up an experiment. We were in luck because someone had already performed our experiment, and we had the opportunity to examine their data and draw conclusions from it. There is something interesting about the hot air balloon example, though. Each hot air balloonist was testing not only a theory about how high or how far a balloon could go, they were also testing the technological design of their balloons. Clearly, a poorly designed and manufactured balloon would not go as high or as far, but which kind of balloon will go the highest or the farthest cannot be known until different designs are tested under controlled scientific conditions.

The very first thing that one would need to know is the variations in balloon design that are possible. Look at Figure 1.15.

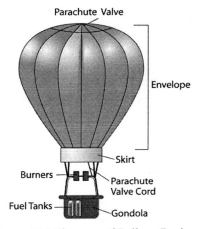

Figure 1.15 Elements of Balloon Design

- The balloon consists of the envelope and the gondola that it carries connected by some kind of lashing or frame.

- The envelope may be made of a variety of different materials including nylon, mylar and polyester; the primary requirement is that material be strong and heat resistant.

- The balloon may be lifted by air, a lighter-than-air gas like helium or hydrogen, or a combination of air with lighter-than-air gas. Whatever lifting gas is used, it is usually heated by an on-board fuel for greater buoyancy. The greater the volume of the envelope, the more lifting gas it can accommodate.

- The gondola may vary in size to accommodate one or several people and their supplies, as well as the necessary fuel tanks, instrumentation and communications devices.

- Notice that there is no steering wheel on the gondola or the envelope. The balloon must travel with air currents by heating (to rise) and turning off the heat (to descend).

These are the main points to consider when designing the balloon. Knowing even these few things, you can already evaluate the following questions.

– If the lifting gas to be used is air, is a heater needed? Why or why not?

– Hydrogen is a flammable gas. Should hydrogen be used as the lifting gas in a balloon equipped with a propane fuel burner? Why or why not?

– What advantages might helium have as a lifting gas, if compared to air alone?

– Steel is strong and heat resistant. Would steel be a good material with which to construct the envelope? Why or why not?

– For an around-the-world-trek, would you want a larger or a smaller envelope?

– What do you think are the practical limitations on the size of the gondola?

– None of the Global Contenders actually made it around the globe during the1997/1998 race. Besides the construction of the balloon itself, what do you think are factors that help determine the success or failure of the experiment for each team?

These questions are intended to bring you to a key point of understanding about the "best" way to execute an experiment: there are usually some practical constraints that must be worked around, and one must make a great many judgments in order to determine the optimal path.

Another consideration is that the cost and time to perform an experiment in the optimal way may be prohibitive. In some cases, the money and man hours needed are so great that only an entity like a government can undertake the experiment. As an example, let's go back to the US Navy's Stratolab program. Stratolab balloons I–V were created and tested as one of the United States' many steps toward manned space flight. They were part of a much larger experiment. The fact that Stratolab V reached an altitude higher than any other balloon before or since is noteworthy. But the fact that the program generated so much data that was important to the space program and to the body of scientific knowledge in general is why the trip was undertaken in the first place and what makes the feat so important.

So, what is the distinction between the experiments conducted by the Global Contenders and the Stratolab teams? The Global Contenders were testing the *technological design* of their balloon, and of course, their own ability to pilot the vessel. The Stratolab pilots were doing the same thing, but more importantly they were engaged in a *scientific investigation* to explore the limits of the Earth's atmosphere, and the human ability to function in that environment. Technological innovation and scientific investigation are intimately linked, but distinguishable concepts.

Section Review 2:   Scientific Investigation and Technological Design

A. Define the following terms.

investigation   technical design

B. Choose the best answer.

1. Without knowing the ultimate purpose of each activity, which of the following would MOST LIKELY be a part of a scientific investigation?

    A. traveling to the rain forest

    B. extracting DNA samples from eight varieties of rain forest beetles

    C. moving to the rain forest to see if you can survive there

    D. listening to the music of native indians

2.   Which of the following is a technological design investigation?

    A. buying a go-cart

    B. installing a new bumper

    C. finding ways to make the go-cart faster

    D. painting the go-cart

3.   Lamar really likes spiders and wants to do a Science Fair project on some aspect of spiders. If the theme of the Fair that year was "Innovations" which topic would make an acceptable entry for Lamar?

    A. "Spiders Throughout History"

    B. "New Applications for Spider Venom"

    C. "Comparing Spider DNA to Human DNA"

    D. "The Everyday Lives of Spiders"

4.   Scientist are often forced to design new instruments and software during the course of their investigations. Design engineers do the same. Which statement BEST describes the difference?

    A. Only the scientist operates the instrument in order to make it work more efficiently.

    B. Only the design engineer gets data from the instrument.

    C. Only the scientist gets data from the instrument.

    D. The design engineer's goal is to perfect the instrument, the scientist's goal is to get results that relate to his hypothesis.

Thought Activity

You are a very resourceful young scientist and decide to build four miniature hot air balloons. Each is about a foot tall, and all have equivalent frames and gondolas. All four have a burner derived from a butane lighter. The only difference in the four balloons is the material of the envelope. You use polyester from a raincoat, Mylar from a balloon, nylon from your mom's stockings and aluminum foil from your kitchen. You go out to your high school football field on a day with no wind, place all of the balloons on the 20 yard line and turn on a large fan to simulate an air current. Then you light the burners. The balloons rise and begin to travel.

1. What are the independent, dependent and control variables in the experiment?

2. What measurements should you record?

3. Describe the technological design that you are testing.

4. What are some possible goals of your scientific investigation?

5. Can you name any problems with the experiment?

6. The nylon and polyester envelopes catch fire, even though the research that you did indicated that many balloonists use these materials. What are possible explanations?

7. Can you suggest any modifications to the experiment?

CHAPTER 1 REVIEW

1. A judgement based on data gathered in an experiment is

   A. a skill.　　　　B. a conclusion.　　　　C. a hypothesis.　　　　D. an observation.

2. Large amounts of petrified wood are found in northeast Arizona. Using inductive reasoning, four inferences are made. Which is the MOST reasonable?

   A. All wood becomes petrified.

   B. A living forest once stood there.

   C. No forests grew in other parts of Arizona.

   D. Wood only becomes petrified in northeast Arizona.

3. Which of the following information sources is MOST likely to undergo peer-review?

   A. *Sports Illustrated*　　　　　　　　C. the daily newspaper

   B. *New England Journal of Medicine*　　D. a news Web site

Use the following information to answer questions 4 and 5.

> Keisha observes goldfish in an outdoor pond. The goldfish seem to be more active when the weather is warm than when it is cold. She asks herself, "How do temperature changes affect goldfish?"

4. If she were to do an experiment, which of the following would be the BEST hypothesis to test?

   A. Do goldfish like warm water or cold water?

   B. Goldfish are more active in warm water than in cold water.

   C. Goldfish live in warm and cold water.

   D. Temperature changes will kill goldfish.

5. What sort of variable would temperature be in Keisha's experiment?

   A. independent　　B. dependent　　C. control　　D. responding

6. A hypothesis is checked by

   A. research in journals.　　　　C. experimentation.

   B. making a prediction.　　　　D. researching on the Internet.

7. Ryan noticed that his cola loses its carbonation as it warms. He knows that it is carbon dioxide that causes cola to fizz. Ryan decides to do a scientific experiment to research this phenomenon. What is the next step Ryan should take?

    A. ask a question

    B. draw a conclusion

    C. make an observation

    D. form a hypothesis

8. Andrika has learned that the hot water in her house is always gone by 6:30 am. She knows that this is because her sisters and mother always get to the shower before her. She decides to experiment with her morning routine to see if she can get a hot shower in the morning. Over the course of a week, she changes the time that she gets up, making it 10 minutes earlier each day. What is the dependent variable in this experiment?

    A. the time she gets up

    B. the volume of hot water her family uses

    C. the temperature of the water in the water heater

    D. the temperature of the water in Andrika's shower

Municipal Solid Waste (MSW) is what goes into landfills. Basically, it is the garbage we put out at the curb. It can be divided up by type.

9. What is the BEST way to display this data?

    A. circle graph

    B. bar graph

    C. multiple line graph

    D. circle or bar graph

Category	Percentage
Rubber, Leather and Cloth	7.3
Yard Trimmings	13.1
Food Scraps	11.7
Wood	5.7
Other	3.4
Metals	7.6
Paper	34.2
Plastics	11.9
Glass	5.2

10. Which of the following phrases contains quantitative data?

    A. Green leaves surround white flowers.

    B. Ricky's football jersey is number 85.

    C. Seeds sprout more quickly when it is warm.

    D. Water evaporates at a rate of 2 mL per minute.

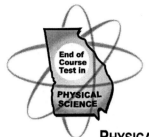

Chapter 2
Laboratory Safety

PHYSICAL SCIENCE STANDARDS COVERED IN THIS CHAPTER INCLUDE:

SCSh2 a – c	Students will use standard safety practices for all classroom laboratory and field investigations.

SAFETY PROCEDURES IN THE LABORATORY

Safety procedures are set up to protect you and others from injury. Hopefully, you will never have to use them! The most important safety rule is to always follow your teacher's instructions. Before working in the laboratory, fully read all of the directions for the experiment. Laboratory accidents can be easily avoided if safety procedures are followed. Be sure to dress appropriately for the laboratory environment. Know where eyewash stations and safety showers are located. Determine what personal protective equipment, like aprons, goggles and/or gloves are necessary to ensure the safety of yourself and others. If there is an accident, spill or breakage in the laboratory, report it to your instructor immediately. *REMEMBER: You must be concerned about your own safety as well as the safety of others working around you.*

Glassware Safety

- To avoid being cut, never use broken or chipped glassware. Broken or chipped glassware should be properly disposed of in an appropriately labeled container.

- Only heat glassware that is thoroughly dry.

- Never pick up any glassware unless you are sure it is not hot. Remember, hot glass looks the same as cold glass. If glassware is hot, use heat-resistant gloves or tongs to handle it to avoid burns.

- To prevent glassware from cracking, do not bring glassware that is hot into contact with anything cold, especially cold water.

Sharp Instrument Safety

- Always use single-edged razors.
- Handle any sharp instrument with extreme care.
- Never cut any material toward you. Always cut away from you. Immediately notify your teacher if you receive a cut.
- Dispose of used or ruined sharp instruments in an appropriately labeled container.

Fire and Heat Safety

- Always wear safety glasses or goggles when working with an open flame.
- Never reach across a flame.
- Never heat anything (particularly chemicals) unless instructed to do so.
- Never heat anything in a closed container.
- Always use a clamp, tongs or heat-resistant gloves to handle hot objects.
- When using a Bunsen burner to heat a substance in a test tube, move the test tube in and out of the flame. Never leave the test tube directly in the flame for extended periods of time.
- Fire extinguishers should be located in or near the lab in case of a fire. Do not tamper with the extinguishers in any way. Only use an extinguisher if you have received proper training. Do not remove an extinguisher from its mounting unless instructed to by your teacher and/or during a fire.

Animal Safety

- Do not cause pain, discomfort or injury to a live animal.
- Follow your teacher's directions when handling animals.
- Wash your hands thoroughly after handling animals or their cages.

Electrical Safety

- If an extension cord is needed to plug in an electrical device, use the shortest extension cord possible. Never use an extension cord that is frayed or worn.
- Do not use socket multipliers to overload an electrical outlet.
- Never touch an electrical appliance or outlet with wet hands.
- Always be sure to keep electrical cords away from standing water.

Chemical Safety

- Always wear a safety apron or lab coat and protective gloves when handling chemicals. This provides protection from chemical spills. If a chemical comes into contact with your skin, rinse immediately for a minimum of 15 minutes and notify your instructor.
- If instructed by your teacher to smell a chemical, never smell the chemical directly. Instead, hold the container with the chemical away from your face and use your hand to waft the chemical odor toward your nose.
- Use proper ventilation in the lab. If chemicals (particularly organic solvents) are handled in the lab, a chemical fume hood should be available.
- When not in use, keep all chemicals properly stored in the appropriately labeled containers.
- Ensure that all chemicals are properly disposed of as instructed by your teacher.

Eye and Face Safety

- Wear safety goggles when handling chemicals.
- When you are heating a test tube or bottle, always point it away from you and others.
- Remember, chemicals can splash or boil out of a heated test tube, beaker or other container.
- If a chemical comes into contact with your eyes, rinse immediately at an eyewash station for a minimum of 15 minutes and notify your instructor.

Proper Dress

- When working in a laboratory setting, wear clothes that cover as much of your skin as possible. This means long-sleeved shirts and long pants rather than tank tops or shorts.
- Wear shoes that completely cover the toes.
- Tie back long hair to prevent it from coming into contact with chemicals or an open flame.
- Remove or tie back any dangling jewelry or loose clothing to prevent them from getting caught on any equipment or causing unsafe situations.

Through the Department of Labor, the United States Government runs the **Occupational Safety and Health Administration**, also called **OSHA**. The goal of OSHA is to protect the health and safety of America's workers. OSHA has many regulations and procedures that help maintain safe work environments. It also has a great deal of guidance for workers and employers from all industries. The national OSHA Web site is at www.osha.gov.

Manufacturers of chemicals are required to produce, update and maintain a safety data sheet for each chemical they produce. This document is called a **material safety data sheet**, or **MSDS**. An MSDS lists information on chemical structure, chemical appearance, chemical properties and personal safety. It also contains information on safe storage and disposal of chemicals.

An MSDS comes with every hazardous chemical that is purchased. In fact, there is an MSDS for every chemical known, even water and air! They are not discarded, but kept on file. If you want to see the MSDS for a chemical that you are working with, ask your teacher.

Official Safety Information

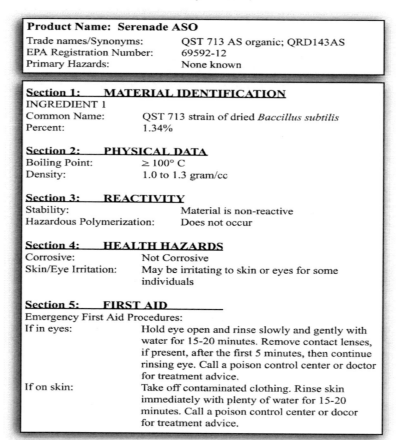

Source: http://www.agraquest.com/products/serenade/pdfs/Serenade_ASO-MSDS.pdf

Figure 2.1 Example of an MSDS

Section Review 1: Safety Procedures in the Laboratory

A. List at least two rules for ensuring the various safety concerns below are met.

glassware safety   animal safety   fire and heat safety   chemical safety
sharp instrument safety   electrical safety   eye and face safety

B. Choose the best answer.

1. How should you pick up a piece of hot glassware?
   - A. with bare hands
   - B. with heat-resistant gloves
   - C. with the sleeve of your shirt
   - D. with a spatula

2. How should you hold a test tube containing a chemical?
   - A. pointed away from your face
   - B. above your head
   - C. held to your nose
   - D. held up to your partner's face

3. Why shouldn't you wear dangling jewelry and baggy clothing to the laboratory?
   - A. The baggier the clothes, the more chemical fumes are absorbed.
   - B. The metal in the jewelry changes the expected reaction.
   - C. Lab coats don't fit over baggy clothes.
   - D. Jewelry and clothing could get caught on equipment, and clothes can catch on fire.

4. When you are done with an experiment, how should you dispose of any chemicals used?
   - A. Mix them all up in a waste container and dump them in the trash.
   - B. Pour them all down the sink.
   - C. Follow the instructions given to properly dispose of the particular chemical(s).
   - D. Mix the chemicals in a flask and heat the mixture until it evaporates into the air.

C. Answer the following questions.

1. Kara and Mitch are partners in physical science lab. Their class is conducting an experiment on supersaturated solutions. Kara and Mitch put on safety goggles and safety aprons and read the experiment's directions. The experiment directs them to add sugar to water in a beaker, heat the beaker with the solution on a hot plate, add more sugar to the solution, remove the beaker with the solution from the hot plate and allow the solution to cool undisturbed. What additional safety equipment will Kara and Mitch need to use for this experiment?

2. Mr. Ohm's physical science class is making soap. The students will be using sodium hydroxide, which is a potent chemical. Which types of safety equipment will the class most likely need?

LABORATORY SAFETY

Walking into science class on Monday morning, you see that materials are all set up for a lab. YES! You love lab days because you get to actually DO science. You observe the classroom on the way to your seat. Before doing anything else, you draw a picture of what you see going on in the classroom. The picture looks something like the one below.

Figure 2.2 A Classroom in Chaos

Your teacher sees your drawing and is horrified! Clearly, many students have forgotten the lab safety rules that were reviewed on Friday. She asks your permission to photocopy it for the class. Then she passes it out for homework the next day as a part of the following assignment:

1. What are two unsafe activities shown in the illustration? Why are they unsafe?

2. List two correct lab procedures depicted in the illustration.

3. What should Bob do after the accident?

4. What should Sue do to avoid an accident?

5. Find three things shown in the lab that should not be there.

6. Compare Joe's and Carl's lab techniques. Who is doing it the correct way?

7. List three items in the illustration that are there for the safety of the students in the lab.

Before reading on, please take some time to examine the picture and answer the questions for yourself. Then we'll give you our perspective.

1. What are two unsafe activities shown in the illustration? Why are they unsafe?

There is SO much to choose from! Let's take the activities of Tim and Ray first. Tim is hitting Ray over the head with a book. This is a DEFINITE no-no. First, Ray could get hurt. Additionally, other people could get hurt, even if they are not fooling around. *No horseplay is allowed in the lab; accidents happen when people are not paying attention.*

Next, take a look at what Joe and Jim are about to do: they are about to drink their experiment. That is EXTREMELY unsafe. *When in the laboratory, you should never put anything to your nose or mouth, unless specifically directed by your teacher to do so.*

2. List two correct lab procedures depicted in the illustration.

Tina is doing a great job holding the test tube over the flame with the proper tool (called tongs). Carl and Tina are both wearing proper safety goggles and are focused on their work.

3. What should Bob do after the accident?

The first thing Bob should do is *let the teacher know the accident has occurred!* In fact, that is what all students should do ANY time there is an accident in the lab. Next he should (carefully) clean up the glass with a glass collection broom and dustpan. He should make sure to *follow his teacher's directions* on whether to put the broken glass in the trash can or into another receptacle that might be designated specifically for glass.

4. What should Sue do to avoid an accident?

Never leave long hair loose in the lab. Sue may not like this, but if she doesn't do something to pin down her beautiful golden locks of hair they are going to catch on fire! Given the choice between securing her hair and having it singed, she'll choose to find a hair clip or hair band!

5. **What are three things shown in the lab that should not be there?**

Some of these are obvious, and some are not. Well, first, there is a rabbit loose in class! If you look closely, you'll see a pair of scissors that definitely should not be in the electric socket. Third, there should not be a beaker and spill on the floor next to Tim. Now you name three more unsafe situations.

_____

_____

_____

_____

6. **Compare Joe's and Carl's lab techniques. Who is doing it the correct way?**

Way to go Carl! Just say NO to Joe! *Never put anything in the lab in your mouth, especially not a liquid that is labeled with the symbol for poison!*

7. **List three items in the illustration that are there for the safety of the students in the lab.**

If you look in the upper right hand corner you should see the *fire extinguisher, safety blanket and first aid box*. It's important to know where all three of these items are located at all times. They are there for your safety and the safety of others. Of course, in our picture, the first aid kit is flapping open and the fire extinguisher is missing. *Let your teacher know if laboratory safety equipment is damaged or missing.*

It's also important to note that some of the students are *wearing safety glasses*. You should know where these are and make sure to wear them during lab.

The most important safety precautions you can take in a science lab are to *always follow instructions,* and when something happens that shouldn't make sure to *inform your teacher as soon as possible.*

Section Review 2: Safety Procedures in the Laboratory

1. Various safety rules apply in the laboratory. In order to protect your clothing, you should

    A. wear an apron or a lab coat.

    B. wear clothing treated with Teflon.

    C. wear clothing treated with Scotchgard™.

    D. wear as many layers as possible.

2. Reaching across a flame is

    A. never acceptable.

    C. sometimes acceptable.

    B. always acceptable.

    D. seldom acceptable.

3. Identify when you should report a chemical spill to your teacher.

    A. immediately

    B. after you've cleaned up the spill

    C. only if you think the spill is dangerous

    D. after you've finished the experiment so your results are not ruined

4. Identify the lab activity that should be conducted under a fume hood.

    A. measuring very high velocities

    B. using high voltage sources of laser light

    C. mixing chemicals that produce dangerous vapors

    D. massing a series of objects

5. What is the best way to avoid eye damage from chemical splashes in the laboratory?

    A. Wear your eyeglasses.

    B. Wear your contact lenses.

    C. Wear your safety glasses or goggles over your eyeglasses.

    D. Stay near the eyewash station and first aid kit throughout class.

THINK WHILE YOU WORK

The ability to **infer causes** and **predict outcomes** should not only be applied to your experiments. You must apply these skills in life also! They will help you make reasonable decisions about many things, including safe behavior in the lab. The following activities will show you how.

Challenge Activity

Rodrigo fills a glass beaker with distilled water and places it on a hotplate. He heats the water, measuring the temperature every three minutes. His results are shown below.

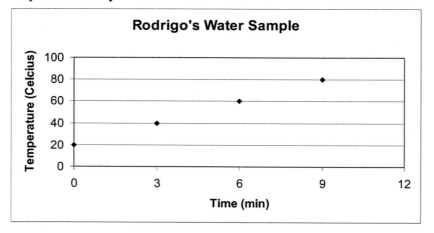

1. What temperature did the water sample start at? Was it warm or cold?

2. What do you predict the temperature will be at 12 minutes?

3. When the experiment is over, should Rodrigo remove the beaker from the hot plate with his bare hands?

4. Is it safe to breathe around the boiling sample, or should Rodrigo wear a face mask?

Challenge Activity

Marita places a beaker containing chemical A on a triple beam balance. She records the mass. She adds chemical B to the beaker and records the mass. As the chemicals begin to react, fumes are produced, and mass is lost. Marita records the mass of the beaker every 10 seconds. Her results are shown below.

A

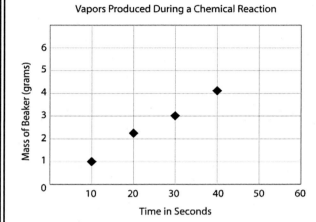

Vapors Produced During a Chemical Reaction

B

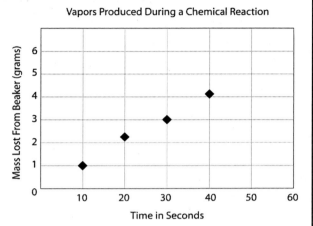

Vapors Produced During a Chemical Reaction

1. Which of these two graphs reflects the scenario outlined above?

2. Where should this experiment be performed?

3. Predict how many grams will be lost at the 60-second mark.

4. Where has the mass gone?

Challenge Activity

Circle graphs (or pie charts) are another way of presenting data. They show parts of a whole. For instance, let's look at the data from an imaginary study. The study shows the percentage of all laboratory injuries that are caused by certain unsafe activities. Each activity is a slice of the pie. The results are shown below.

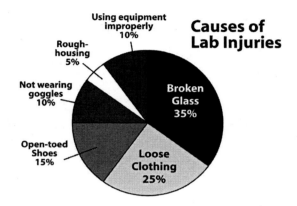

1. Based on this graph, what can you infer to be the greatest threat to student safety?

2. Look back at Figure 2.2 on page 46. Which students are practicing the unsafe behaviors shown in this circle graph?

3. Make a circle graph of your own. How many students are practicing each unsafe behavior?

4. Does your circle graph show the same patterns as the national study? Why do you think there are differences?

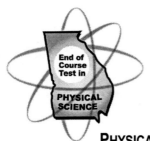

Chapter 3
Equipment and Measurement

PHYSICAL SCIENCE STANDARDS COVERED IN THIS CHAPTER INCLUDE:

SCSh2 a – c	Students will use standard safety practices for all classroom laboratory and field investigations.
SCSh4 a – c	Students will use tools and instruments for observing, measuring and manipulating scientific equipment and materials.
SCSh5 a – e	Students will demonstrate the computation and estimation skills necessary for analyzing data and developing reasonable scientific explanations.

EQUIPMENT AND MATERIALS

Laboratory **equipment** and **materials** are tools used in scientific investigations. Examples are glassware and weighing dishes. **Instruments** are an example of technological design and can be used to enhance the ability of our senses to observe. Examples are balances and calipers.

Each piece of equipment in the lab has a specific purpose. Part of behaving safely is the ability to identify these items and recognize their use. Inappropriate use of equipment and materials cause accidents. If you don't know how to operate an instrument, ask your teacher.

Glassware for Handling Liquids:

An **Erlenmeyer flask** is used to mix liquids; its narrow mouth prevents splashing and lessens the dispersion of noxious fumes. Although sometimes it is marked to make volume measurements, they are only approximate values.

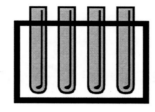

Test tubes are used to mix, measure or heat liquids. Test tubes are not usually marked with measurements, so they are only used to make approximate measurements.

Beakers are used to mix and heat liquids. Like the Erlenmeyer flask, they are not intended for accurate volume measurement.

An **eyedropper** is used to dispense small measurements of a liquid.

Equipment for Heating:

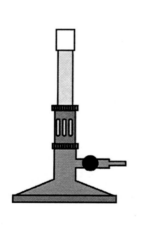

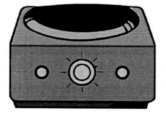

A **hot plate** is a source of electrical heat.

A **Bunsen burner** is a source of gas heat.

Tongs are used to grasp heated material.

A **tripod** holds glassware above a Bunsen burner.

Wire gauze usually goes on top of a tripod to hold the glassware being heated.

Equipment for Measuring Mass:

Lab tip: Remember to weigh the container that holds your sample before adding your sample. Then you can subtract the container's mass from the total mass to obtain the sample mass.

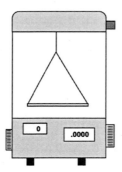 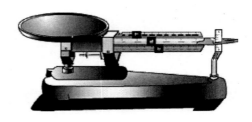

A **analytical pan balance** is used to accurately determine mass to the nearest ten thousandth of a gram. The balance above is tared (zeroed out).

A **triple-beam balance** is used to determine the mass of heavier materials to the nearest gram.

Equipment for Measuring Volume:

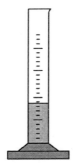 

Graduated cylinders are "graduated" or marked with a scale for measurement. They are used to accurately measure liquid volume.

Pipets are used to accurately measure small liquid volumes. Pipets are usually marked TD (to deliver). When using a TD pipet, it delivers the exact volume on marked on the side; do not "blow out" excess liquid left in the tip as you dispense. Shown above is an automatic pipet.

Equipment for Measuring Length:

 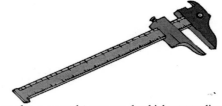

A **meter stick** measures length or width.

A **caliper** is used to accurately measure the thickness or diameter of·an object, on smaller scale than a ruler. The jaws of the caliper are closed on the object to be measured, then the distance between the jaws is read. Calipers work best on firm, solid objects.

Section Review 1: Equipment

A. Equipment Check

Look around your laboratory and determine which pieces of equipment are there. Are pieces broken or missing? Offer to help your teacher organize equipment drawers and keep equipment clean.

B. Choose the best answer.

1. Which of the following is used as a source of heat in the laboratory?

   A. thermometer   B. Bunsen burner   C. thermostat   D. gasoline

2. Which has specific markings for measurement and is used to accurately measure liquid volume?

   A. test tube   B. beaker   C. ruler   D. graduated cylinder

3. Which of the following pieces of equipment is used to handle liquids but is not intended for accurate measurement?

   A. beaker   B. test tube   C. Erlenmeyer flask   D. all of the above

4. If you were instructed to heat something on the Bunsen burner, you would need to set your container on a _____ to hold your container over the burner.

   A. watch glass   C. a piece of wire gauze held by a tripod

   B. hotplate   D. Petri dish

5. Which material would you use a caliper to measure the width of?

   A. a cube of jello   C. a cube of butter

   B. a cube of sugar   D. a pea

6. Which piece of equipment would be MOST appropriate for determining the mass of a lead brick?

   A. a beaker   C. a triple beam balance

   B. an analytical balance   D. a hot plate

7. Your instructor gives you an unknown sample, contained in a 5mL vial. You are to add 1mL of a chemical to your liquid and observe the reaction. In which piece of equipment should you mix your chemicals?

   A. 25 ml beaker   C. eyedropper

   B. 10 ml test tube   D. 50 ml Erlenmeyer flask

SCIENTIFIC MEASUREMENT

When scientists study the world around them, they often make measurements of various phenomena as part of their observations. It is important that these measurements are accurate. It is equally important that measurements are reproducible. That means similar results should be produced each time the experiment is repeated as long as the procedure is repeated correctly. This makes intuitive sense, right? Wouldn't you be skeptical of a result that only one person in the world could seem to obtain? These requirements mean that communication is an important component of all science.

One of the best examples of the need for clear communication in science is the system of measurement that is used when data from experiments is collected. Imagine Sergio is a scientist measuring the width of a rock and writes in his lab notebook "The fragment is as wide as my thumb." Unless someone has access to Sergio's thumb, no one can know how wide the rock is. Sergio might have been more accurate and written "2.1", though there's no way of knowing what 2.1 means because there is no unit written next to it. He might be more accurate and write, "a few centimeters," but that is still an estimate. To properly record data and to ensure that others know exactly how wide the rock is, Sergio must write "2.1 centimeters."

There are a few important points to keep in mind about recording scientific measurements:

The unit is half of the answer. When Sergio wrote "2.1", we didn't know if it meant 2.1 pounds, 2.1 seconds or 2.1 feet. Each of these measurements has a *very* different meaning. There are only a few cases in science in which a measurement has no units associated with it.

The unit must be part of an agreed-upon system of measurement. Sergio's thumb is not a standard measure that all scientists have access to. Having a system in place that is agreed-upon ensures that the measurement is effectively communicated to everyone so that everyone can universally know how wide the rock is. The most common system used is the **metric system**.

The number should be in the proper form, usually as a decimal. Although it is common to use fractions to describe measurements such as "half a mile" or "quarter past two o'clock", the use of fractions does not make sense with all units. It is not often that you hear someone say, "a third of a centimeter." Writing the value as a decimal avoids any problems communicating the measurement—and it makes calculations easier too!

INTRODUCTION TO SI UNITS

The **SI units** of measurement are used throughout the world when performing calculations related to scientific investigations. It stands for **Le Système International d'Unites** and was established in France about 200 years ago. SI units were adapted from the metric system. The base units are meter, gram and second to measure length, mass and time, respectively. In addition, volume, density and temperature are measurements frequently used in the laboratory.

The English system of measurement, also called the **U.S. customary system**, is used in the United States. In this system, the foot is the standard length, the pound is the standard weight, and the second is the standard for time. Although you are probably more familiar with the English system, the SI units are used in the scientific community, and throughout the world. Therefore, SI units will be the standard system of measurement used in this book. Some units and conversions are listed in Table 3.1.

Table 3.1 English and Metric Systems (with abbreviations)

English			Metric		
Length					
12 inches (in)	=	1 foot (ft)	1000 millimeters (mm)	=	1 meter (m)
3 ft	=	1 yard (yd)	100 centimeters (cm)	=	1 m
5,280 feet (ft)	=	1 mile (mi)	1000 m	=	1 kilometer (km)
Mass					
16 ounces (oz)	=	1 pound (lb)	1000 milligrams (mg)	=	1 gram (g)
2000 lbs	=	1 ton	1000 g	=	1 kilogram (kg)
Volume					
16 fluid ounces (fl oz)	=	1 pint (pt)	1 cubic centimeter cm^3	=	1 milliliter (mL)
2 pts	=	1 quart (qt)	1000 mL	=	1 liter (L)
4 qts	=	1 gallon (gal)			

Table 3.2 English-Metric Conversions

English		Metric
Length		
1 inches (in)	=	2.54 cm
3.281 ft	=	1 m
Mass		
0.035 oz	=	1 g
1 lb	=	0.453 kg
Volume		
33.8 fl oz	=	1 L
1 gal	=	3.78 L

STANDARD SI MEASUREMENTS

Length measures the distance from one point to another and can be used to determine a person's height in meters, the distance between your home and your school in kilometers, the length of an almond in centimeters or the thickness of a quarter in millimeters. The standard SI unit of measurement to determine length is meter (m). To better visualize a meter, it is helpful to know that 1 meter is equal to 3.28 feet. A ruler or **meter stick** is commonly used to measure length, as seen in Figure 3.1 below.

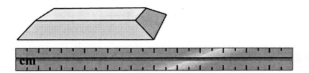

This pencil eraser measures about 6cm in length.

Figure 3.1 Metric Ruler

Mass is the measure of the amount of matter in an object. Its standard SI unit is the kilogram (kg), and its tool of measurement is the balance. The mass of a needle, a rock and a person would be expressed in milligrams, grams and kilograms, respectively.

Figure 3.2 Triple-beam Balance

The terms mass and weight are often used interchangeably, but they are NOT the same. Mass is a property of an object related to the quantity of matter the object consists of. **Weight** is a measurement of the gravitational force that attracts an object to the Earth, or to any other center of gravity (as on another planet). So, the weight of an object depends on both the object's mass and its location. Therefore, the mass of an object on Earth is the same as it is on the Moon, but the weight of the object will be different there. Because the Moon is a lot smaller and has less mass than the Earth, it does not have as strong of a gravitational force. In fact, an object that weighs one pound on Earth will weigh only 0.167 pounds on the Moon. Let's do a conversion. Let us say that Lois has a mass of 60 kg. She stands on two scales, one located on the Earth and one on the Moon. Let's see what Lois will weigh in the two locations.

60 kg $\times$ (2.2 pounds/1kg) = 132 Earth pounds

132 Earth pounds $\times$ (0.167 Moon pound/Earth pound) = 22.04 Moon pounds

So, Lois's weight will differ depending on the degree of gravitational force that is acting on her. Scientists prefer to use mass when reporting the results of an experiment because it does not vary.

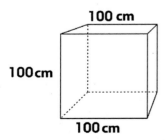

Figure 3.3 Volume of a Cube

Volume is the amount of space occupied by an object. Volume is determined in different ways depending on the shape (i.e. cube, sphere, irregular) and state of matter (i.e. solid, liquid, gas) of the object. For a regularly shaped object, like a cube, volume is determined by multiplying the length times the height times the width of the object ($V = l \times h \times w$). The units used for volume are cubic centimeters (cm^3 or cc) or milliliters (mL). Figure 3.3 shows this relationship. One cubic centimeter is equal to one milliliter, which is equal to one thousandth of a liter.

A **graduated cylinder** is used to measure the volume of liquids. When liquids are placed in a graduated cylinder, a meniscus will form. A **meniscus** is the curve of liquid at its surface. It forms as a result of how the liquid interacts with the glass surface. The meniscus may curve down or up, depending on the liquid. To read the volume of the liquid, get eye level with the meniscus and measure from the bottom of the curve of the meniscus if it curves downward or the top of the meniscus if it curves upward. Figure 3.4 shows how to read a meniscus by getting eye level with it and measuring at the center point.

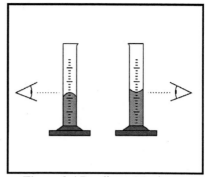

Figure 3.4 Reading a Meniscus

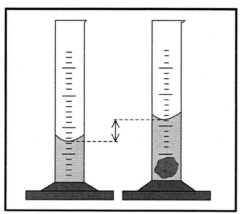

Figure 3.5 Water Displacement Method

Many objects are irregular in shape. In these cases, volume must be measured using a different approach. It turns out that the volume property of an object is independent of what the object is made of. This means that 1 mL of air occupies the same volume as 1 mL of lead. To determine the volume of irregularly shaped objects, the **water displacement** method is used. Typically, this method produces reliable results only if the object is a solid substance. To measure volume by water displacement, place an amount of water in a container and determine its volume. Then add the object. When the object is placed in the container of water, the water level will rise. Measure the volume again. To determine the volume of the object, simply subtract the first measurement from the second.

Although this method sounds very scientific, you already have some experience with this phenomena. Have you ever seen the water level rise in a bathtub or jacuzzi when you get in? If you had a proper way of determining how much the water increased by, you could determine your volume. How else is an irregularly-shaped human to find out their volume?

There is a great usefulness to volume determination. Volume and mass can be used together to obtain the density of an object. **Density** is a measure of how closely packed matter is, within a given space.

$$D = \frac{m}{V}$$

The standard SI unit for density is kg/m^3, but it is also commonly expressed in units of grams per cubic centimeter (g/cm^3) or grams per milliliter (g/mL). Density is a characteristic material property; thus the density of two objects of the same material is always the same even if the objects have different masses. For example, imagine you have two items: a gold coin and a gold brick. The gold brick has a volume ten times larger than the coin. The density is a property of the gold, so both the coin and the brick will have the same density. However, since the volume of the brick is ten times larger than the coin, we also know that the mass of the brick must be ten times larger as well. This is the only way that the density will be the same for both. Density, then, is a measure of how much matter is occupying a certain amount of space.

Density explains why some things float, and other things sink. A rock at the bottom of a stream is denser than water, so it sinks to the bottom, whereas a piece of styrofoam is less dense than the water, so it floats. If an object sinks, it is denser than the liquid it is placed in. If an object floats, it is less dense than the liquid it is placed in. The same is true of gases. Remember the hot air balloons from Chapter 1? Heating the lifting gas causes the molecules in the envelope to move around rapidly, becoming father apart. The gas inside the envelope is less dense (the molecules are farther apart) than the gas outside of the envelope (unheated air), and so the hot air balloon floats.

Temperature measures how hot or cold something is. All measurements for temperature are taken in degrees. In the metric system, **Celsius** is the unit of temperature. The SI unit for temperature is **Kelvin**, and the English unit is **Fahrenheit**. Both Celsius and Fahrenheit are written in their abbreviated forms with a degree symbol, as in °C and °F, whereas Kelvin is abbreviated simply as K (not degrees Kelvin). To convert from one unit to another, use the following formulas:

$$C = \frac{(F - 32)}{1.8} \qquad F = 1.8\,C + 32 \qquad C = K - 273.15 \qquad K = C + 273.15$$

C is degrees Celsius; **F** is degrees Fahrenheit; **K** is Kelvin.

Figure 3.6 Temperature Conversion Formulas

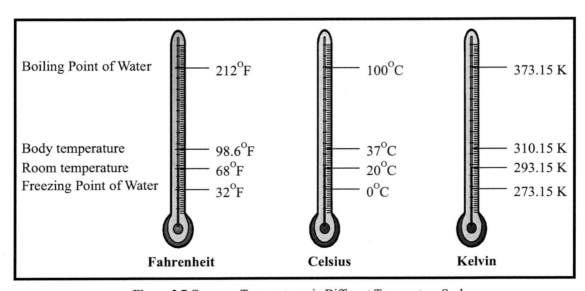

Figure 3.7 Common Temperatures in Different Temperature Scales

METRIC UNIT CONVERSIONS

The units in the metric system are defined in multiples of 10 from the standard unit. The metric prefixes indicate which multiple of 10 the standard unit should be multiplied or divided by. Multiply when changing from a greater unit to a smaller one: divide when changing from a smaller unit to a larger one. The chart below is set up to help you know how far and which direction to move a decimal point when making conversions from one unit to another. Each space on the chart stands for a multiplication factor of 10. To convert a kilometer (km) to a meter (m), move 3 spaces to the right. So, multiply (km) (10^3) = (km) $(10 \times 10 \times 10)$ = (km) (1000) = m. To convert m to km, divide the meter value by 1000.

Prefix	kilo (k)	hecto (h)	deka (da)	unit (m, L, g)	deci (d)	centi (c)	milli (m)
Meaning	1000	100	10	1	0.1	0.01	0.001

DIMENSIONAL ANALYSIS

Now that we have covered the units themselves and talked about adjusting their magnitude, we need to discuss converting the identity of the units. This is important because you will often encounter measurements in common units (remember Sergio's thumb?) which must be converted to SI units. This is done by the process of dimensional analysis. **Dimensional analysis** is a structured method of helping you to convert units by using conversion factors. A dimension is a property that can be measured, such as length, time, mass or temperature. It may also be derived by multiplying or dividing other dimensions. Some examples of derived dimensions include length/time (velocity), length^3 (volume) or mass/length^3 (density). Dimensions are *not* the same as units. The dimensions of a physical quantity can be measured in any appropriate unit. For instance, velocity can be measured in mph, m/s, etc., but it will always be a measure of length divided by time. Therefore, the dimensions of velocity are length/time.

A **conversion factor** is a defined relationship between two units. They are similar to the expressions shown in Tables 3.1 and 3.2, but they are written as fractions that are always equal to 1. For instance, the conversion from ounces to pounds is 16 oz = 1 lb. We can write two conversion factors using this information:

$$\frac{16 \text{ oz}}{1 \text{ lb}} \quad \textbf{and} \quad \frac{1 \text{ lb}}{16 \text{ oz}}$$

Ratios of equivalent values expressed in different units like these are known as conversion factors. To convert given quantities in one set of units to their equivalent values in another set of units, we set up dimensional equations. We will write our dimensional equations so that the old units cancel and we are left with only the new units. So you will have to choose which form of the conversion factor you need to use. How will you know? In order to eliminate a unit in the numerator, you will need to cancel it out by choosing a conversion factor that places that unit in the denominator. Likewise, if you want to eliminate a unit that is in the denominator, you will choose a conversion factor that places that unit in the numerator. Because any factor divided by itself is equal to 1, this process will eliminate factors that you do not need.

Example 1: How many cubic centimeters are in 2 liters?

Step 1. Begin by writing the term that needs to be converted:

$$2 \text{ L}$$

Step 2. Identify the unit that the term needs to be converted into:

$$2 \text{ L} = \underline{\quad} \text{ cm}^3$$

Step 3. Next, identify the conversion formulas that will be needed:

$$1 \text{ cm}^3 = 1 \text{ mL} \textbf{ and } 1000 \text{ mL} = 1 \text{ L}$$

Step 4. Write both forms of the conversion factors as fractions:

$$\frac{1 \text{ cm}^3}{1 \text{ mL}} \text{ or } \frac{1 \text{ mL}}{1 \text{ cm}^3} \textbf{ and } \frac{1000 \text{ mL}}{1 \text{ L}} \text{ or } \frac{1 \text{ L}}{1000 \text{ mL}}$$

Step 5. Select the correct conversion factors that will eliminate unwanted units:

$$2 \text{ L} \times \frac{1000 \text{ mL}}{1 \text{ L}} \times \frac{1 \text{ cm}^3}{1 \text{ mL}} = \underline{\quad} \text{ cm}^3$$

Step 6. Cross out the units that cancel and multiply the rest together:

$$2 \cancel{\text{L}} \times \frac{1000 \cancel{\text{mL}}}{1 \cancel{\text{L}}} \times \frac{1 \text{ cm}^3}{1 \cancel{\text{mL}}} = 2000 \text{ cm}^3$$

Notice that the units of "mL" and "L" cancel, leaving you with cm^3.

WRONG: If you had used the conversion factors incorrectly, this is what you would have:

$$2\text{L} \times \frac{1\text{L}}{1000\text{mL}} \times \frac{1\text{mL}}{1\text{cm}^3} = \frac{2\text{L}^2}{1000\text{cm}^3}$$

Notice, liters multiplied by liters are liters squared (L^2). None of the units cancel, so you know right away that this is a wrong approach.

A grid-like format is a different way to represent multiplying several conversion factors together. Each column contains a conversion factor that is needed to convert your units. Let's try to convert a rate of speed and see how this works for you.

Example 2: 36 kilometers per hour is how many meters/sec?

$$\frac{36 \cancel{\text{km}}}{1 \cancel{\text{hour}}} \left| \frac{1 \cancel{\text{hour}}}{60 \cancel{\text{min}}} \right| \frac{1 \cancel{\text{min}}}{60 \text{ s}} \left| \frac{1000 \text{ m}}{1 \cancel{\text{km}}} \right| = \frac{36 \times 1000 \text{ m}}{60 \times 60 \text{ s}} = \frac{36000 \text{ m}}{3600 \text{ s}} = 10 \text{ m/s}$$

JUDGING MEASUREMENTS

PRECISION AND ACCURACY

Science is not built on single results but the collection of large amounts of data from many experiments. In fact, one of the tests for something being scientifically correct is whether it can be repeated anywhere and still produce similar results. But experiments do not always produce the exact *same* result every time. This happens because there are many factors that can affect the experiment, and it is difficult to control all of them. Typically, a set of experiments will produce a range of results. But how can a scientist tell the difference between acceptable and an unacceptable range of data?

Scientists must analyze their data for precision and accuracy. **Precision** is the degree of closeness within a range of results. If you were throwing a ball repeatedly against a wall and hit the same spot every time, your aim would be very precise. **Accuracy** is the degree of agreement between a measured result and an accepted value. For example, let's say your family has a garage sale. You estimate that you will make $1000 but instead only made $150. Clearly, your estimate was very inaccurate. If, on the other hand, you sold $975, your estimate would be much more accurate. A helpful way to think of the difference between precision and accuracy is to consider a dart game with a target as in Figure 3.8. The bull's eye in the center is the "accepted value" that you want to hit. The first instance shows random hits that are far from the center. So the precision and accuracy are both poor. The precision is good when the darts all hit the same location. The dart throws are accurate when they hit close to the bull's eye. But only when the darts hit close together and hit the center are the throws both precise <u>and</u> accurate.

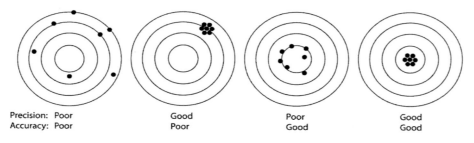

| Precision: Poor | Good | Poor | Good |
| Accuracy: Poor | Poor | Good | Good |

Figure 3.8 Precision and Accuracy

Precision has an additional meaning related to the scale of a measurement device. The smaller the measurement increment that an instrument can distinguish, the more precise the instrument. So, a pipet marked in 0.10 mL increments is more precise than one marked in 1 mL increments.

ERROR

All measurements have varying degrees of certainty. When there is disagreement between a measured value and an exact or accepted value, then **error** is present. There are many reasons for error when taking measurements. For example, it's easy to see how the quality and/or precision of the instrument can affect the measured value. There are also factors that are difficult to control, such as maintaining a constant wind speed on a spring day. Human error, commonly called operator error, can occur because of poor technique or just simple mistakes. Certain amounts of error are common and expected, having little impact on the values obtained. Other error can be chronic, making the data completely useless.

Section Review 2: Scientific Measurement

A. Define the following terms.

graduated cylinder	volume	meter stick	dimensional analysis
metric system	meniscus	length	conversion factor
tripod	water displacement	mass	error
SI units		weight	
U.S. customary system	density	Kelvin	precision
	temperature	Fahrenheit	accuracy
	Celsius		

B. Answer the following questions.

1. Alan would like to determine how the amount of salt dissolved in distilled water (measured in grams per liter) changes at different temperatures. List the pieces of lab equipment that he should use and explain how each piece of equipment would be used.

2. In her physics class, Geri needs to find the volume of one small BB (a metallic sphere). She does not trust her ability to take an accurate measurement of its diameter in order to calculate its volume. Suggest another way that Geri could experimentally find the volume of the small sphere. Be specific as to how she should carry out the experiment.

Use the following scenario to answer questions 3 – 7.

Mario, Jed, Tate and Rufus are lab partners. They are given a cube of metal and told to characterize it. They record that the metal is grey and shiny, and that it seems light for its size. They use a triple beam balance and determine that the mass of the cube is 48 grams. They decide to determine its density. Each boy measures the cube's length, width and height and records his data in the lab notebook.

Mario	Jed	Rufus	Tate
2.7 cm	2.65 cm	2.67 cm	3 cm
2.6 cm	2.57 cm	2.58 cm	2 cm
2.6 cm	2.59 cm	2.60 cm	3 cm

3. Which boy's data is the most precise? Least precise?

4. What methods and equations should be used to determine the volume of the metal cube? Which data set or sets should be used?

5. If you dropped this cube into a beaker of water, how much water would be displaced?

6. What is the density of the cube?

7. Perform a dimensional analysis to convert your answer to kg/m^3.

CHAPTER 3 REVIEW

Choose the best answer.

1. Identify a piece of equipment used to measure mass.

   A. spring scale

   B. beam balance

   C. caliper

   D. graduated cylinder

2. Select the freezing point of water on the Kelvin temperature scale.

   A. −273.15 K. B. 0 K. C. 32 K. D. 273.15K

3. Identify the correct conversion of 4.2 grams (g) to kilograms (kg).

   A. 4.2 g = 0.0042 kg

   B. 4.2 g = 0.042 kg

   C. 4.2 g = 42 kg

   D. 4.2 g = 4,200 kg

4. Identify the reason why scientists from countries around the world use the same measurement system.

   A. to simplify international copyright and patent laws

   B. to make it easier to understand and compare published results

   C. to make it easier for scientists to plagiarize the work of other scientists

   D. to simplify monitoring of the code for the humane treatment of animals

5. Graduated cylinders are marked in units of

   A. grams. B. meters. C. millimeters. D. milliliters.

6. Density is a good way to identify an object because

   A. different masses of the same object will always have different densities.

   B. different masses of the same object will always have the same density.

   C. the same volume of the same object will always have different densities.

   D. the same mass of two different objects will have the same density.

7. What is the BEST way to read the volume of a liquid in a graduated cylinder?

   A. Read the level of the liquid going up the side of the cylinder.

   B. Make sure five people in the laboratory read it before you write it down.

   C. Glance at the cylinder and write down the first number you see.

   D. Read the level of liquid at the middle of the meniscus at eye level.

Chapter 4
Structure, Properties and
Bonding of Elements

PHYSICAL SCIENCE STANDARDS COVERED IN THIS CHAPTER INCLUDE:

SPS1 a – b	Students will investigate our current understanding of the atom.
SPS4 a – b	Students will investigate the arrangement of the periodic table.

THE STRUCTURE OF ATOMS

MODERN ATOMIC THEORY

The **atomic theory** states that all matter is made up of tiny particles called atoms. **Matter** is defined as anything that has mass and takes up space. **Atoms** are the basic unit of all things. Everything that has matter is made up of smaller particles called atoms.

ATOMIC STRUCTURE

Atoms are made up of **subatomic particles**. These particles include protons, neutrons and electrons. **Protons** (p) have a positive charge, and **electrons** (e) have a negative charge. **Neutrons** (n) have neither a positive nor negative charge; they are neutral. Figure 4.1 shows a simplified model of a helium atom. The **nucleus** of the atom consists of protons and neutrons. The electrons are outside the nucleus. The overall charge of the atom is neutral because the number of protons equals the number of electrons.

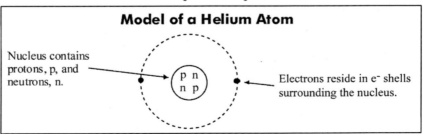

Figure 4.1 Model of a Helium Atom

The negatively-charged electrons are electrically attracted to their oppositely charged counterparts, the protons. This attraction holds them in orbit around the nucleus. The area that they occupy is called an **orbital**. These orbitals are designated s, p, d and f, each of which has a different shape. When associated with their quantum mechanical **energy level** (1, 2, 3…), these orbitals define the electron distribution of an atom. The s orbital is found closest to the nucleus; it can be imagined as a sphere around the nucleus. The smallest atom, hydrogen (H), consists of 1 proton and 1 electron. The proton is in the nucleus (in fact, for hydrogen, the proton essentially *is* the nucleus) and the electron orbits the nucleus in the 1s orbital. The next largest atom is helium (He), which consists of 2 protons, 2 neutrons and 2 electrons. As shown in Figure 4.1, the 4 protons and neutrons of the helium atom are held together in the nucleus, while the 2 electrons orbit the nucleus in the 1s orbital.

The next element in the Periodic Table is lithium (Li), which has 3 protons, 3 neutrons and 3 electrons. An s orbital will only hold two electrons, however. Two of lithium's electrons will go into the 1s orbital, and the third will go into the 2s orbital, as shown in Figure 4.2. While having the same orbital designation (s) as the 1s orbital, the 2s orbital has a higher quantum number (2), and is thus a higher energy orbital, located farther from the nucleus. The greater the distance between two charged particles, the weaker the electrical force that holds them together. Therefore, since the lithium electron in the 2s orbital spends most of its time farther away from the nucleus than the atom's 1s electrons, it is less tightly bound to the nucleus.

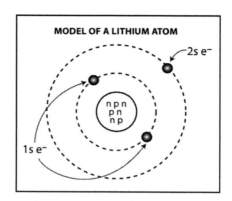

Figure 4.2 Lithium Atom Model Including Electron Shells

Even without explicitly addressing the quantum mechanical considerations necessary to examine larger atoms, we can still understand a bit about how atoms are put together. The quantum number and orbital designation of each electron can be accounted for in an atom's **electron configuration**. This is the organizational concept behind the periodic table, and will be discussed in the next section. For now, it is sufficient to recognize that electrons sequentially fill various quantum energy levels (1,2,3, etc…), and the various shells within those energy levels. As each energy level becomes full, electrons begin to fill the next highest level. The highest energy level orbital containing electrons is the atom's **valence shell**; it contains the electrons that exist farthest away from, and thus the least tightly bound to, the nucleus of the atom. These "outer electrons" are called **valence electrons**, and are free to participate in bonding with other atoms. Table 4.1 shows the electron configuration for sulfur, which has 16 electrons. It has four valence electrons in the 3p orbital. Note that the p orbital consists of three sub-orbitals — p_x, p_y and p_z — each of which holds a maximum of two electrons, for a total of six.

Table 4.1 Electron Configuration of Sulfur

Energy Level	s	Px	Py	Pz	Total e⁻ in energy level
1	2	-	-	-	2
2	2	2	2	2	8
3	2	2	1	1	6

Section Review 1:   The Structure of Atoms

A. Define the following terms.

atomic theory	proton	neutron	electron configuration
matter	electron	nucleus	energy level
valence shell	atom	orbital	
subatomic particles			

B. Choose the best answer.

1. Which of the following parts of an atom has a positive charge?

   A. protons   B. neutrons   C. electrons   D. electron shells

2. Which of the following parts of an atom has a negative charge?

   A. protons   B. neutrons   C. electrons   D. the nucleus

3. Which of the following parts of an atom has no charge?

   A. protons   B. neutrons   C. electrons   D. the nucleus

4. Which subatomic particles are found in the nucleus of an atom?

   A. protons and electrons   C. protons and neutrons

   B. electrons and neutrons   D. protons, neutrons and electrons

5. What is the maximum number of electrons that are contained in an s orbital?

   A. 1   B. 2   C. 3   D. 4

6. Which of the following are transferred or shared between atoms that have chemically bonded?

   A. valence shells   C. protons

   B. valence electrons   D. nuclei

C. Answer the following questions.

1. Compare and contrast protons, neutrons and electrons.

2. What is a valence electron?

3. The diagram at right shows a typical electron distribution pattern in a 1s orbital. You know that a 1s orbital can contain, at most, only 2 electrons. What is your interpretation of the meaning of the large dot in the center of the diagram, and of many dots shown as a cluster around it? (HINT: Think of this figure as the result of a series of snapshots together.)

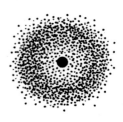

ORGANIZATION OF THE PERIODIC TABLE

ATOMIC NUMBER AND ATOMIC MASS

Elements are substances that cannot be further broken down by simple chemical means. An element is composed of atoms with the same number of protons. Each element has its own name, symbol, atomic number, atomic mass and electron shell arrangement (electron configuration). The **atomic number** represents the number of protons found in a given atom; this number defines the elemental identity of the atom.

The mass of an atom, referred to as **atomic mass**, is related to the number of protons, electrons and neutrons in the atom. Protons and neutrons account for the majority of the atom's mass. The unit of atomic mass, as expressed in the periodic table, is called an **atomic mass unit (amu)**. One atomic mass unit is defined as a mass equal to one-twelfth the mass of one atom of carbon-12. The amu is also known as the **dalton (Da)**.

To find the number of neutrons most commonly found in an element, subtract the atomic number from the atomic mass and round to the nearest whole number.

As an example, let's look at Carbon, represented in the periodic table as follows:

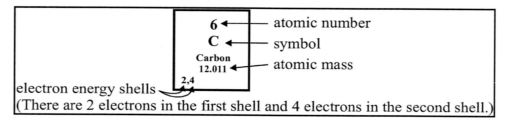

Figure 4.3 Periodic Table Information for Carbon

To find the neutrons most commonly found in an atom of carbon, subtract the atomic number, 6, from the atomic mass, 12.011, to get 6.011. Round to the nearest whole number to get 6. Carbon atoms most often have 6 neutrons in their nuclei.

PERIODIC TABLE

Look at Figure 4.4. As you already know, this is called the **Periodic Table**. The Periodic Table arranges all known elements by atomic number, starting with atomic number 1 (hydrogen-H) and "ending" with atomic number 111 (roentgenium-Rg). However, if the Periodic Table were only organized by atomic number, it would not be very useful. (It would simply be a list of elements in order of increasing atomic number). It also organizes the elements by their properties. The horizontal rows of the table are called **periods**. By moving across the periods from left to right, one can determine two things: how many valence electrons a given element has and the order in which their orbitals fill (called the electron configuration). The vertical columns of the Periodic Table are called **groups** or **families**; all members of any vertical group have the same number of valence electrons in the same orbital. An element's placement in the rows and columns of the table has meaning and enables the observer to understand many properties of that element.

Figure 4.4

THE PERIODIC TABLE OF THE ELEMENTS

Legend:
- Atomic Number → 36
- Symbol → Kr
- Name → Krypton
- Atomic Mass → 83.80

Noble Gases

	1 IA	2 IIA	3 IIIB	4 IVB	5 VB	6 VIB	7 VIIB	8 VIIIB	9 VIIIB	10 VIIIB	11 IB	12 IIB	13 IIIA	14 IVA	15 VA	16 VIA	17 VIIA	18 VIIIA
1	1 H Hydrogen 1.0079																	2 He Helium 4.0026
2	3 Li Lithium 6.941g	4 Be Beryllium 9.01218											5 B Boron 10.81	6 C Carbon 12.011	7 N Nitrogen 14.0067	8 O Oxygen 15.9994	9 F Fluorine 18.998403	10 Ne Neon 20.179
3	11 Na Sodium 22.9898	12 Mg Magnesium 24.305											13 Al Aluminum 26.98154	14 Si Silicon 28.0855	15 P Phosphorus 30.97376	16 S Sulfur 32.06	17 Cl Chlorine 35.453	18 Ar Argon 39.948
4	19 K Potassium 39.0983	20 Ca Calcium 40.08	21 Sc Scandium 44.9559	22 Ti Titanium 47.90	23 V Vanadium 50.9415	24 Cr Chromium 51.996	25 Mn Manganese 54.9381	26 Fe Iron 55.847	27 Co Cobalt 58.9332	28 Ni Nickel 58.69	29 Cu Copper 63.546	30 Zn Zinc 65.38	31 Ga Gallium 69.723	32 Ge Germanium 72.61	33 As Arsenic 74.9216	34 Se Selenium 78.96	35 Br Bromine 79.904	36 Kr Krypton 83.80
5	37 Rb Rubidium 85.4678	38 Sr Strontium 87.62	39 Y Yttrium 88.9059	40 Zr Zirconium 91.22	41 Nb Niobium 92.9064	42 Mo Molybdenum 95.94	43 Tc Technetium 97.91	44 Ru Ruthenium 101.07	45 Rh Rhodium 102.9055	46 Pd Palladium 106.4	47 Ag Silver 107.868	48 Cd Cadmium 112.41	49 In Indium 114.82	50 Sn Tin 118.71	51 Sb Antimony 121.75	52 Te Tellurium 127.60	53 I Iodine 126.9045	54 Xe Xenon 131.30
6	55 Cs Cesium 132.9054	56 Ba Barium 137.33	57 La Lanthanum 138.9055	72 Hf Hafnium 178.49	73 Ta Tantalum 180.9479	74 W Tungsten 183.84	75 Re Rhenium 186.2	76 Os Osmium 190.2	77 Ir Iridium 192.22	78 Pt Platinum 195.09	79 Au Gold 196.9665	80 Hg Mercury 200.59	81 Tl Thallium 204.383	82 Pb Lead 207.2	83 Bi Bismuth 208.9808	84 Po Polonium 208.9824	85 At Astatine 209.98704	86 Rn Radon 222.02
7	87 Fr Francium 223.01976	88 Ra Radium 226.0254	89 Ac Actinium 227.02779	104 Rf Rutherfordium 261.1	105 Db Dubnium 262.11	106 Sg Seaborgium 263.12	107 Bh Bohrium 262.12	108 Hs Hassium 264.13	109 Mt Meitnerium 266.14	110 Ds Darmstadtium 271	111 Rg Roentgenium 272	112	113	114	115	116	117	118

Lanthanide Series

58 Ce Cerium 140.12	59 Pr Praseodymium 140.9077	60 Nd Neodymium 144.24	61 Pm Promethium 144.91279	62 Sm Samarium 150.4	63 Eu Europium 151.96	64 Gd Gadolinium 157.25	65 Tb Terbium 158.9254	66 Dy Dysprosium 162.50	67 Ho Holmium 164.9304	68 Er Erbium 167.26	69 Tm Thulium 168.9342	70 Yb Ytterbium 173.04	71 Lu Lutetium 174.967

Actinide Series

90 Th Thorium 232.0381	91 Pa Protactinium 231.0359	92 U Uranium 238.029	93 Np Neptunium 234.0482	94 Pu Plutonium 244.06424	95 Am Americium 243.06139	96 Cm Curium 247.07035	97 Bk Berkelium 247.07030	98 Cf Californium 251.0796	99 Es Einsteinium 252.08	100 Fm Fermium 257.09515	101 Md Mendelevium 258.1	102 No Nobelium 259.100	103 Lr Lawrencium 262.11

Figure 4.5 shows a portion of the Periodic Table. At the head of each column is the group name. For example, the first column contains Group 1, which may also be called Group IA. Both names are correct, although the use of the Arabic numerals (1,2,3...) is more common than the use of the Roman numerals I, II, III. Moving toward the right across the Periodic Table, the Group number increases form 1 to 18. At the beginning of each row is the number defining the energy level of that period. The lower you go on the Periodic Table, the higher the energy level of the period; the highest energy level elements currently on the table are in Period 7.

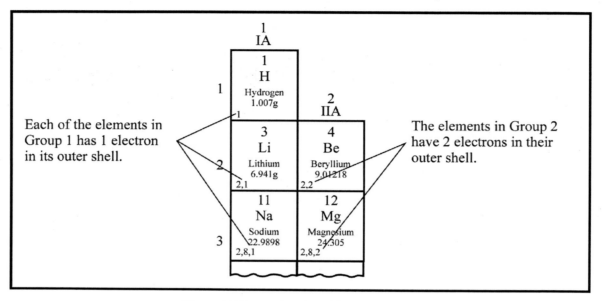

Figure 4.5 Groups 1 and 2 of the Periodic Table

Challenge Activity

Look at Figure 4.5. The arrows point to the number of valence electrons in each group: 1 valence electron in each Group 1 element and 2 in each Group 2 element. Can you figure out what the other numbers are? (Hint: look back at Table 4.1.)

ELEMENTAL CLASSIFICATION

Elements can all be classified as metals, nonmetals or metalloids depending on where they are located in the Periodic Table.

Metals make up the majority of the elements on the Periodic Table, more than 75%! They are located on the left side of the table and in the center. Group 1 metals are called **alkali metals**. (Hydrogen is the only exception — it is a gas at room temperature and considered a nonmetal.) Group 2 metals are called **alkaline earth metals**. The block of elements in the center of the Table (Groups 3 – 12) is called the **transition metals**. Here are a few important properties of metals:

- They have metallic shine, or **luster**.
- They are usually solids at room temperature.
- They are **malleable**, meaning that they can be hammered, pounded or pressed into different shapes without breaking.
- They are **ductile,** meaning that they can be drawn into thin sheets or wires without breaking.
- They are good **conductors** of heat and electricity.

Nonmetals are on the right side of the periodic table in Groups 14 – 18. There are only 18 elements that fall into this category. Nonmetals are usually gases or dull, brittle solids at room temperature. Some examples of nonmetals are hydrogen, helium, carbon, nitrogen, oxygen, fluorine and neon. Here are a few important properties of nonmetals:

- They rarely have metallic luster.
- They are usually gases at room temperature.
- Nonmetallic solids are neither malleable nor ductile.
- They are poor conductors of heat and electricity.

The **halogens** are a group of elements that are all non-metals. They are found in Group 17. The halogens react easily with the alkali metals to form salts like NaCl (sodium chloride). Group 18 also contains non-metals. This group is called the **noble gases**. They do not usually react with any other elements; another way of saying this is that they are **inert** (a chemical property).

The elements diagonally between the metals and the nonmetals are called **metalloids**. There are 7 elements that fall into this category. These are boron (B), silicon (Sc), germanium (Ge), arsenic (As), antimony (Sb), tellurium (Te) and polonium (Po). Metalloids have properties of both metals and nonmetals. One important property is that most metalloids are **semiconductors**. This means that, at certain temperatures, they conduct electricity very well; at other temporaries, they do not. Metalloids are frequently used in computer chips.

These are general categories that allow us to group elements by their physical properties. The Periodic Table may also be used to discover important information about the chemical properties of the elements. It tells us how the elements "like" to combine with other elements! This combining of atoms is called **bonding**. The process of reorganizing atoms into different bonded clusters (called **molecules)** is what happens in a **chemical reaction**. The number of protons and neutrons in a chemical reaction does not change, but the number of electrons does. We will look at chemical reactions in the next few sections of this chapter.

HISTORICAL DEVELOPMENT OF THE PERIODIC TABLE

The trends explained by the Periodic Table as we know it today were first identified in the 19th century. At that time, scientists began to recognize that certain elements exhibited similar properties, but the reasons were not yet clear. There were several attempts to arrange the elements to fit scientific observations, but each of these arrangements had problems.

Then, in 1869, the Russian chemist **Dmitri Mendeleev** (1834 – 1907) constructed his periodic table. In this table, the elements were arranged in order of increasing atomic mass. Mendeleev found that, in the table, similar properties were seen at regularly spaced, periodic intervals. Some of the elements were not known in Mendeleev's time; therefore, he had to leave blank spots in his table in order to group elements with similar properties into the same column. He predicted the properties and atomic masses of elements yet to be discovered that fit into these blank spots. These elements have since been discovered, and Mendeleev's predictions have been found to be very accurate.

There were some inconsistencies in Mendeleev's periodic table. For example, he had potassium (K) listed before argon (Ar) in his table because the atomic mass of argon is greater than that of potassium. However, the inert gas argon obviously did not belong in a group with such highly reactive elements as lithium and sodium. It was not until 1913 that scientists were able to determine the atomic number of elements. They found that with few exceptions, the order of increasing atomic number is the same as the order of increasing atomic mass. Argon and potassium are one of those exceptions. The atomic number of argon is less than the atomic number of potassium. With this information, argon was correctly placed in a group with the other inert gases. The modern Periodic Table that chemists use today appears very similar to that of Mendeleev. However, the modern Periodic Table is organized in order of increasing atomic *number*, instead of mass.

The last major modification of the Periodic Table occurred in the middle of the 20th century, when **Glenn Seaborg** (1912 –1999) discovered plutonium (Pu) and the other transuranic (past-uranium) elements between 94 and 102. He modified the table by placing the **actinide** series below the **lanthanide** series. Although the basic structure of the Periodic Table now appears to be correct, new elements called the **transactinides** (past the actinides) are being created at labs across the world. After each element is created and fully characterized, it is submitted to the **International Union of Pure and Applied Chemistry (IUPAC)** for confirmation and naming.

Section Review 2:   Organization of the Periodic Table

A. Define the following terms.

elements	group (family)	malleable	semiconductors
atomic number	alkali metal	ductile	bonding
atomic mass	metal	conductors	molecules
atomic mass unit (amu)	alkali earth metal	nonmetal	IUPAC
dalton	alkaline metals	halogens	actinides
Periodic Table	transition metals	noble gas	transactinides
periods	luster	inert	lanthanide
		metalloid	

B. Choose the best answer.

1. Lithium and sodium are in the same group of elements in the Periodic Table. Which of the following statements is true regarding these two elements?

    A. They have the same number of electrons in their valance shell.

    B. They have the same number of protons in their nucleus.

    C. They are both noble gases.

    D. They are in the same row of the Periodic Table.

2. Which of the following is NOT a property of most metals?

    A. solid at room temperature   C. conduct heat and electricity well

    B. have luster   D. do not react readily with any other elements

3. Where might you find a metalloid element used?

    A. computer motherboard   C. electrical power lines

    B. kitchen potholder/oven mitt   D. atmospheric gas mixture

4. The current Periodic Table is arranged in what order?

    A. in order of increasing atomic number   C. in order of increasing electrons

    B. in order of increasing atomic mass   D. in order of increasing chemical reactivity

C. Answer the following questions.

1. Name two physical properties of nonmetals.

2. Name two physical properties of metals.

3. Which Group of elements is very stable and does not react readily?

REACTIVITY OF ELEMENTS IN THE PERIODIC TABLE

In general, an element is most stable when its valance shell is full. Recall that the valance shell is the highest energy level orbital shell containing electrons. Period 1 elements (hydrogen and helium) have the valence shell 1s, which can only contain 2 electrons. Period 2 elements (lithium through neon) may have a 2s or 2s, 2p valence shell configuration that can hold up to 8 electrons. The 2s orbital can contain up to 2 electrons, and the 2p orbital can contain up to 6 (two in each of the sub-orbitals p_x, p_y and p_z) for a total of 8. Look at the periodic table in Figure 4.4 and count this out.

It is important to realize that bonding between elements occurs primarily because of the placement of electrons in the valence shell, particularly the unfilled orbital of the valence shell. Remember this: *Bonding is all about energy!*

For instance, the energy needed to remove an electron from an atom (that is, to ionize the atom) is called the **ionization energy.** Another term is directly related to ionization energy: **electronegativity.** The electronegativity of an atom is a description of the atom's energetic "need" for another electron. An atom with a high electronegativity "wants" another electron; it would be very difficult to remove an electron from an atom that already wants another electron. Therefore, the ionization energy of that atom would also be high. Elements in the same Group tend to have similar chemical reactivity based on their willingness to lose or gain electrons. We will look at some of these trends in the following section.

ELEMENTAL FAMILIES

Group 1(IA) elements, with the exception of hydrogen, are called the alkali metals. All the elements in Group 1 are very reactive. Since they only have one electron in their valance shell, they will give up that one electron to another element in order to become more **stable**. In chemistry, stability describes an atom or molecule's energy, the more stable the atom or element is.

When an element loses or gains an electron, it forms an **ion**. An ion is an atom that has lost or gained electrons. Ions have either a positive or a negative charge. When the elements in Group 1 give up the one electron in their valence shell, they form positive ions (or **cations**) with a +1 charge. The positive +1 charge comes from having one more proton than electron. The alkali metals become more reactive as you move down the Periodic Table because the lone electron in the valence shell is further from the positive charge of the nucleus, and thus the electrical attraction is less. *Group 1 elements form ions with a +1 charge.*

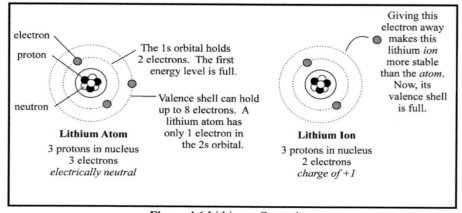

Figure 4.6 Lithium - Group 1

Group 2 (IIA) elements are called the alkaline earth metals. They have 2 electrons out of a possible 8 in their valence shell. These metals are less reactive than the alkali metals but are still very reactive. The alkaline earth metals will give away both of their electrons in their valence shell in order to be more stable. Therefore, they form positive ions with a +2 charge. The +2 charge comes from having two more protons than electrons. The alkaline earth metals also become more reactive as you move down the periodic table. ***Group 2 elements form ions with a charge of +2.***

Groups 1 and 2 are sometimes called the s-block, because their valence electrons are in the s orbital.

Groups 3 – 12(IIIB-IIB) elements in the middle of the Periodic Table are called **transition metals**. They are sometimes referred to as the d-block because their valence electrons are in the d orbital. In general, the reactivity of these metals increases as you go down the Periodic Table and from right to left.

Group 13 – 15 (IIIA, IVA and VA) contain both metals and non-metals. In Group 13, boron is a metalloid; going down the column, all other elements are metals. Group 13 elements form oxides with the general formula R_2O_3. Group 14 is headed by carbon, a prominent nonmetal; going down the column, there are both metalloids (silicon and germanium) and metals. Group 14 elements form oxides with the general formula RO_2. Having four valence electrons (a half-full valence shell) lends these elements a special stability. Group 15 also shows the variation from nonmetal (nitrogen and phosphorous) to metalloid (arsenic and antimony) to metal (bismuth). These elements generally form oxides of the formula R_2O_3 or R_2O_5. ***Group 13 elements form +3 cations and Group 15 elements form negatively charged, −3 ions (or anions). Group 14 elements are generally too stable to ionize.***

Group 16 (VIA) elements have 6 out of a possible 8 electrons in their valence shell. These elements want to gain two electrons to fill the valence shell. Said another way, Group 16 elements have a high electron affinity, particularly oxygen. ***Group 16 elements form anions with a −2 charge.***

Group 17 (VIIA) elements are called the halogens. They have seven electrons in their valence shell, and only require one more to achieve a full valence shell. They have a very high electron affinity and are the most reactive nonmetal elements. They are generally designated with the symbol X and exist in the form X_2, as in Cl_2 gas. They also react with hydrogen, as in HC1. ***Group 17 elements form ions with a −1 charge.***

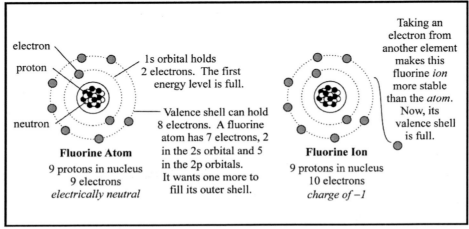

Figure 4.7 Fluorine - Group 17

Group 18 (VIIIA) are the noble gases. The noble gases have 8 electrons in their outer shells with the exception of helium, which fills its first energy level with only 2. (Remember, the first energy level will only hold 2 electrons.) The noble gases are very stable elements because their outermost electron shell is completely filled. They will not react readily with any other elements. *Group 18 elements are inert, and do not form ions under normal circumstances.*

Groups 13 – 18 are sometimes called the p-block. Why? you guessed it: their valence electrons are located in the p orbital.

SUMMARY OF PERIODIC TRENDS OF ELEMENTS

- Reactivity of metals increases *down* the Periodic Table.
- Reactivity of non-metals increases *up* the Periodic Table.
- In general, atomic radius increases *down* the Periodic Table.
- Atomic radius decreases *left to right* across the Periodic Table. This trend may seem opposite from what you would guess. Since the atoms increase in number of protons, neutrons and electrons, you may think the atomic radius would also get larger. However, the opposite is true. Since the atoms have an increasing number of protons, the positive charge in the nucleus increases. The greater the positive charge in the nucleus, the closer the electrons are held to the nucleus due to the electrical force between them. So, in general, the atomic radius decreases from left to right on the Periodic Table.
- In general, ionization energies increase *left to right* across the Periodic Table and decrease down the Periodic Table. Ionization energy is a measure of how tightly an electron is bound to an atom.
- In general, electronegativity increases from *left to right*, and decreases going *down* the Periodic Table. Fluorine has the highest electronegativity.

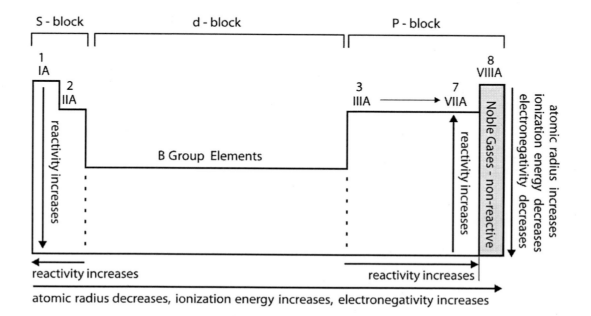

Figure 4.8 Trends of the Elements in the Periodic Table

76

Section Review 3: Reactivity of Elements in the Periodic Table

A. Define the following terms.

valence electron	electronegativity	cation
ionization energy	chemical reactivity	anion
stable	ion	ionization energy

B. Choose the best answer.

1. Given the following set of elements as found in the Periodic Table, which 2 elements would have the most similar chemical properties?

3 Li Lithium 6.941g 2,1	4 Be Beryllium 9.01218 2,2
11 Na Sodium 22.9898 2,8,1	12 Mg Magnesium 24.305 2,8,2

A. lithium and beryllium

B. lithium and sodium

C. sodium and beryllium

D. sodium and magnesium

2. Which of the following statements is NOT true of noble gases?

A. Except for helium, they have 8 electrons in their outer subshell.

B. They do not react readily with other elements.

C. They usually exist as ions.

D. They are in Group 18 (VIIIA).

C. Answer the following questions.

1. What does an atom become when it gains or loses an electron?

2. Which group of elements is the most stable? Why?

3. Look at the block of atoms in the diagram. Which of the elements is most reactive and why?

7 N Nitrogen 14.0067 2,5	8 O Oxygen 15.9994 2,6	9 F Fluorine 18.998403 2,7	10 Ne Neon 20.179 2,8

4. If an atom gains two electrons, what is the charge of the resulting ion? What if it loses 1?

5. What characteristic do all elements in a Group share?

6. Why do alkali metals become more reactive as you move down the Periodic Table?

BONDING OF ATOMS

A **compound** is a substance composed of two or more atoms joined together. A molecule is the smallest particle of a chemical compound that retains the properties of that compound. Atoms of different elements can combine chemically to form molecules by sharing or by transferring valence electrons. Valence electrons are either lost, gained or shared when forming compounds.

IONIC BONDS

An **ion** is an atom with a charge. It is formed by the *transfer* of electrons. When one atom "takes" electrons from another atom, both are left with a charge. The atom that took electrons has a negative charge. (Recall that electrons have a negative charge). The atom that "gave" electrons has a positive charge. The bond formed by this *transfer* is called an **ionic bond**. Ionic bonds are very strong. Ionic compounds have high melting points and high boiling points. These compounds tend to have ordered crystal structures and are usually solids at room temperature. Ionic compounds will usually dissolve in water, and they have the ability to conduct electricity in an aqueous (dissolved in water) or a molten state.

Aluminum oxide is an example of a compound with an ionic bond. In aluminum oxide, two atoms of aluminum react with three atoms of oxygen. The two aluminum atoms give up three electrons each to form positive ions with +3 charges. The three oxygen atoms gain two each of the six electrons given up by the two aluminum atoms to form negative ions with –2 charges. Figure 4.9 illustrates this electron transfer. Note that the orbital shape (circular) has been simplified for clarity.

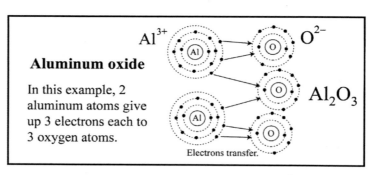

Aluminum oxide

In this example, 2 aluminum atoms give up 3 electrons each to 3 oxygen atoms.

Electrons transfer.

Figure 4.9 Ionic Bonding in Aluminum Oxide

COVALENT BONDS

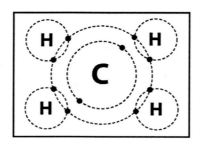

Figure 4.10 Methane Molecule (CH$_4$)

Covalent bonds are formed when two or more elements *share* valence electrons in such a way that their valence electron orbital is filled. The sharing arrangement creates a more stable outer electron structure in the bound elements than was present in their elemental state. In general, there are two rules about which elements form covalent bonds:

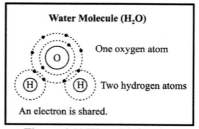

Water Molecule (H$_2$O)

One oxygen atom

Two hydrogen atoms

An electron is shared.

Figure 4.11 Water Molecule

1. Elements with similar electronegativities form covalent bonds.

2. Non-metals form covalent bonds.

The compounds that result from covalent bonding have low melting points and low boiling points. They are usually liquids or gases; if solid, they are brittle. In general, they do not conduct electricity well, although there are some exceptions to that rule. Let's look at two examples of covalent compounds.

Carbon and hydrogen have very similar electronegativities and commonly form covalent bonds. Methane (CH_4) is a good example of a covalent compound. Each of the four hydrogen atoms shares one electron with a single carbon atom. Likewise, the carbon atom shares its four valence electrons – one is shared with each of the four hydrogen atoms. This arrangement gives the carbon atom a full **octet** of eight electrons and each hydrogen atom a full octet of two electrons (remember that hydrogen's valence orbital is the 1s orbital, which can only contain 2 electrons). Note how the valence orbitals of carbon and hydrogen are drawn in Figure 4.10; the overlap of orbitals represents shared electrons.

Water is another example of covalent bonding. Two hydrogen atoms and one oxygen atom combine to form one molecule of water. Figure 4.11 shows how the atoms in water share electrons. However, oxygen has a greater electronegativity than hydrogen. This means that it draws electrons away from hydrogen and toward itself. This lends an "ionic character" to the bond.

POLAR COVALENT AND HYDROGEN BONDS

The covalent bond will sometimes have an "ionic character," depending on the identity of the atoms involved in the bonding. This means that one of the two atoms participating in the bond "wants" electrons more than the other, and thus pulls them closer; this atom has a partially negative charge symbolically shown as δ^-. The other atom, which has allowed its electrons to be pulled away a bit, has a partially positive charge symbolically shown as δ^+. These molecules are called **polar** molecules, and water is an excellent example. The oxygen atom in water pulls electrons toward it; the hydrogen atom is left with a partially positive charge. Figure 4.12 shows three molecules, including water, that exhibit hydrogen bonding.

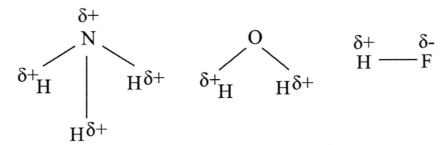

Figure 4.12 Polar Covalent Bonds

The presence of these partial charges creates an electrical attraction between polar molecules: the partially positive end (that is, the hydrogen) lines up in such a way that it is close to the partially negative end (the oxygen) of another polar molecule. The resulting orientation is highly stabilizing, and powerful enough to be called a form of bonding: **hydrogen bonding.** Hydrogen bonds are not as powerful as covalent bonds, but are highly stabilizing and represent a significant organizing force.

Didn't we say that covalent compounds were generally poor conductors of electricity? Well, water is one of the exceptions to that rule. The electrical attraction between the polar water molecules makes a kind of path for electricity to flow through. Free hydrogen ions can also move through water to transport charge. When other compounds, like NaCl, are dissolved in water, it becomes even more electrically conducting. We will talk more about solution conductivity in Chapter 8, Solutions.

Section Review 4: Bonding of Atoms

A. Define the following terms.

compound   covalent bond   hydrogen bond

ionic bond   polar molecule

B. Choose the best answer.

1. A covalent compound has which of the following characteristics?

    A. high melting and high boiling points   C. conducts electricity

    B. atoms share electrons to bond   D. all of the above

2. Hydrogen bonding takes place between

    A. polar molecules containing hydrogen.

    B. non-polar molecules containing hydrogen.

    C. all ionic compounds.

    D. all covalently-bound molecules.

3. What type of bond is formed when atoms transfer electrons?

    A. covalent   B. hydrogen   C. ionic   D. polar

4. Which of the following molecules is non-polar?

    A. NaCl   B. HF   C. CH_4 D. H_2O

5. Which of the following polar molecules could NOT exhibit hydrogen bonding?

    A. HCl   B. CCl_4 C. NH_4 D. HBr

6. Which of the following molecules is MOST likely to have a covalent bond?

    A. O_2 B. NaCl   C. MgO   D. Fe_2O_3

C. Answer the following questions.

1. What kind of bonding do you think is found in a crystal of table sale (NaCl)? How about octane (C_8H_{18}, a primary component of gasoline)? How about in ethanol (C_2H_5OH)?

2. Look at Figure 4.9. How many valence electrons do Al and O each have? How many total electrons?

CHAPTER 4 REVIEW

Choose the best answer.

1. Look at the element of fluorine as it appears in the Periodic Table shown below. How many neutrons are in the nucleus of most fluorine isotopes?

A. 9   C. 18

B. 10   D. 19

2. Why are Group 16 atoms generally quite reactive?

A. They want to gain one electron to become stable.

B. They want to gain two electrons to become stable.

C. They want to lose one electron to become stable.

D. Their outer shell is full of electrons.

3. Choose the valence shell configuration of chlorine (Cl).

A. $3s_2, 3px_2, 3py_1, 3pz_1$ C. $3s_2, 3px_1, 3py_1, 3pz_1$

B. $3s_2, 3px_2, 3py_2, 3pz_1$ D. $3s_2, 3px_2, 3py_2, 3pz_2$

4. Look at the following blocks of elements as they appear in the Periodic Table. Which two elements would have the most similar chemical properties?

9 F Fluorine 18.998403 2,7	10 Ne Neon 20.179 2,8
17 Cl Chlorine 35.453 2,8,7	18 Ar Argon 39.948 2,8,8

A. fluorine and chlorine

B. fluorine and neon

C. fluorine and argon

D. chlorine and neon

5. Which of the following is a characteristic of an ionic bond?

A. low melting point

B. shares electrons

C. good conductor of electricity in aqueous solution

D. insoluble

6. Look at the following block of atoms as they appear in the Periodic Table. Which of the elements is MOST reactive?

A	**B**	**C**	**D**
15 P Phosphorus 30.97376 2,8,5	16 S Sulfur, 32.06 2,8,6	17 Cl Chlorine 35.453 2,8,7	18 Ar Argon 39.948 2,8,8

7. Elements in the same Group have similar chemical properties because

   A. their electrons are inside the nucleus.

   B. they have the same number of valence electrons.

   C. they have the same number of neutrons in their nucleus.

   D. they have similarly-sized nuclei.

8. Which Group of elements contains 8 electrons in its valence shell?

   A. noble gases   B. metals   C. non-metals   D. metalloids

9. An ionic bond results from the transfer of electrons from

   A. one orbital to another within the same atom.

   B. a valence shell of one atom to a valence shell of another atom.

   C. the valence shell of one atom to the nucleus of another atom.

   D. the nucleus of one atom to the nucleus of another atom.

10. The element magnesium (Mg), has 12 electrons. In which energy level will its valence electrons be found?

   A. first   B. second   C. third   D. fourth

11. Which of the following statements correctly describes compounds containing covalent bonds?

   A. Covalent compounds have high melting points.

   B. Covalent compounds conduct electricity well.

   C. Covalent compounds have high boiling points.

   D. Covalent compounds tend to be brittle solids.

12. What is the most common charge of an oxygen ion?

   A. +1   B. +2   C. −1   D. −2

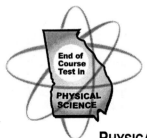

Chapter 5
Nuclear Processes

PHYSICAL SCIENCE STANDARDS COVERED IN THIS CHAPTER INCLUDE:

SPS3 a – d	Students will distinguish the characteristics and components of radioactivity.

RADIOACTIVITY, FISSION AND FUSION

RADIOACTIVITY

As you know, **isotopes** are atoms of the same element with different numbers of neutrons. The nucleus of an atom can be unstable if there are too many neutrons for the number of protons. An unstable nucleus is **radioactive**, and unstable isotopes are called radioactive isotopes. All elements with atomic numbers greater than 83 are radioactive. Radioactive atoms give off radiation in the form of alpha particles, beta particles and gamma rays.

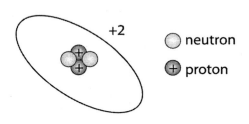

Figure 5.1 Model of an Alpha Particle

An **alpha particle** is equivalent to a helium nucleus, with 2 protons and 2 neutrons, as shown in Figure 5.1. When an alpha particle is released from the nucleus of an atom, the atomic number of the parent nucleus is reduced by two. Alpha particles cannot penetrate a piece of paper or even a thin layer of cloth. However, if ingested, they will do more damage to internal tissue than other forms of radiation.

Beta particles are electrons emitted by an unstable atom. Beta particles are more able to penetrate matter than alpha particles. However, lead is capable of stopping them. **Gamma rays** are high energy X-rays, and only thick lead or concrete can stop them.

Table 5.1 Radioactive Particles

Radiation	Symbol	Particles/Waves	Electric Charge	Energy	Energy stopped by
Alpha particle	α	2 protons, 2 neutrons	positive	low	a piece of paper
Beta particle	β	1 electron	negative	medium	lead 1 cm thick
Gamma rays	γ	wave of energy	no charge	high	thick lead or concrete

A radioactive atom that emits an alpha particle, beta particle or gamma ray is going through a process of **radioactive decay**. Radioactive decay causes an atom of one element to become a different element by reducing its atomic number.

Each isotope decays in its own characteristic way. It will emit α particles, β particles and/or γ rays in a particular order, over a particular period of time. The amount of time that it takes for ½ of the atoms of a radioactive sample to decay is called the **half life** of the isotope. For instance, radium-226 has a half-life of 1,602 years. Let's say a sample of 10 grams of ^{226}Ra is placed in a weighing dish and left in a locked vault. After 1,602 years, the vault is opened. How much ^{226}Ra is in the weighing dish now? That's right, only 5 grams remains. One half of the sample has decayed to something else. But what? That is where it becomes important to know *how* the isotope decayed.

Radium-226 decays by alpha particle emission, as shown in the following equation.

$$^{226}_{88}\text{Ra} \longrightarrow\, ^{222}_{86}\text{Rn} + {}^{4}_{2}\alpha$$

By releasing an alpha particle, the radium-226 atom has lowered its energy and transformed itself into a radon-222 atom.

So, you have seen that unstable nuclei can emit an α particle, β particle or γ ray to become more stable. However, there is another way for an unstable nucleus to lower its energy: the process of nuclear fission.

FISSION

Fission occurs when the nucleus of an atom that has many protons and neutrons becomes so unstable that it splits into two smaller atoms. Fission may be spontaneous or induced.

Spontaneous fission is a natural process that occurs mostly in the transactinide elements, like rutherfordium (Rf). However, some of the actinides (which are a little bit lighter than the transactinides) decay partially by spontaneous fission, including isotopes of uranium (U) and plutonium (Pu). For example, a ^{235}U atom has 92 protons and 143 neutrons. When fission occurs, it may split into a krypton atom and a barium atom, plus 2 neutrons, as shown in the following equation and in Figure 5.2.

$$\ _{92}^{235}\text{U} \longrightarrow\ _{36}^{94}\text{Kr} +\ _{56}^{139}\text{Ba} + 2\ _{0}^{1}\text{n}$$

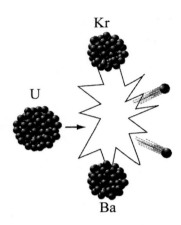

Figure 5.2 Spontaneous Fission

The process of spontaneous fission wasn't well-known or understood until fairly recently. In fact, it was only discovered as a by-product of the investigation into induced fission. **Induced fission** is the process of firing neutrons at heavy atoms, to induce them to split. It was first investigated by **Enrico Fermi** in the 1930s. The theory was proven in 1939, with the discovery by **Lise Meitner** and **Otto Frisch** that the use of neutron projectiles had actually caused a uranium nucleus to split into two pieces, as shown in Figure 5.3 (except that more neutrons were emitted). Meitner and Frisch named the process nuclear fission. Fermi proceeded to co-invent the first nuclear reactor. This design led to the invention of nuclear reactors found in nuclear power plants, as well as nuclear bombs.

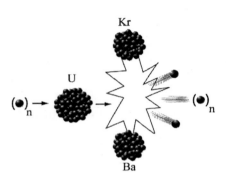

Figure 5.3 Induced Fission

FUSION

During this time, another nuclear process was being investigated: nuclear fusion. **Fusion** is the exact opposite of fission, involving the joining (fusing) of two small atoms to form one larger atom. Fusion reactions occur in the Sun (and other stars), where extremely high temperatures allow hydrogen isotopes to collide and fuse, releasing energy. In 1939, **Hans Bethe** put forth the first quantitative theory explaining fusion, for which he later won the Nobel Prize.

The most commonly-cited fusion reaction is the fusion of hydrogen's two isotopes, deuterium (^{2}H) and tritium (^{3}H), to form a helium nucleus and a neutron. This is shown in Figure 5.4.

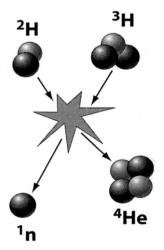

Figure 5.4 Fusion

Section Review 1: Radioactivity, Fission and Fusion

A. Define the following terms.

induced fission	isotope	alpha particle	half-life
spontaneous fission	radioactive	beta particle	fission
	gamma ray	radioactive decay	fusion

B. Choose the best answer.

1. Where would you find a nuclear fusion reaction occurring?
   A. in a nuclear power reactor   C. in an X-ray machine
   B. in the Sun   D. in a microwave oven

2. Palladium-100 has a half-life of 4 days. If you started with 20 grams of palladium-100, how much would remain after 12 days?
   A. 10 grams   B. 0 grams   C. 5 grams   D. 2.5 grams

C. Answer the following questions.

1. Describe the contributions of the following people to the development of our nuclear understanding and technology.
   A. Lise Meitner and Otto Frisch   B. Enrico Fermi

2. What is the difference between induced fission and spontaneous fission?
   occurs naturally   *forcefully*

3. Would it be a good idea to build a nuclear power reactor that utilized spontaneous fission? Why or why not?
   No, because it happens at any moment

Use the figure to answer questions 4 and 5.

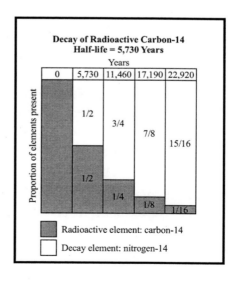

Decay of Radioactive Carbon-14
Half-life = 5,730 Years

4. Does carbon decay by α-particle emission? How do you determine this from the figure?

5. An initial sample of 30 grams of ^{14}C is allowed to decay for 11,460 years. How much does the sample weigh at that time?

INDUCED FISSION

Induced fission is the process of bombarding radioactive atoms with neutrons to cause them to split apart. What are the products of these processes? There are several, including fission fragments, neutrons and energy. First, let's look at the fission fragments and neutrons.

FISSION FRAGMENTS AND NEUTRONS

Look back at Figures 5.2 and 5.3. The illustrations simplify the fission process and depict an atom of uranium always splitting into krypton and barium. In actuality, however, the nuclear products are much more diverse, as shown in Figure 5.5.

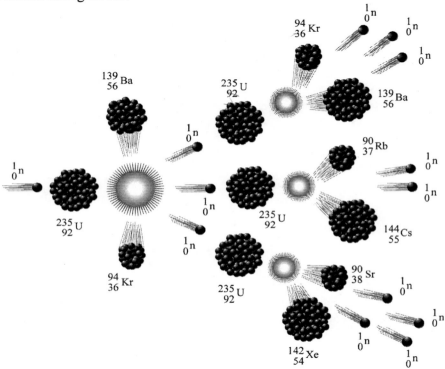

Figure 5.5 Production of Fission Fragments

Besides barium and krypton, rubidium, cesium, strontium and xenon are also produced. These **fission fragments** are the products of an atom split by neutron bombardment. The average mass of ^{235}U fission fragments is 118, but as Figure 5.6 indicates, a fragment of mass 118 is rarely detected. Instead, ^{235}U tends to split into uneven fragment masses around 95 and 137. To see this in another way, look again at the mass numbers and atomic numbers of the fragments shown in Figure 5.5.

Each of the fission fragments is an isotope with a half-life of its own, which may range from seconds to millions of years. As the half-life of each isotope passes, the isotope decays by emitting one or more forms of radiation, like alpha and beta particles or gamma rays. The result is a new isotope called a **daughter**, which may or may not be **stable**. If the atom is **unstable** (meaning that it is still radioactive), it will decay to yet another isotope. If the atom is stable, it will remain as it is, with no further transformation. The succession of decays is called a **decay chain**.

One common pair of fragments is xenon and strontium. The fission is illustrated by the following reaction.

$$^{235}U + n \longrightarrow {}^{236}U^* \longrightarrow {}^{140}Xe + {}^{94}Sr + 2n$$

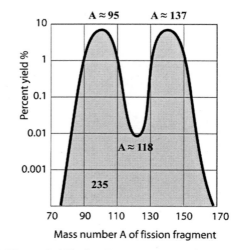

Figure 5.6 Fission Fragment Mass Distribution

U-236 has an asterisk (*) because it only lasts a moment after absorbing the neutron. The forces within the nucleus redistribute themselves allowing for the fission decay, in this case to xenon and strontium isotopes. Xenon-40 is a highly radioactive isotope with a half-life of 14 seconds. It undergoes a series of decays, finally ending with cerium-140. Strontium-94, with a half-life of 74 seconds, decays by beta emission to yttrium-94. Let's look at a partial decay chain of those isotopes, as in Figure 5.7.

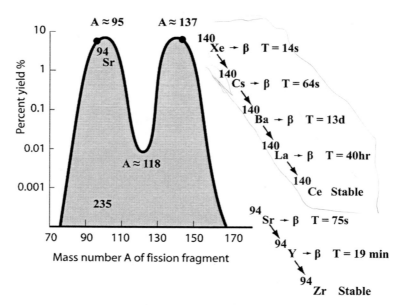

Figure 5.7 Decay Chain

These decay chains show only beta (β) emissions, but other fission fragments may have other types of radiative decay. Even different isotopes of xenon and strontium will decay differently. For instance, we have been looking at Xe-140 and Sr-94. Look back at Figure 5.5. See that the isotopes of strontium and xenon noted there are Xe-142 and Sr-90. The reaction that produces those fragments would be:

$$^{235}U + n \longrightarrow {}^{236}U^* \longrightarrow {}^{142}Xe + {}^{90}Sr + 4n$$

These isotopes will have a different decay chain than that illustrated by Figure 5.7. Try going to the Internet to find their decay chains. Surf around the Brookhaven National Lab's national nuclear database at http://www.nndc.bnl.gov.

NUCLEAR ENERGY

When a nucleus splits, or fissions, a great deal of energy is also released. In fact, the scientific world was surprised by how much energy was generated. **Neils Bohr**, the Danish physicist who first modeled the atom, wrote to Lise Meitner to comment on how unexpectedly large the energy release was. The energy release was much larger than calculations had predicted, it turns out. Up until this point, fission research had been performed simply to understand more about the atom. Now, though, the stakes began to rise: a new energy source had been found.

How much energy are we talking about, though? The **nuclear energy** produced by fission and fusion reactions requires only a small amount of matter. After all, an atom is a very small amount of matter. Einstein's famous **mass-energy equation**, $E = mc^2$, states this fact very simply. Einstein's equation, written in word form, is Energy = mass × speed of light × speed of light. Since the speed of light is 3×10^8 meters per second and this term is squared, we can still have a very small amount of matter and end up with a large amount of energy. A nuclear fission reaction, utilizing one U-235 atom, will produce 50 million times more energy than the combustion (burning) of a carbon atom.

Today we use nuclear reactors to harness this power for the production of electricity. Figure 5.8 shows the process. Fissile material, like uranium-235, is manufactured into pellets that are bound together into long rods, called **fuel rods**. Fuel rods are bundled together with **control rods** and placed in the reactor core. Here is what happens.

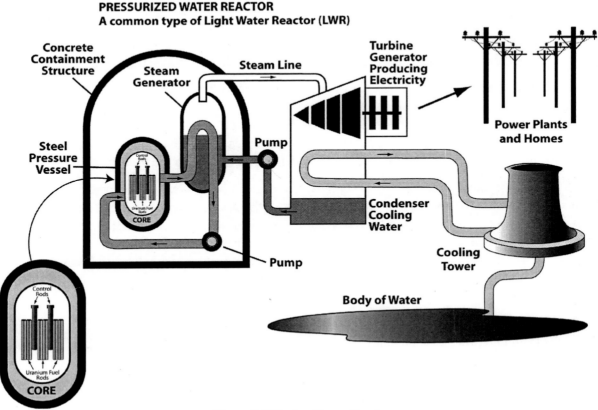

Figure 5.8 Nuclear Power Reactor

Every time a uranium atom fissions, it releases neutrons, which cause another atom to fission. This process is called a **chain reaction**, and it produces energy in the form of heat. The water surrounding the reactor core gets very hot. It is pumped through another water tank by way of a pipe. Note that the water from the core never touches any reactor component outside the core. The continuous pumping of the super-hot water from the reactor core heats the secondary tank water to produce a continuous supply of steam. The steam turns the turbines of a generator, which generates electricity. The steam is then diverted to a cooling tower.

Nuclear Power Plant
Figure 5.9 Cooling Tower

This structure, as shown in Figure 5.9, is commonly associated with nuclear power plants, though it actually has nothing to do with energy production. It is where the steam condenses and cools before its release into a body of water, like a river.

ENERGY AND ENVIRONMENTAL CONSEQUENCES

Nuclear power is a very attractive energy option because it is clean and cheap. However, as with every energy option, there are environmental consequences. The two that are the most important to prevent are **supercriticality** and **environmental contamination** from general operation.

SUPERCRITICALITY

Inside a nuclear power reactor, uranium fuel is used to create energy. Long fuel rods formed of small U-235 pellets are arranged into bundles and submerged in some coolant, usually water. In order for the reactor to work, the submerged bundles of rods must be *slightly* **supercritical**. This means that, left to its own devices, the uranium in the rods would eventually overheat and melt.

To prevent this, control rods are used. **Control rods** are made of a material, like cadmium, that absorbs neutrons. Inserted into the bundle of uranium, control rods allow operators to control the rate of the nuclear reaction. If more heat is needed, the rods are raised out of the uranium bundle. To lessen heat, the rods are lowered into the uranium bundle. The rods can also be lowered completely into the uranium bundle to shut the reactor down in the case of an accident or to change the fuel.

These control rods are the safeguard of the power plant. Without them, true supercriticality could be reached. Were this to happen, the uranium would melt the reactor core, causing a **breech** (a crack or hole) and subsequent release of radioactive isotopes, encased in superheated steam and melted metals. Depending on the scale of the breech, this could be an environmental disaster. The Three Mile Island accident in the US was not a disaster; very little radioactivity was released. It was a warning, however, for the U.S. to increase safety and maintenance precautions. The Chernobyl accident in the former Soviet Union was a disaster and one that the region has yet to recover from.

The issue of environmental impact must be studied whenever an effort to produce energy is planned. Drilling for oil, damming rivers and erecting windmills all have environmental impacts. These must be weighed against the value of the energy produced and the ultimate cost of failure.

ENVIRONMENTAL CONTAMINATION

We have noted that Sr-90 is one product of the induced fission of U-235. This isotope of strontium has an intermediate half-life of around 30 years. This is a difficult time span for environmental contaminants. If you are asking "why," consider this. A short half-life of minutes, days or weeks indicates that the contaminant will be gone (decay) quickly and not have a chance to do much damage, particularly in low concentrations. A long half-life of hundreds, thousands or even millions of years indicates that the isotope releases radioactive particles so infrequently that little damage is done. An intermediate half-life, however, can do great damage.

In addition, strontium mimics the properties of calcium. Look where it is on the Periodic Table — in the same group as calcium. This means that strontium is taken up by living organisms that utilize calcium; those organisms incorporate Sr-90 into their bones. There the Sr-90 decays, emitting radiation that can cause cancer. While strontium is *very unlikely* to enter the environment from a nuclear power reactor, it is one of several isotopes that would have a negative environmental effect if released. In addition to the normal security and operational controls of a nuclear power plant, the area surrounding the reactor must be continually monitored to ensure that no such release has occurred.

Another, more pressing, example of environmental contamination is the issue of radioactive waste. Remember that many different kinds of radioactive isotopes, each of which decays in a different way, are the result of the fission of ^{235}U. This occurs *within the core of the reactor*; during normal operation, no radioactive components come in contact with any other part of the facility. However, a reactor core does not last forever; periodically, fuel rods and control rods must be replaced to maintain optimal function of the reactor. The spent rods still contain a great deal of radioactive material, mostly from the still-decaying daughters of the fission fragments.

The processing of this waste, to separate and neutralize the individual components, is not always possible or feasible. At present, there is no ideal storage solution for this waste. In order to avoid contamination, it must be stored in a highly absorbing material and allowed to decay in a location that will remain secure for many years. **Yucca Mountain** (in Nevada) is the prospective site for nuclear waste storage in this country. Other countries, like France, almost completely reprocess their nuclear waste; this leaves little need for waste storage.

ONGOING RESEARCH

Three kinds of research are being performed that may revolutionize the way nuclear processes are used in power production.

1. New fission reactor designs are now under construction that make nuclear power even cheaper, safer and more efficient.

2. New waste re-processing technologies are being investigated to help us deal with dangerous and long-lived nuclear waste.

3. Fusion reactors are still being investigated. Fusion reactions, as described earlier in this section, produce a great deal of energy — potentially much more than fission reactions. They have fewer reactants, fewer products and produce little waste. Scientists are still trying to overcome the obstacle of the extremely high temperatures necessary for fusion to occur and sustain itself.

Keep an eye on these technologies, as well as other energy technologies. Remember, you will be paying the power bills one day soon.

Section Review 2: More About Nuclear Energy

A. Define the following terms.

stable	unstable	decay chain	control rod
fission fragments	supercritical	breech	fuel rod

B. Choose the best answer.

1. In the following reaction, how many neutrons are produced?

$$^{235}U + n \longrightarrow {}^{236}U^* \longrightarrow {}^{90}Rb + {}^{144}Cs + \underline{\hspace{1.5cm}}$$

    A. 1   B. 2   C. 3   D. 4

2. Which subatomic particle is used as a projectile to induce fission reactions?
    A. the proton   B. the neutron   C. the electron   D. the alpha particle

C. Answer the following questions.

1. Describe the use of control rods in a nuclear power reactor.

2. Search the terms "Three Mile Island" and "Chernobyl" on the Internet. From what you find, describe what happened and what the difference was in the two accidents.

3. Describe the environmental impact of nuclear power plants.

4. It was noted in this chapter that many different fission fragments are produced during a fission process. Does this have an impact on the handling of nuclear waste?

5. Nuclear fission reactions are used to make nuclear energy. Name one advantage and one disadvantage of using nuclear fission as an energy source.

6. A nuclear reactor uses fission to produce harnessed energy that we can use. A nuclear bomb produces a nuclear explosion of unharnessed energy. What is the difference between these two nuclear devices?

7. Why would a fusion reactor be more desirable than a fission reactor? Why are fusion reactors not used?

8. How is nuclear fission similar to nuclear fusion? How are these two types of nuclear reactions different?

CHAPTER 5 REVIEW

Choose the best answer.

1. A scientist detected radiation escaping from a material encased in a thick block of concrete. Identify the type of radiation the scientist MOST likely detected.

   A. beta particles   C. gamma radiation

   B. alpha particles   D. radio nuclides

2. Given 100.0 g of a radioactive isotope that has a half-life of 25 years, identify the amount of that isotope that will remain after 100 years.

   A. 50.0 g   B. 25.0 g   C. 12.5 g   D. 6.3 g

3. The half-life of an isotope is the time required for half of the nuclei in the sample to undergo

   A. induced fission.   C. fusion.

   B. spontaneous fission.   D. radioactive decay.

4. Which of the following radioactive emissions is the MOST dangerous if ingested?

   A. α-particle   C. X-ray

   B. β-particle   D. microwave

5. Identify the element that *cannot* participate in nuclear fission reactions.

   A. plutonium   C. uranium

   B. hydrogen   D. thorium

6. Identify the issue that has NOT been a factor in any new nuclear power plants having been built in over twenty years.

   A. construction costs   C. availability of nuclear fuel

   B. political opposition   D. disposal of radioactive by-products

7. Describe the reaction illustrated by:

   $$^1H + {}^2H \rightarrow {}^3He$$

   A. spontaneous fission   C. decay

   B. induced fission   D. fusion

8. Which of the following is an appropriate material to use in making control rods?

   A. hydrogen   B. cadmium   C. plutonium   D. uranium

9. The following reaction shows the alpha decay of uranium-238 to thorium-234. The nuclear mass, in grams, is written beneath each nuclide symbol. What is the change in mass (Δm) for this reaction?

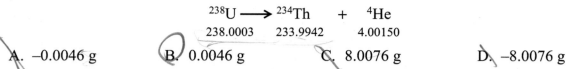

$$^{238}U \longrightarrow {}^{234}Th + {}^{4}He$$
$$238.0003 \qquad 233.9942 \qquad 4.00150$$

A. −0.0046 g   B. 0.0046 g   C. 8.0076 g   D. −8.0076 g

10. Every mass has an associated energy, and every energy has an associated mass. This is described by Einstein's equation $E=mc^2$. When the mass of a product set is different than the mass of a reactant set, what has happened to the mass?

A. It has been eliminated.

B. It has been converted to energy.

C. It has been accelerated to the speed of light.

D. It has been accelerated to the speed of light, squared.

11. Complete the following equation. What nuclei belongs in the first blank and how many neutrons are produced (second blank)?

$$^{1}n + {}^{235}U \longrightarrow {}^{136}I + \_\_\_\_ + \_\_\_\_ {}^{1}n$$

A. ^{96}Y, 3   B. ^{94}Sr, 4   C. ^{96}Y, 4   D. ^{94}Sr, 3

12. A decay chain ends when

A. the product nucleus decays to zero grams.

B. the product nucleus undergoes fission.

C. the product nucleus is stable.

D. the product nucleus undergoes fusion.

13. When a reaction is supercritical,

A. small amounts of neutrons are being produced.

B. large amounts of neutrons are being produced.

C. all the fission fragments in the core are unstable.

D. all of the fission fragments in the core are stable.

14. Which of the following is NOT an isotope of hydrogen?

A. ^{1}H B. ^{2}H C. ^{3}H D. ^{4}H

Chapter 6
Chemical Equations and Reactions

PHYSICAL SCIENCE STANDARDS COVERED IN THIS CHAPTER INCLUDE:

SPS2 b – e	Students will explore the nature of matter, its classifications, and its system for naming types of matter.

In Chapter 4, we discussed the characteristics of individual elements at the atomic level. It should be clear that the number of valence electrons that an atom of an element has is the primary factor in determining the kind of bonding arrangements that atom forms with atoms of other elements. Once bound together, individual atoms become a **molecule**. In this chapter, we will examine these molecular arrangements and the chemical interaction between molecules.

UNDERSTANDING CHEMICAL FORMULAS

A **chemical formula** is a group of symbols that show the makeup of a molecule. For example, the chemical formula for a molecule of water is H_2O. The **subscript**, or small number, after the elemental symbol indicates the number of atoms of the element present in the molecule. The chemical formula for water, H_2O, indicates that 2 atoms of hydrogen combine with 1 atom of oxygen. In aluminum oxide, Al_2O_3, 2 atoms of aluminum combine with 3 atoms of oxygen (look back to Figure 4.9 to see how). In sodium chloride, NaCl, 1 atom of sodium combines with 1 atom of chlorine.

Atoms bind together to form molecules like ammonia, NH_3, which is a gas. Notice that the NH_3 molecule is neutral, meaning that it has no charge. Does the fact that the molecule is neutral mean that it will not interact with other molecules? Nope! Ammonia may be neutral, but that does not mean that it is chemically unreactive. Remember that N and H have different electronegativities, so this will be a polar molecule. Watch what happens when gaseous ammonia is bubbled through a beaker of liquid water.

$$NH_3 + H_2O \longrightarrow NH_4^+ + OH^-$$

New molecules have formed, but these have a charge. Recall that atoms can be ionized by removing an electron from their valence shell. A similar thing has occurred in this situation: the electron arrangement of the ammonia and water molecules has been changed by their interaction with each other. The result is two charged molecules called **ions**.

Let's look at the bonding in the molecules and ions, as shown in Figure 6.1. Covalent bonds are shared electrons. In the neutral ammonia molecule, NH_3, each hydrogen atom shares an electron with the central nitrogen atom. This results in three covalent bonds (represented by lines) in the ammonia molecule. Nitrogen also retains one **lone pair** of electrons, shown as two dots above the nitrogen atom. At this point, nitrogen has 5 valence electrons surrounding it, one from each covalent bond, plus two from the lone pair. If you look at the Periodic Table, nitrogen is placed in Group 15 (or VA), and so you know that it should have 5 valence electrons in its neutral state. When the ammonia gas comes in contact with liquid water, its electron arrangement changes. Here is what happens:

1. Ammonia takes a hydrogen atom from the water molecule.

2. The hydrogen atom leaves its electron with oxygen.

3. The two electrons that had been nitrogen's lone pair are now used to form a covalent bond with the "stolen" hydrogen atom.

4. The nitrogen atom now has four valence electrons surrounding it, one from each covalent bond. Since it should have five valence electrons, it now shows a deficit of one electron (5-4=1) and so it becomes an ion with a +1 charge.

Figure 6.1 The Reaction of Ammonia with Water

Practice Exercise 1:   Covalent Bonding

Based on this information, can you describe what has happened to the water molecule?

<u>Before interacting with ammonia:</u>

1. How many covalent bonds does the water molecule have? _____

2. How many lone pairs does the oxygen atom in water have? _____

3. How many valence electrons does oxygen have in the water molecule? _____

4. On the Periodic Table, what element Group is oxygen found? _____

5. What is the charge on the water molecule? _____

<u>After interacting with ammonia:</u>

1. How many covalent bonds does oxygen now have? _____

2. How many lone pairs does oxygen now have? _____

3. How many valence electrons now surround oxygen? _____

4. What is the charge on the new OH^- ion? _____

Since opposite charges are drawn to each other by **electrostatic attraction**, the two new ions are usually written as a molecule, NH_4OH. A whole bunch of these molecules together are referred to as a compound. Where would you find a whole bunch of NH_4OH molecules? Well, if you look in the laundry cabinet at your house, you will probably see a jug containing this compound: ammonium hydroxide, or liquid bleach.

It is important to know that chemical formulas of individual ions are often written together as uncharged molecules. If you can tell when this has been done, you will know when an ionic bond is present. Recall that an ionic bond is a transfer of electrons. Sometimes a chemical formula clearly shows you what the ions are, by using parentheses, as in the calcium hydroxide compound, $Ca(OH)_2$. This chemical formula shows a calcium ion, Ca^{2+}, ionically bound to two OH^- ions. How many atoms are in a calcium hydroxide molecule?

To find the number of atoms of each element, multiply the subscript number inside the parentheses by the subscript number outside the parentheses.

Example 1: $Ca(OH)_2$ contains 2 groups of OH ions. Therefore, the number of atoms in a calcium hydroxide molecule equals 1 atom of calcium, 2 atoms of oxygen and 2 atoms of hydrogen.

$$Ca \left\langle \begin{array}{c} OH \\ OH \end{array} \right.$$

Example 2: $Al(NO_3)_3$ has 1 atom of aluminum, 3 atoms of nitrogen and 9 atoms of oxygen.

$$Al \left\langle \begin{array}{c} NO_3 \\ NO_3 \\ NO_3 \end{array} \right.$$

If you look at the Periodic Table, you will see that calcium is a metal in the s-block (on the left side of the Periodic Table) and aluminum is a metalloid in the p-block (on the right side). Ionic bonding that involves metalloids and metals (including the metals of the d-block in the middle of the Periodic Table) results in ionic solids. In the solid form, these compounds often take on an ordered structure that is referred to as a **crystal lattice**. To emphasize this, their chemical formula is sometimes written with the notation (cr), as in NaCl (cr). This convention is not always observed, however, and you will also see ionic solids written like other solids, as in NaCl (s).

Now try counting up the atoms on your own. As you are doing so, try also to think about the kind of bonding arrangements in each of these compounds.

Practice Exercise 2:   Chemical Formulas

For each chemical formula, give the ratio of atoms present for each element.

Formula   **Number of atoms of each element**

1. $Mg(NO_3)_2$ _____

2. $Al_2(SO_4)_3$ _____

3. $Ba(OH)_2$ _____

4. H_3PO_4 _____

Now that we know what elements make up each of these chemical formulas, let's try to name them. The **International Union of Pure and Applied Chemistry (IUPAC)** has systematized the naming of all chemical compounds. We will just look at diatomic and binary compounds for now, but you can always go to www.iupac.org to see more.

DIATOMIC MOLECULES

Diatomic molecules consist of two atoms bound together into a molecule. A diatomic molecule may be **homonuclear** (two atoms of the same element, like O_2) or **heteronuclear** (two atoms of different elements, like HCl).

Oxygen, hydrogen and nitrogen, as well as all of the halogens, form homonuclear diatomic molecules as their most stable elemental state. Note that these are all gases, as indicated by the (g) in $O_2(g)$, $H_2(g)$ and $Cl_2(g)$. Even metals form homonuclear diatomic molecules when in a gaseous state. In this case, the molecule is just called by its elemental name.

Heteronuclear diatomic molecules, like NaCl, are a subclass of a larger category of molecules, called binary compounds.

BINARY COMPOUNDS

A **binary compound** has two different elements that have reacted to form a molecule. Some examples are CCl_4, HBr, NaCl and $FeCl_3$. Note that HBr and NaCl are also heteronuclear diatomic molecules, which contain two atoms from two different elements. On the other hand, CCl_4 contains 5 atoms (one carbon atom and four chlorine atoms) from two different elements and $FeCl_3$ contains 4 atoms (one iron atom and three chlorine atoms) from two different elements. These two compounds are not diatomic but *multi*-atomic. However, all four compounds can correctly be called "binary," since they are made from two elements.

Also notice from these four examples that the bonding in a binary can be either ionic or covalent. In fact, the bonding arrangement must be known in order to correctly name the compound.

BINARY COVALENT COMPOUNDS

Covalent compounds are named using a few rules.

- Binary covalent compounds have two words in their name. Name them as their formulas are written, from left to right. The first word is simply the name of the element. For instance, in CCl_4, carbon (C) will be the first word.

- The second word is the name of the other atoms, with "ide" replacing the end of the element name. For instance, HBr would be called hydrogen bromide.

- Sometimes a prefix is needed to indicate how many of each element makes up the compound. Refer to Table 6.1 for the necessary prefixes. In CCl_4, carbon does not require the "mono" prefix; the only time that mono is used is when oxygen is being named. However, the four chlorides do require a prefix. The full, correct name is carbon tetrachloride.

- There are a few common molecules that are not named this way. Water is one of them. It is called water, rather than dihydrogen monoxide. Ammonia (NH_3) is another.

Number of Atoms	Prefix
1	mono- (use only for oxygen)
2	di-
3	tri-
4	tetra-
5	penta-
6	hexa-
7	hepta-
8	octa-

Table 6.1 Numerical Prefixes

BINARY IONIC COMPOUNDS

Binary ionic compounds are named similarly to binary covalent compounds.

- The first word is the name of the first element in the formula. This will always be the cation (+ charge ion). In NaCl, for instance, the cation is Na^+ and the first word in the compound's name is sodium.

- The second word is the name of the anion (– charge ion). Since we are naming binary compounds, the anion is a single element, like chlorine. When the anion is a halogen (F, Cl, Br, I, etc), simply replace the –ine with an –ide. Halogen anions are then fluoride, chloride, bromide and iodide. So, NaCl is called sodium chloride. Sometimes the anion will be oxygen; in that case, use the anion name oxide.

- Some elements (particularly d and f-block elements) form cations that can have more than one possible charge. $FeCl_3$ and $FeCl_2$ are good examples. Iron in $FeCl_3$ has a +3 charge; iron in $FeCl_2$ has a +2 charge. At this point we would call both of them iron chloride. (Notice that we do not distinguish a binary ionic compound by using the prefixes in Table 6.1; they are named by charge of the ions, not by the number of atoms.) If more than one charge state is possible, then the charge must be specified in the name. How do you know? Until you are more familiar with chemical formulas, you will have to use a reference like Figure 6.2 (on the page 101).

- If you determine that the compound you are naming has more than one charge state, a Roman numeral is used to specify the charge state by the following formula.

$$Roman\ numeral = -\frac{[(charge\ on\ anion) \times (number\ of\ anions)]}{(number\ of\ cations)}$$

To find out the charge on the anion, look back to Chapter 4 for the descriptions of the ions formed by various families in the p-block of elements, on the right side of the Periodic Table. <u>It will be useful to remember that the halogens always form anions with a -1 charge; oxygen always forms anions with a -2 charge</u>.

For $FeCl_3$, we get $-\dfrac{[(-1) \times (3)]}{(1)} = +3$, which means we use the Roman numeral (III).

The final name for $FeCl_3$ is then iron (III) chloride

POLYATOMIC IONS

Many atomic species form common combinations that are identified with common names, as found in Table 6.2. Using the same rules that you have learned in this section, you can see that the compound $KMnO_4$ would be called potassium permanganate. The compound $NaOH$ is sodium hydroxide.

Table 6.2 Polyatomic Ions

Polyatomic Ions	
NH_4^+	Ammonium
$C_2H_3O_2$	Acetate
ClO_3^-	Chlorate
MnO_4^-	Permanganate
NO_3^-	Nitrate
OH^-	Hydroxide
CO_3^{2-}	Carbonate
CrO_4^{2-}	Chromate
SO_4^{2-}	Sulfate
PO_4^{3-}	Phosphate

										13 Al			
21 Sc +3	22 Ti +2, +3, +4	23 V +2, +3, +4, +5	24 Cr +2, +3, +6	25 Mn +2, +3, +4, +7	26 Fe +2, +3	27 Co +2, +3	28 Ni +2, +3	29 Cu +1, +2	30 Zn +2	31 Ga +3	32 Ge +2, +4		
39 Y +3	40 Zr +4	41 Nb +3, +5	42 Mo +8	43 Tc +4, +6, +7	44 Ru +3	45 Rh +3	46 Pd +2, +4	47 Ag +1	48 Cd +2	49 In +3	50 Sn +2, +4	51 Sb +3, +5	
71 Lu +3	72 Hf +4	73 Ta +5	74 W +6	75 Re +4, +6, +7	76 Os +3, +4	77 Ir +3, +4	78 Pt +2, +4	79 Au +1, +3	80 Hg +1, +2	81 Tl +1, +3	82 Pb +2, +4	83 Bi +3, +5	84 Po +2, +4
103 Lr +3	104 Rf	105 Db	106 Sg	107 Bh	108 Hs	109 Mt							

57 La +3	58 Ce +3, +4	59 Pr +3	60 Nd +3	61 Pm +3	62 Sm +2, +3	63 Eu +2, +3	64 Gd +3	65 Tb +3	66 Dy +3	67 Ho +3	68 Er +3	69 Tm +3	70 Yb +3
89 Ac +3	90 Th +4	91 Pa +4, +5	92 U +3, +4, +5, +6	93 Np +3, +4, +5, +6	94 Pu +3, +4, +5, +6	95 Am +3, +4, +5, +6	96 Cm +3	97 Bk +3, +4	98 Cf +3	99 Es +3	100 Fm +3	101 Md +2, +3	102 No +2, +3

Figure 6.2 Charge states of the transition metals, lanthanides and actinides.

Now, let's see how well you use these rules.

Practice Exercise 3

Use the rules to name each compound.

Formula

1. I_2 ____________________
2. SbF_5 ____________________
3. SF_4 ____________________
4. N_2O_4 ____________________
5. $FePO_4$ ____________________
6. TiO_2 ____________________
7. $CaCrO_4$ ____________________
8. KOH ____________________

Section Review 1: Understanding Chemical Formulas and Equations

A. Define the following terms.

IUPAC	binary compound	crystal lattice
chemical formula	diatomic molecule	heteronuclear
lone pair	electrostatic attraction	homonuclear
subscript		

B. Choose the best answer.

1. One molecule of calcium carbonate, $CaCO_3$, has how many atoms of calcium, Ca?

   A. 0   B. 1   C. 2   D. 3

2. How many atoms of oxygen are present in one molecule of H_2SO_4?

   A. 1   B. 2   C. 4   D. 8

3. What is the ratio of atoms present in ammonia, NH_3?

   A. 1 atom of nitrogen to 3 atoms of hydrogen

   B. 3 atoms of nitrogen to 1 atom of hydrogen

   C. 1 atom of nitrogen to 1 atom of hydrogen

   D. the ratio varies

4. What kind of compound is $MgCl_2$?

   A. a homonuclear diatomic molecule   C. a binary ionic compound

   B. a heteronuclear diatomic molecule   D. a binary covalent compound

5. You have a weighing dish containing table salt. What is the correct way to describe it?

   A. as a sample of the NaCl molecule

   B. as a sample of NaCl atoms

   C. as a sample of the compound, NaCl

   D. as a sample of the binary covalent compound, NaCl

C. Answer the following questions.

1. Determine the names of CuO_2 and AgI using the rules for binary ionic compounds.

2. What is the name of the compound $N_2(g)$?

3. Determine the names of SF_6, CO_2 and H_2S using the rules for naming binary covalent compounds.

BASIC CHEMICAL EQUATIONS

A **chemical equation** expresses a chemical reaction. A **chemical reaction** is a process in which one or more elements or compounds (reactants) form new elements or compounds (products). The **reactants** are the starting substances. The **products** are the substances formed by the reaction. In a chemical equation, an arrow separates the reactants and the product. When reading a chemical equation aloud, you say that the reactants yield the products. The arrow represents the "yield" part of the equation. Many times, the chemical equation also contains information about the state of the reactants and products. The equation lists the physical states of the substances in parentheses. The right side of Figure 6.3 lists some of the common physical states and their abbreviations.

$NaOH(aq) + HCl(aq) \rightarrow NaCl(aq) + H_2O(l)$	(aq) aqueous (dissolved in water)
	(g) gas
	(l) liquid
reactants yield products	(s) solid; sometimes (cr) crystalline

Figure 6.3 Example of a Chemical Equation

BASIC CHEMICAL REACTIONS

All chemical reactions involve one or more reactants that interact to form one or more products. From the huge array of elements in the periodic table, we can assume that there is an equally wide variety of possible interactions between these elements. These interactions are divided into several different categories.

$AX + BY \rightarrow BX + AY$

Synthesis reactions: Small molecules combine to form larger ones.

$$H_2(g) + Cl_2(g) \rightarrow 2HCl(aq)$$

Decomposition reactions: The opposite of synthesis reactions. Large molecules break apart to form smaller molecules.

$$2H_2O_2(l) \rightarrow 2H_2O(l) + O_2(g)$$

Single displacement reaction: When a pure element switches places with one of the elements in a compound.

$$Mg(s) + 2HCl(l) \rightarrow MgCl_2(aq) + H_2(g)$$

Double displacement reaction: The components of ionic compounds switch places.

$$AgNO_3(aq) + NaCl(aq) \rightarrow AgCl(s) + NaNO_3(aq)$$

Each of these is a **balanced equation**. We will see why this is so in the next section.

WRITING BALANCED CHEMICAL EQUATIONS

CONSERVATION OF MASS

Chemical equations must maintain balance. There must be the same number of atoms of each element on both sides of the equation. The **Law of Conservation of Mass** states that matter is conserved, which means that you can neither create nor destroy it. The amount of matter remains the same before and after a chemical reaction. An atom of hydrogen remains an atom of hydrogen, but it may chemically bond to form a different compound.

BALANCING CHEMICAL EQUATIONS

Look at the equation in Figure 6.4. On the side of the reactants, there is 1 atom of Na, 1 atom of O, 2 atoms of H, and 1 atom of Cl. On the product side of the reaction, there is 1 atom of Na, 1 atom of Cl, 2 atoms of H, and 1 atom of O. The number of atoms of each element is equal, so this is a balanced equation.

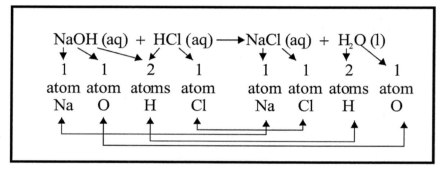

Figure 6.4 Example of a Balanced Equation

Now look at the following equation. There are 2 atoms of hydrogen reacting and 2 atoms of hydrogen as products, so the hydrogen in the equation is balanced. However, there are 2 atoms of oxygen reacting but only 1 atom of oxygen shown as products. This is not a balanced equation.

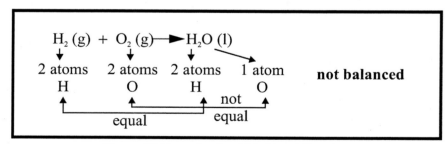

Figure 6.5 Example of an Unbalanced Equation

How can we balance the equation in Figure 6.5? We balance the equation by **inspection**.

Step 1: Put a 2 in front of the H_2O. Now, we have 2 atoms of oxygen to balance the oxygen, but the number of hydrogen atoms increases to 4.

Step 2: Put a 2 in front of the H_2. Now, we have 4 atoms of hydrogen on each side of the equation, and the equation is completely balanced.

Balancing equations is a matter of trial and error. Change the numbers in front of each element until the number of atoms of each element is equal on both sides. Remember, you can never change the number of the subscripts. Changing the number of the subscripts changes the identity of the compound, which consequently changes the meaning of the equation.

Up until now, we have said that equations are balanced by balancing the number of atoms on the reactant side with the number of atoms on the product side. This is true. It is rare, however, that chemists work with such tiny amounts. Usually they are working with some tangible quantity, like milligrams or grams. A gram of, say, magnesium, contains a LOT of atoms of magnesium. So many, in fact, that chemists came up with the **mole concept**. One mole of an element is equal to 6×10^{23} atoms of the element. One mole of a compound equals 6×10^{23} molecules of that compound. That large number, 6×10^{23}, is called **Avogadro's number**. Do not let the size of it scare you away from using it.

Let us look back at the four primary reaction types again, and use words to describe those reactions.

Synthesis reactions: In words, we can say that 1 mole of hydrogen gas reacted with 1 mole of chlorine gas to form 2 moles of aqueous (in water) hydrochloric acid.

Decomposition reactions: Here, 2 moles of hydrogen peroxide decomposed to 2 moles of water and one mole of oxygen gas.

Single displacement reaction: Here, 1 mole of elemental magnesium reacted with 2 moles of hydrochloric acid to form one mole of magnesium chloride (dissolved in water) and 1 mole of elemental hydrogen gas.

Challenge Activity

Now it is your turn to describe the reaction in words.

Double displacement reaction: _____

_____

_____

REDOX REACTIONS

Redox reactions are a category of chemical reactions that involve the transfer of electrons between the reacting elements, molecules or ions. Redox reactions are not separate from synthesis, decomposition or single replacement; each of these reaction types may also be a redox reaction. Only the double displacement reaction is never a redox process.

The term redox is the abbreviation of "oxidation-reduction reactions."

- The *oxidation* half of the reaction shows the *loss* of electrons by a reactant.
- The *reduction* part of the reaction shows the *gain* of electrons by the reactant.

Metals tend to oxidize (lose electrons). Highly electronegative elements, like oxygen and the halogens, tend to be reduced (gain electrons). For example, when the metal iron reacts with oxygen, it forms iron oxide, which we call rust. The chemical equation describes the redox reaction of iron and oxygen.

$$4Fe(0) + 3O_2(0) \longrightarrow 2Fe_2(+3)O_3(-2)$$

Note that this redox reaction is also a synthesis reaction. The reactants are the element iron (Fe) and the homonuclear diatomic molecule oxygen (O_2). The product is the solid compound rust (Fe_2O_3).

So, what are the numbers in parentheses? Those are the oxidation states of the reactants and products; they allow you to see the transfer of electrons. The **oxidation state** is the hypothetical charge of an atom. Notice that there is no actual charge (indicated by a superscript) on the reactants or products in the above chemical equation. So what are the + and − signs for? Those show how the electron distribution has changed. In this reaction, oxygen "takes" electrons; its oxidation state is reduced from 0 to −2. Iron "gives" electrons; its oxidation state increases from 0 to +3. *The oxidation state has changed, but not the actual charge on the element or molecule.* This sometimes makes it hard to tell from the written chemical equation when a redox reaction has taken place. You will learn more about determining oxidation states and balancing redox equations in your high school and/or college chemistry classes. For now it is important for you to be familiar with redox reactions as the cause of a variety of chemical changes, which we will discuss in the next section.

Section Review 2: Chemical Equations

A. Define the following term.

Law of Conservation of Mass   chemical reaction   products

Avogadro's number   chemical equation   balanced equation

reactants   mole concept

B. Answer the following questions.

The following formula describes how iron and oxygen react to form iron oxide (rust). Use this equation to answer questions 1–4.

$$4Fe(s) + 3O_2(g) \rightarrow 2Fe_2O_3(s)$$

1. Write out the equation in words, and include the state of each substance.

2. Which substances are the reactants and which ones are the products?

3. How many atoms of iron are in one molecule of rust?

4. What kind or kinds of reaction does the formula describe?

C. Balance the following equations.

1. $H_2O_{2(l)} \longrightarrow H_2O_{(l)} + O_{2(g)}$

2. $AgNO_3(aq) + NaCl(aq) \rightarrow AgCl(s) + NaNO_3(aq)$

3. $Na(s) + Cl_2(g) \rightarrow NaCl(s)$

4. $N_2(g) + H_2(g) \rightarrow NH_3(g)$

D. For each of the following, determine whether the chemical equation represents a synthesis, decomposition, single displacement or double displacement reaction.

1. $AgNO_3(aq) + KCl(aq) \rightarrow AgCl(aq) + KNO_3(aq)$_____

2. $N_2(g) + 3H_2(g) \rightarrow 2NH_3(g)$_____

3. $Cu(s) + AgNO_3(aq) \rightarrow CuNO_3(aq) + Ag(s)$ _____

4. $Zn(s) + H_2CO_3 \rightarrow H_2(g) + ZnCO_3(aq)$_____

5. $H_2CO_3(aq) \rightarrow H_2O(l) + CO_2(g)$_____

CHEMICAL AND PHYSICAL CHANGES

We have seen that elements and compounds have a distinct name and identity. That identity consists of all of the **chemical properties** of the element or compound. Many of the chemical properties of the element are indicated by its placement on the Periodic Table. This includes characteristics like electronegativity and preferred type of chemical bonding (ionic or covalent).

Other chemical properties are not summarized in the Periodic Table. So, how do you know what *all* the chemical properties of an element or compound are? Well, you are in luck: you can generally look them up in a chemical reference book, like the *CRC Handbook of Chemistry and Physics*. But every piece of information that you find on any substance is the result of someone doing an experiment (or many experiments) to see how that substance reacted when in the presence of other substances. The point is that chemical properties are determined by the interaction of substances, rather than their independent behavior. That is one reason why it is so important that you learn the possible chemical reactions. Let's go over the reaction types that we have seen in this chapter:

- Synthesis Reactions
- Decomposition Reactions
- Single Displacement Reactions
- Double Displacement Reactions
- Redox Reactions

Each chemical reaction causes a chemical change. A **chemical change** produces a new substance that has entirely different chemical and physical properties. The physical evidence that a chemical change has occurred may be a change in smell, function, texture, color or temperature.

A chemical change is very different than a **physical change**, which results in the same substance with different physical properties. A physical change is the result of some physical act, such as cutting, grinding, mashing, compressing, dissolving, cooling, heating or drying. The product of the physical act is the same substance, but with a different appearance.

We will discuss physical changes more in the next chapter. Now, let's look at our chemical reactions and the evidence that they have occurred.

EVIDENCE OF CHEMICAL CHANGE

Sometimes you cannot see the chemical change. For instance, you probably have a dark brown bottle of hydrogen peroxide at home. If you have had it for long enough, it may not be hydrogen peroxide anymore. Look at this decomposition reaction:

$$2H_2O_2 \text{ (l)} \longrightarrow 2H_2O \text{ (l)} + O_2\text{(g)}$$

So, how can you tell if your hydrogen peroxide has decomposed into water and oxygen? Hydrogen peroxide is a clear liquid just like water. Well, there is one thing: it will smell different. Water has no smell, but hydrogen peroxide definitely does. So, sniff the bottle (by wafting of course!). Another way to tell is more hands-on: the next time you get a scrape, pour the hydrogen peroxide on it. If you don't see any of the bubbling and foaming action that hydrogen peroxide normally produces upon contact with blood, then all you have is a bottle of water!

> **Evidence of the chemical change:** Change in smell and function.

Often, though, there is more direct visual evidence that a chemical reaction has occurred. For instance, you can see that rust has formed in the synthesis and redox reaction of iron with oxygen. This chemical change is called **corrosion**. Other materials, especially metals, also corrode by oxidation. The tendency to corrode is a chemical property. If you have any gold or platinum jewelry, you will note that it does not corrode. A chemical property of those **noble metals** is that they are impervious to corrosion.

> **Evidence of the chemical change:** Change in color and texture of the metal, called corrosion.

Another chemical property is the tendency to burn. This is called **combustion**, and it is another example of a redox reaction. In this chemical process, a reactant combines with oxygen and gives off heat in the process. Organic (carbon-containing) substances will usually burn. For example, this chemical reaction shows the combustion of the organic compound CH_4 (commonly known as methane).

$$CH_4(g) + 2O_2(g) \longrightarrow CO_2(g) + 2H_2O(l) + heat$$

A chemical reaction that gives off heat is **exothermic.** One that absorbs heat is **endothermic.**

> **Evidence of the chemical change:** Production of energy in the form of heat and light, called combustion.

Solubility is another chemical property, one that we will discuss more fully in Chapter 8 on solutions. Right now, let's look at solubility as evidence that a chemical reaction has occurred. Remember the examples of single and double displacement reactions in the last section? Here they are again:

Single Displacement Reaction: $Mg(s) + 2HCl(l) \longrightarrow MgCl_2(aq) + H_2(g)$
Double Displacement Reaction: $AgNO_3(aq) + NaCl(aq) \longrightarrow AgCl(s) + NaNO_3(aq)$

In the single displacement reaction, dissolving solid magnesium in hydrochloric acid gives magnesium chloride and gaseous hydrogen. The hydrogen gas will bubble out of the aqueous $MgCl_2$ solution. Evolution of the gas is evidence that a chemical reaction has taken place. Without seeing the gas, we might just assume that the solid magnesium had dissolved, and that is just a physical change.

> **Evidence of the chemical change:** Evolution of gas.

In the double displacement reaction, solid silver chloride is formed as a product. If you perform this reaction in a beaker in your laboratory, you will see solid AgCl begin to fall out of the solution and sit on the bottom of the beaker as it is formed. A chemical property of silver chloride is that it is insoluble. You have formed a **precipitate**!

> **Evidence of the chemical change:** Formation of a precipitate.

Section Review 3:   Chemical and Physical Changes

A. Define the following terms.

chemical properties   noble metal
chemical change   combustion
physical change   precipitate
corrosion   exothermic
              endothermic

B. Choose the best answer.

1. Which of the following processes would result in a chemical change?

    A. boiling   C. dissolving

    B. cutting   D. burning

2. Rusting is an example of

    A. oxidation.   C. a physical change.

    B. combustion.   D. precipitation.

3. You heat 50 mL of salt water on a Bunsen burner until all the water has evaporated. NaCl crystals are left behind. Which statement describes the result of this action correctly?

    A. The water has undergone a chemical change.

    B. The salt has undergone a chemical change.

    C. The salt and water have decomposed.

    D. The salt and water have undergone a physical change.

4. A solid compound is poured into a beaker of liquid. You do not know the identity of either substance. Which of the following is NOT evidence that a chemical reaction has occurred between the two?

    A. The solid compound dissolves.   C. The beaker gets very hot.

    B. Gas is evolved from the beaker.   D. A strong smell wafts from the beaker.

5. A gaseous compound is bubbled through a tube into a beaker of liquid. You do not know the identity of either substance. Which of the following is NOT evidence that a chemical reaction has occurred between the two?

    A. A precipitate is formed.   C. The beaker gets very cold.

    B. Gas is evolved from the beaker.   D. A strong smell wafts from the beaker.

CHAPTER 6 REVIEW

A. Choose the best answer.

1. The chemical formula for glucose is $C_6H_{12}O_6$. How many atoms of carbon make up one molecule of glucose?

   A. 1   B. 3   C. 6   D. 12

2. The reaction for photosynthesis is $6CO_2 + 6H_2O \rightarrow C_6H_{12}O_6 + 6O_2$. How many molecules of diatomic oxygen are released for every 1 molecule of glucose, $C_6H_{12}O_6$, produced?

   A. 1   B. 2   C. 6   D. 12

3. Which of the following represents a balanced chemical reaction?

   A. $H_2 + O_2 \rightarrow H_2O$

   B. $CO_2 + H_2O \rightarrow 2H_2CO_3$

   C. $CH_4 + O_2 \rightarrow CO_2 + 2H_2O$
   C-1 H-4 O-2   C-1   O-2   H-4 O-1

   D. $N_2 + 3H_2 \rightarrow 2NH_3$
   N-2 H-6   N-2 H-6

4. Which of the following is a true statement?

   A. Matter is conserved in a chemical reaction.

   B. Matter is created in a chemical reaction.

   C. Matter is destroyed in a chemical reaction.

   D. All of the above statements can be true depending on the reaction.

5. Group 17 (or VIIA) of the Periodic Table is the halogens. Which of the following halogens is the MOST reactive?

   A. fluorine   C. bromine

   B. chlorine   D. iodine

6. Which of the following is NOT a binary compound?

   A. HCl

   B. H_2O

   C. $MgSO_4$

   D. CCl_4

7. The chemical formula for sugar is $C_6H_{12}O_6$. Sugar placed in a test tube and then heated over a Bunsen burner turns black and eventually disappears completely. Which of the following statements explains what happens to the sugar that causes it to disappear?

    A. The heat destroys the elements that make up the sugar.

    B. As the sugar burns, it combines with oxygen in the air to form water and carbon dioxide. Water vapor and carbon dioxide escape into the atmosphere.

    C. The sugar is converted to nitrogen gas and is released into the atmosphere.

    D. All of the sugar is converted to energy that cannot be seen.

8. In chemistry class, Mr. Smoak adds a small piece of sodium metal to a glass of water. The sodium reacts violently with the water, producing a flame. The end products are hydrogen gas and sodium hydroxide. Which of the following is the correct balanced chemical equation for the reaction described above?

    A. $2Na + 2H_2O \rightarrow 2NaOH + H_2$

    B. $Na + H_2O + O_2 \rightarrow 3NaOH + H_2$

    C. $H_2O_2 + 2Na \rightarrow 2NaOH + H_2$

    D. $2NaOH + H_2 \rightarrow 2Na + 2H_2O$

9. Which of the following equations is balanced?

    A. $Ga + 3H_2SO_4 \rightarrow 2Ga_2(SO_4)_3 + 2H_2$

    B. $PdCl_2 + HNO_3 \rightarrow Pd(NO_3)_2 + HCl$

    C. $O_2 + Sb_2S_3 \rightarrow Sb_2O_4 + SO_2$

    D. $RbBr + AgCl \rightarrow AgBr + RbCl$

10. The carbonate anion (CO_3^{2-}) is insoluble in water, except when it forms compounds with Group 1 (or IA) alkali metals. Which of the following reactions would NOT result in a *carbonate* precipitate?

    A. $CaO(aq) + CO_2(g) \longrightarrow CaCO_3(s)$

    B. $Na_2SO_4(aq) + CaCO_3(s) + 2C(s) \longrightarrow Na_2CO_3(aq) + 2CO_2(g) + CaS(s)$

    C. $Mg^{2+}(s) + 2HCO_3^-(aq) \longrightarrow MgCO_3(s) + CO_2(g) + H_2O(l)$

    D. All of these would produce a carbonate precipitate.

11. What type of reaction can be represented by the following general chemical equation?

    $$AX + BY \longrightarrow BX + AY$$

    A. synthesis

    B. decomposition

    C. single displacement

    D. double displacement

12. Which of the following steps below includes a chemical change?

    A. Carlos cuts down a large oak tree.

    B. He strips the tree of its limbs and leaves and chips them into smaller pieces.

    C. He then burns all of the small twigs and leaves.

    D. Finally, he cuts the trunk into fire logs.

13. Which of the following combinations would result in a substance that is chemically different than its components?

    A. carbon and oxygen form carbon dioxide

    B. a bowl of Cheerios, blueberries and milk

    C. a pitcher of lemonade made from a powdered mix and water

    D. oxygen and nitrogen form the air that we breathe

14. Which of the following involves a chemical change?

    A. snow melting into water   C. boiling water until vapor forms

    B. an apple rotting on a tree   D. making sweet iced tea

15. Which combination of mole quantities correctly balances the following double displacement reaction?

$$\_CaCl_2(aq) + \_AgNO_3(aq) \longrightarrow \_Ca(NO_3)_2(aq) + \_AgCl(s)$$

    A. 1,1,1,1   ca-1   B. 1,2,1,2   Ag-1   C. 2,1,2,1   D. 1,2,2,2
              Cl-2   Ag-2   N-1
              aq-1   N-20-6 0-3

16. Which combination of mole quantities correctly balances the following synthesis reaction?

$$\_CO_2 + \_H_2O \longrightarrow \_H_2CO_3$$

    A. 1,1,1   B. 1,2,1   C-1   H-2   C. 2,1,2   D. 1,2,2
                                                      H-2
                            O-2   O-1   0-3
                                                C-1
                                              4-2

17. The electrolysis of water is performed by passing an electric current through water to break the chemical bonds that hold it together. What kind of reaction is this?

$$2H_2O \longrightarrow 2H_2 + O_2$$

    A. synthesis   C. single displacement

    B. decomposition   D. double displacement

18. The following reaction is given to you. Based only on the chemical equation, determine which of the following statements provides correct evidence that a chemical change has taken place.

$$Mg^{2+}(s) + 2HCO_3^-\ (aq) \longrightarrow MgCO_3(s) + CO_2(g) + H_2O(l)$$

A. Solids are present.

B. Carbon dioxide gas is evolved.

C. The equation is balanced.

D. The charges are balanced.

19. Silver (Ag) is a transition metal. As a cation, Ag always carries a +1 charge. Bromine (Br) is a halogen. As an anion, Br always carries a -1 charge. Which of the following chemical formulas correctly represents 2 mols of silver bromide?

A. $2AgBr$ B. $Ag(Br)_2$ C. Ag_2Br_2 D. $2Ag_2Br_2$

20. What type of compound is $FeCl_3$?

A. binary

B. heteronuclear diatomic

C. homonuclear diatomic

D. both A and B are correct

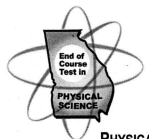

Chapter 7
Matter and Energy

PHYSICAL SCIENCE STANDARDS COVERED IN THIS CHAPTER INCLUDE:

SPS2 a	Students will explore the nature of matter, its classifications, and its system for naming types of matter.
SPS5 a – b	Students will compare and contrast the phases of matter as they relate to atomic and molecular motion.
SPS7 b – d	Students will relate transformations and flow of energy within a system.

The structural details of the atom are important for understanding the basic building blocks of matter. However, from a human point of view, we do not actually observe individual atoms when we look at an object. Instead, we observe the properties that arise from the combination of many atoms interacting together. The properties of matter that we observe with our senses are known as **physical properties**.

Physical properties help to describe matter. The state (or phase) of matter is of primary interest when observing and recording the physical properties of a sample. However, there are many other physical properties that can be observed and measured. These are divided into two categories: extrinsic (or extensive) properties and intrinsic (or intensive) properties.

Extrinsic properties depend on the amount of matter present. Mass, volume and energy are all extrinsic properties of matter. **Intrinsic properties** of a substance do not depend on the amount of matter present in the sample. Color, melting point, boiling point, hardness and electrical conductivity are all intrinsic properties. Another important intrinsic property is density.

STATES OF MATTER

Matter exists in different states, called **phases**. The four states of matter are **solid**, **liquid**, **gas** and **plasma**.

- **Solid-** The atoms or molecules that comprise a solid are packed closely together, in fixed positions relative to each other. Therefore, the solid phase of matter is characterized by its rigidity. Solids are also resistant to changes in volume: that is, they are **incompressible**. A solid does not conform to the container that it is placed in.

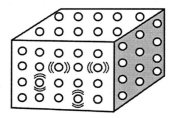

Particles can vibrate, but remain in fixed positions, with strong association between them.

Figure 7.1 Particle Motion in Solids

Particles can vibrate, rotate and translate. Particles are not fixed, but do associate with one another.

Figure 7.2 Particle Motion in Liquids

- **Liquid-** The molecules that comprise a liquid can move relative to one another, but are fixed within the volume of the liquid by temperature and pressure. A liquid does conform to the container that it is placed in, but may not fill that container. Liquids are **slightly compressible**. The bottom of any liquid sample will always have a higher pressure than the top because the liquid molecules are pressed closer together. This is most noticeable in vary large liquid samples. Think of the ocean, where the pressure at the ocean floor is much greater than at the surface.

- **Gas-** The atoms and molecules that comprise a gas move independently of one another. Because the particles of a gas are far apart, gases are **compressible**. The amount of space between them is determined by the temperature and pressure of the gas, as well as the volume of the container in which it is placed. A gas placed in a container will spread out to uniformly fill that container.

Translation is the primary mode of movement for these fast-moving particles. There is little attraction between particles.

Figure 7.3 Particle Motion in Gases

- **Plasma-** A plasma is an ionized gas. This means that atoms and molecules that make up a plasma are charged. As a result of this charge, the atoms and molecules of a plasma "communicate" with each other; they move together, because each particle interacts simultaneously with many others. A plasma is characterized by its temperature, density and electrical conductivity. Its particles are very far apart and so are very compressible. Figure 7.4 shows a plasma lamp, which many stores sell as a decorative item. If you have ever touched one of these lamps, you know that the filaments of ionic gas reach out toward the conducting surface, that is, your hand. If the lamp were just filled with un-ionized gas, there would be no collective movement of the state in reaction to a stimulus (your hand).

Figure 7.4 Plasma Lamp

Table 7.1 Common Substances for Each State of Matter

Solids	Liquids	Gases	Plasma
silver	water	oxygen	fire
diamond	milk	helium	lightening
copper	alcohol	carbon dioxide	the Sun and stars
rocks	syrup	hydrogen	the ionosphere
wood	oil	nitrogen	neon signs

The particles making up matter are in constant motion. In liquids, gases and plasmas, it is easier to think of particles moving around, since molecules in both states can flow (that is, they are **fluids**). But a solid is…well…it is solid! How can the particles be moving? Look at Figure 7.1 – they vibrate! Think of a classroom of little kids. They have been told to sit in their seats, but they want to play so badly. So they remain in the chair, but wiggle and squirm continuously until dismissed.

The phase of the matter depends on the amount and type of motion of those particles. In general, the particles of the gas and plasma states have the highest kinetic energy, while solids have the least. According to kinetic theory, particle motion increases as temperature increases. Adding or subtracting thermal energy in the form of heat changes matter from one state to another. These are called **phase changes**.

Figure 7.5 Squirmy Kids

Section Review 1: States of Matter

A. Define the following terms.

physical properties	solid
extrinsic properties	liquid
intrinsic properties	gas
phases	incompressible
plasma	phase changes

B. Choose the best answer.

The following figure shows the three phases of a material, X, in a closed container. Use it to answer question 1.

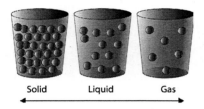

1. Tina uses a vice to squeeze each container. Which turns out to be the MOST compressible?

   A. the solid phase container

   B. the liquid phase container

   C. the gas phase container

   D. The temperature must be known to answer this question.

2. What is translation, with respect to particle motion?

   A. movement that changes the position of the particle

   B. movement that rotates the particle

   C. movement that vibrates the particle

   D. movement seen only in ionized particles

3. Select the primary difference between a gas and a plasma?

   A. ionization of particles

   B. compressibility

   C. particle motion

   D. ability to conform to container

4. Which of the following is an extrinsic property?

   A. conductivity   C. energy

   B. boiling point   D. color

PHASE CHANGES

The phase of matter is determined by the physical condition of that matter. When the physical conditions change, a phase change may occur. Two physical conditions of primary importance are temperature and pressure. To determine how temperature and pressure changes affect phase, we must define **phase barriers**—that is, the point at which matter changes phase.

The **freezing point** of a substance is the temperature at which a liquid becomes a solid or freezes. The **melting point** of a substance is the temperature at which a solid becomes a liquid or melts. The freezing point and the melting point for a given substance are the same temperature. For example, liquid water begins to freeze at 0°C. Likewise, a cube of ice begins to melt at 0°C. So the difference between the freezing and melting points has to do with the initial and the final states of matter. In other words, the different names reflect the direction of change at the phase barrier.

The **boiling point** of a substance is the temperature at which a liquid becomes a gas. The **condensation point** is the temperature at which a gas becomes a liquid. The boiling point and the condensation point for a given substance are the same temperature. For example, water boils at 100°C, and water vapor (steam) cooled to 100°C begins to condense. Again, the difference between the boiling and condensation points is the direction of change.

Sublimation is the evaporation of a substance directly from a solid to a gas without melting (or going through the liquid phase). For example, mothballs and air fresheners sublime from a solid to a gas. Dry ice, which is frozen carbon dioxide, is also a common example of sublimation because the solid dry ice immediately sublimes into carbon dioxide gas (looking like "fog"). In fact, if you have ever had ice cubes in a tray become smaller while they sit for days in the freezer, you have already seen sublimation in action.

Deposition is the condensation of a substance directly from a vapor to a solid, without going through the liquid phase. This term is mostly used in meteorology (the study of weather) when discussing the formation of ice from water vapor. The phase changes between solid, liquid and gas are summarized in Figure 7.6.

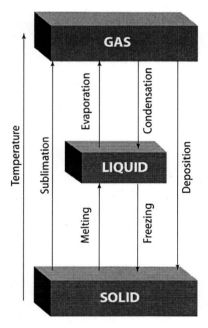

Figure 7.6 Possible Phase Changes

Depending on the temperature and pressure, water exists in all four states of matter. Therefore, it is a good example of how matter changes states. Figure 7.7 shows a common way to illustrate these transitions, called a **phase diagram**.

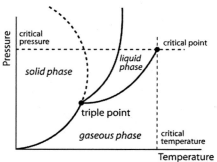

Figure 7.7 A General Phase Diagram

Phase changes can also be illustrated in terms of the amount of heat added. Figure 7.8 shows this perspective.

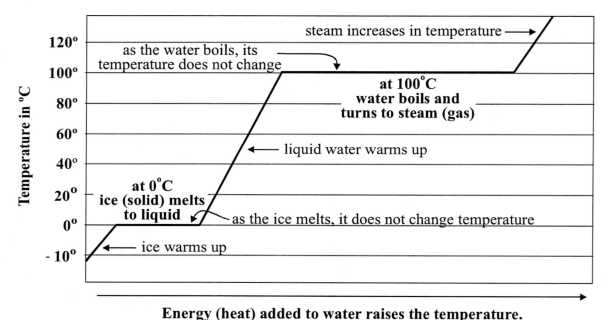

Energy (heat) added to water raises the temperature.

Figure 7.8 The Changing States of Water

Ice remains solid at temperatures below 0°C, but once ice warms to 0°C, it starts to melt. Notice that as ice melts, it continues to absorb energy, but the temperature of the ice-water mixture does not change. As we apply heat to the ice cube, the heat energy breaks up the molecular bonds of the ice, rather than raising the temperature of the surrounding water. The temperature does not change again until all of the ice melts. Once in a liquid state, the temperature of the water increases until it reaches 100°C. At 100°C, the water boils and turns to steam. While the liquid changes to vapor, the liquid absorbs energy, but the temperature does not increase. This is the reason that water can never get hotter than its boiling point (at standard temperature and pressure, anyway). Once all of the liquid turns to steam, the temperature of the steam increases. In fact, steam can be much more damaging to your skin than liquid water because steam absorbs all that energy pumped into it and can easily transfer it to other surfaces. Once all of the liquid turns to steam, the temperature of the steam increases, but only if you can keep it around and continue to heat it. In summary, the temperature remains constant through any phase change whether it be melting, freezing or boiling. The temperature does not increase during a phase change because the energy is being used to break and/or form molecular bonds rather than to heat the substance.

So, where is the plasma phase in these diagrams? A plasma is very like a gas in some ways, for instance, it has no defined volume. It is also greatly influenced by temperature. If you were to place the plasma state in the phase diagram shown in Figure 7.7, it would be at the extreme right if the diagram, beyond the gas phase. Remember that a plasma is an ionized gas; enough energy must be added to the plasma in order to keep the electrons separate from the ions in the plasma. This is done by adding heat.

The top temperature shown in Figure 7.8 is 130°C (which is about 400 Kelvin). Steam will begin to dissociate (split) into hydrogen and oxygen atoms at around 1500 K. Above 4000 K, hydrogen ions will begin to ionize, generating a "water plasma." Lowering the pressure and adding an electric field will produce plasma at lower temperatures and at different percentages, but this example allows you to see the amount of heat that must be added to reach the fourth state of matter without those measures.

DENSITY

As a substance undergoes phase changes, its density changes. **Density** (D) is the mass (m) per unit volume (V) of a substance. We express density in units of kg/m³ or g/cm³. At the atomic level, the atomic mass of the element and the amount of space between particles determines the density of a substance. The following equation is used to calculate density.

$$D = \frac{m}{V}$$ **Equation 7.1**

When comparing objects of the same volume, the denser something is, the more mass it has and, therefore, the greater its weight. This explains why even a small amount of pure gold is very heavy. Likewise, an equal amount of pure gold and pure oxygen will occupy very different volumes because the density of oxygen at room temperature is so much less than gold.

The following are general rules regarding density:

Rule 1. **The amount of a substance does not affect its density. The density of iron at 0°C will always be 7.8 g/cm³. It does not matter if we have 100 g or 2 g of iron.**

Rule 2. **Temperature affects density. In general, density decreases as temperature increases. Water is an exception to this rule. The density of ice is less than the density of liquid water; therefore, ice floats.**

Rule 3. **Pressure affects the density of gases and plasmas, but it does not affect solids or liquids since those two states are not very compressible. As the pressure on a gas or plasma increases, density also increases.**

Mixing substances of different densities changes the density of the mixture. For example, the density of fresh water is less than the density of salt water.

Section Review 2:   Phase Changes

A. Define the following terms.

phase barriers   sublimation

freezing point   deposition

melting point   phase diagram

boiling point   density

condensation point

B. Choose the best answer.

1. The density of water is 0.998 g/mL at 25° C and 0.917 g/mL at 0° C. What can you infer about water from these two measurements?

    A. Water is more dense when it is solid.

    B. Water is less dense when it is liquid.

    C. Ice will float on liquid water.

    D. Ice will sink in liquid water.

2. Iron has a density of about 8 g/cm^3. What is the mass of 2 cm^3 of iron?

    A. 4 grams   B. 8 grams   C. 16 grams   D. 24 grams

The figure shows the phase transition of a substance. Use it to answer questions 3 and 4.

3. During which period(s) of time is the substance in the liquid phase, either partially or fully?

    A. 2   C. 3

    B. 2 and 3   D. 2, 3 and 4

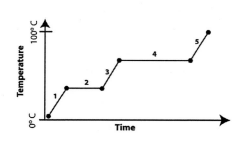

4. During which periods of time is the substance undergoing a phase transition?

    A. 1 and 3   C. 2, 3 and 4

    B. 1, 3 and 5   D. 2 and 4

5. What is the opposite of evaporation?

    A. sublimation   C. deposition

    B. condensation   D. freezing

INTERACTIONS IN GASES

Size and **polarity** of molecules affect the interaction of gases. Substances that are gases at room temperature are most often stand-alone atoms, diatomic molecules, or small, nonpolar molecular compounds. A small, stable atom such as helium has little attraction for other helium atoms; therefore, it exists as a gas at room temperature. These are called **volatile** compounds, because they tend to vaporize. The condensation point for helium or other atmospheric gases is very low. Hydrogen, oxygen and nitrogen exist as diatomic molecules. Carbon dioxide is a small, nonpolar molecular compound. *In general, the smaller the gas molecule, the lower the condensation and freezing point it has.*

GAS LAWS

The collisions of the gas particles against the surface of the container cause the gas to exert pressure upon the container. **Pressure** is a force (push or pull) applied uniformly over an area. The SI unit of pressure is called a **pascal (Pa)**, and the English unit is called an **atmosphere (atm)**. The velocity of the gas particles relates to the temperature of the gas. The **gas laws** describe the relationship between the temperature, pressure and volume of gases.

Table 7.2 Gas Laws

Gas Law	Type of Relationship	Relationship
Boyle's law	**Pressure-Volume (P-V) Relationship:** Increasing the pressure at a constant temperature decreases the volume of the gas. Conversely, decreasing the pressure at a constant temperature will increase the volume of the gas.	$V \propto \dfrac{1}{P}$
Charles' law	**Temperature-Volume (T-V) Relationship:** Heating a fixed amount of gas at constant pressure causes the volume of the gas to increase, and vice versa: Cooling a fixed amount of gas at constant pressure causes the volume of the gas to decrease.	$V \propto T$
Avogadro's law	**Volume-Amount (V-n) Relationship:** At constant pressure and temperature, the volume of a gas increases as the number of molecules in the gas increases.	$V \propto n$

The symbol $\propto$ means "is proportional to." When we say two quantities are **directly proportional**, we mean that when one quantity increases, so does the related quantity. The opposite is also true: when one quantity decreases, so does the related quantity. The quantities in Charles' and Avogadro's laws are directly proportional. Notice that Boyle's law states the volume is proportional to one (1) divided by pressure. So, if volume increases, then the value of the fraction 1/P must also increase. The value of the fraction 1/P is greater when the value for P is smaller. For instance, 1/2 is greater than 1/3, which is greater than 1/4. Thus, in Boyle's law, when the volume increases, the pressure must decrease. The converse is also true: when the volume decreases, the pressure must increase. In order for the fraction 1/P to decrease, the value of P must increase. The relationship in Boyle's law is called an **inversely proportional** relationship.

For the purpose of solving problems, Boyle's law and Charles' law are written in a different form. Another way of stating Boyle's law is P×V is always equal to the same constant as long as the temperature and amount of gas does not change. Boyle's law is expressed by Equation 7.2.

$$P_1V_1 = P_2V_2 \qquad \textbf{Equation 7.2}$$

For a sample of gas under two different sets of conditions at constant temperature. V_1 and V_2 are the volumes at pressures P_1 and P_2, respectively.

> **Example:** A sample of sulfur hexafluoride gas exerts 10 atm of pressure in a steel container of volume 5.5 L. How much pressure would the gas exert if the volume of the container was reduced to 2.0 L at constant temperature?

Step 1. Set up the equation: $P_1V_1 = P_2V_2$

Step 2. Insert the known information. In this problem, we know that the initial conditions were a pressure of 10 atm and a volume of 5.5 L. The final volume is 2.0 L. Therefore, the equation becomes:

$$(10 \text{ atm})(5.5 \text{ L}) = P_2(2.0 \text{ L})$$

Step 3. Solve for P_2. $\qquad P_2 = \dfrac{(10 \text{ atm}) \cdot (5.5 \text{ L})}{(2.0 \text{ L})} = 27.5 \text{ atm}$

Charles' law can be rewritten as

$$\frac{V_1}{T_1} = \frac{V_2}{T_2} \qquad \textbf{Equation 7.3}$$

for a sample of gas under two different sets of conditions at constant pressure. V_1 and V_2 are the volumes at temperatures T_1 and T_2, respectively. Both temperatures are in Kelvin.

> **Example:** Under constant-pressure conditions a sample of methane gas initially at 400 K and 12.6 L is cooled until its final volume is 9.3 L. What is its final temperature?

Step 1. Set up the equation: $\qquad \dfrac{V_1}{T_1} = \dfrac{V_2}{T_2}$

Step 2. Insert the known information. In this problem, we know that the initial conditions were a volume of 12.6 L and a temperature of 400 K. The final volume is 9.3 L.

Therefore, the equation becomes: $\qquad \dfrac{12.6 \text{ L}}{400 \text{ K}} = \dfrac{9.3 \text{ L}}{T_2}$

Step 3. Solve for T_2: $\qquad T_2 = \dfrac{(9.3 \text{ L}) \cdot (400 \text{ K})}{(12.6 \text{ L})} = 295 \text{ K}$

Ideal Gas Equation (pressure-temperature-volume relationship): Heating a gas in a fixed volume container causes the pressure to increase. Conversely, cooling a gas in a fixed volume container causes the pressure to decrease. The ideal gas equation combines the three gas laws into one master equation to describe the behavior of gases,

$$PV = nRT \qquad \textbf{Equation 7.4}$$

where R is the gas constant. When used in the ideal gas equation, R has a value of $0.08206 \; \dfrac{L \cdot atm}{K \cdot mol}$.

Try to remember this equation using the pnemonic "**Piv Nert**," which is how you would pronounce Equation 7.4 if you were to say it aloud as a word instead of as an equation. Each consonant in Piv Nert corresponds with a term in the Ideal gas equation as shown in Figure 7.9.

Results from these properties can be observed around us. Pressurized gases pose hazards during handling and storage. Pressurized gases should not be stored in hot locations or be handled near flames.

Balloons, whose volumes are not fixed, can also illustrate the behavior of gases. For example, if you put a balloon in a freezer, it will shrink because of the decreased pressure inside the balloon resulting from the lower temperature. If you take it to the top of a very high mountain, it will expand because of the decreased atmospheric pressure.

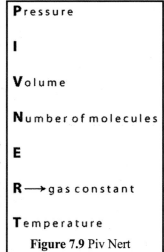

Figure 7.9 Piv Nert

Practice Exercise 1: Gas Laws

1. A gas occupying a volume of 675 mL at a pressure of 1.15 atm is allowed to expand at constant temperature until its pressure becomes 0.725 atm. What is its final volume?

2. A 25 L volume of gas is cooled from 373 K to 300 K at constant pressure. What is the final volume of gas?

3. A sample of gas exerts a pressure of 3.25 atm. What is the pressure when the volume of the gas is reduced to one-quarter of the original value at the same temperature?

4. A sample of gas is heated under constant-pressure conditions from an initial temperature and volume of 350 K and 5.0 L, respectively. The final volume is 11.6 L. What is the final temperature of the gas?

Section Review 3: Physical Properties of Matter

A. Define the following terms.

Piv Nert	pascal	inversely proportional
volatile	atmosphere	Boyle's law
ideal gas equation	gas laws	Charles' law
pressure	directly proportional	Avogadro's law

B. Choose the best answer.

1. Based on particle interactions, which of the following types of substances is MOST volatile?

    A. small, nonpolar molecules

    B. ionic compounds dissolved in a polar liquid

    C. large, polar molecules

    D. small, polar molecules which also exhibit hydrogen bonding

2. Cartridges used to fire paint balls are filled with carbon dioxide gas. Each time a paint ball is fired, some carbon dioxide gas escapes. The volume of the cartridge is rigid and does not change. Hampton buys a new carbon dioxide cartridge. Lisa has the same cartridge, but hers has been used to fire several paint balls. Which of the following is true of the cartridges assuming both cartridges are at the same temperature?

    A. The pressure in Hampton's cartridge is greater than the pressure in Lisa's cartridge.

    B. The pressure in Hampton's cartridge is less than the pressure in Lisa's cartridge.

    C. The pressure in Hampton's cartridge is equal to the pressure in Lisa's cartridge.

    D. No relationship can be determined from the given information.

3. Which Gas Law gives a proportional relationship between temperature and volume?

    A. Boyle's Law   C. The Ideal Gas Law

    B. Charles' Law   D. B and C

4. Which of the following must be constant for Boyles Law $(P_1V_1 = P_2V_2)$ to hold?

    A. temperature   C. amount of gas

    B. pressure   D. both B and C

5. A sample of neon gas is at a constant pressure of 3 atm and an initial temperature of 350K. Its volume is reduced by half. What it the final temperature T_2?

    A. 1050 K   B. 175 K   C. 700 K   D. 950 K

SPECIFIC HEAT CAPACITY

All matter is made up of atoms and molecules. Within these atoms and molecules, there is a lot of action going on. Electrons are constantly in motion within the atoms and molecules due to electrical charges. Additionally, the atoms and molecules that make up the matter are in motion with respect to each other, transferring energy as they move. Fortunately, there are also strong forces inside each atom holding it together. There are also forces holding atoms together with other atoms to form molecules. These electrically charged particles possess energy together known as **internal energy**. When internal energy transfers between materials, we call the transferred energy **heat**, or **thermal energy**. The measure of heat is **temperature**. Energy transfer always occurs from an area of high energy to an area of low energy.

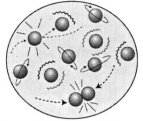

Figure 7.10 Thermal Energy

Let's say you have one container of gas in which the atoms are moving slowly and another container of gas with faster moving atoms. If you mix the two, the atoms will bump into each other. As they do, the faster moving atoms will transfer energy to the slower moving gas atoms. When the gas atoms are all colliding at the same speed, they will have the same internal energy. The energy of the combined gases can then be measured as temperature.

Every substance has a different ability to absorb heat. The **specific heat** of a substance is the number of joules (unit of work and energy) required to raise 1 gram of the substance 1°C or 1K. Table 7.3 shows the specific heat capacity of a few common substances.

Table 7.3 Specific Heat Capacity

Specific Heat Capacity (Cp)	
Substance	(J/kg °C)
Air	995
Aluminum	920
Copper	390
Glass	840
Iron	450
Lead	130
Water	4,200
Ice (0°C)	2,100
Steam (100° K)	2,100

The equation to calculate how much heat energy (Q) is needed to raise one gram of a substance 1°C is:

Heat gained or lost = (mass in kilograms)(specific heat capacity)(change in temperature)

$$Q = mCp\Delta T$$

Equation 7.5

Use the equation above and the table of specific heat values to work the problems on the following page.

Example: How much heat is required to change the temperature of 7 grams of iron by 12°C?

Step 1: Look up the formula for specific heat.

$Q = mc\Delta T$

Step 2: Make sure all values are in the correct units, then place values into the equation and calculate.

$Q = (0.007kg)(450J/kg°C)(12°C)$

$Q = 37.8J$

Lab Activity 1: Specific Heat

Use the equation and table of specific heat on the previous page to answer the following questions.

1. How much heat is required to change 5 grams of iron 10°C?

2. How much heat is lost when 10g of glass cools 15°C?

3. How much heat is needed to raise 50g of water from 20°C to 50°C?

4. 1 kg slav of concrete loses 12,000 J of heat when it cools from 30°C to 26°C. Determine the specific heat capacity of concrete.

There are three common ways to refer to heat transfer: conduction, convection and radiation. Figure 7.11 shows examples of these three means of heating. In **conduction**, kinetic energy is transferred as particles hit each other directly. During this type of heat transfer, the two objects at different temperatures are in direct contact with one another. **Convection** occurs when circulation of heat through gases or liquids raises the temperature of the whole fluid. Finally, **radiation** is the transfer of thermal energy as waves. Various kinds of matter transfer thermal energy to different degrees. **Thermal insulators** such as cork, fiberglass, wool or wood inhibit the transfer of thermal energy. Thermal insulators can improve efficiency by slowing heat loss. **Thermal conductors** are substances that promote thermal energy transfer. Many types of metal, such as copper and aluminum, are good thermal conductors.

Conduction   Convection   Radiation

Figure 7.11 Conduction, Convection and Radiation

EXOTHERMIC AND ENDOTHERMIC REACTIONS

Chemical changes in matter occur because of chemical reactions. Chemical reactions are either exothermic, which means they give off energy, or endothermic, which means they absorb energy. (Physical changes in matter can also be exothermic or endothermic.) The energy is usually given off or absorbed is in the form of heat. This is not always the case, however. Some chemical reactions generate or absorb energy in the form of light or electricity. For example, a burning candle gives off heat, but it also gives off light energy. The burning of fossil fuels also releases heat and light energy. A car battery produces electrical energy, and a recharged battery stores electrical energy. In all cases, energy is conserved, which means it is neither created nor destroyed. The energy is just transferred from one form to another.

EXOTHERMIC REACTIONS

Exothermic reactions release thermal energy. Exothermic reactions or processes are often spontaneous. This release or production of heat warms the surrounding area. One example of an exothermic reaction is combustion. The combustion of fossil fuels is the source of most of the world's energy. Condensing steam is an example of an exothermic process. The steam gives up energy to condense into a liquid form. The liquid state of a substance has less molecular/atomic motion than its gaseous state, and so it has less internal energy. So, going from a gas to a liquid is an exothermic transition. An example of an exothermic chemical reaction is the decomposition of food in a compost pile. Compost made up of grass clippings and leftover vegetable peels gives off heat because bacteria and other organisms break down the matter into simpler substances. Another example is rusting. Iron exposed to oxygen will react to form rust and give off heat. Rust, the product, has less energy than iron and oxygen, the reactants. Other examples of exothermic reactions are personal hand warmers and portable heating pads.

Often, a chemical change or reaction must be started by adding energy or heat. Once the chemical reaction begins, it gives off more energy than was added to start the reaction. The energy needed to start the reaction is called the **activation energy**. If the energy at the end of the reaction is less than the energy at the beginning of the reaction, it is still exothermic. Burning wood gives off energy in the form of light and heat, but wood does not burn spontaneously under ordinary conditions. For example, a match does not burn until friction is added to form a spark. Once the spark ignites the match, it burns and gives off more energy in the form of heat and light than the initial spark. Once the match has burned, it cannot be used again to give off energy. The total energy of the match after it has burned is less than the energy before it burned; therefore, it is an exothermic reaction.

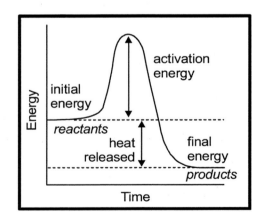

Figure 7.12 Exothermic Reaction

ENDOTHERMIC REACTIONS

Some reactions absorb energy causing the products to have more energy than the original reactants. These endothermic reactions are not as common. In an **endothermic** reaction, heat energy is absorbed. This absorption of energy results in the cooling of the surrounding area. Heat transfers from the surrounding area to the point of the chemical reaction. An example of an endothermic process is melting ice. Ice must absorb energy to melt. The liquid water has more energy than the ice; therefore, it is an endothermic process. Another example of an endothermic chemical reaction is the medical cold pack included in some emergency first aid kits. A membrane separating two chemicals must be broken by bending or kneading the pack. Once the chemicals mix, they react and absorb heat causing it to feel cold.

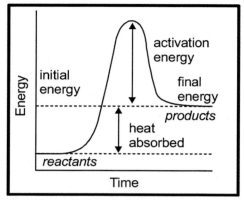

Figure 7.13 Endothermic Reaction

CATALYSTS

Catalysts can increase the rate of reaction. They do this by decreasing the activation energy needed for a reaction. Figure 7.14 shows what an energy graph of a reaction might look like with and without a catalyst. Notice that the beginning energy and the final energy are the same for both reactions, but the energy needed for the reaction to occur is less with a catalyst.

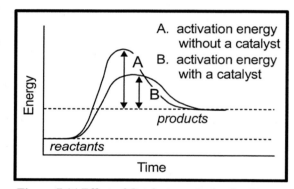

Figure 7.14 Effect of Catalysts on Activation Energy

Section Review 4:   Heat

A. Define the following terms.

thermal energy	temperature	radiation
specific heat capacity	conduction	thermal insulator
heat	convection	thermal conductor
	endothermic reaction	exothermic reaction

B. Choose the best answer.

Use the Table to answer questions 1–5.

Specific Heat Capacity	
Substance	(J/kg °C)
Air	995
Aluminum	920
Copper	390
Glass	840
Iron	450
Lead	130
Water	4,200
Ice (0°C)	2,100
Steam (100° K)	2,100

1. Paul removed 2 kg cubes of ice, copper, lead and glass from a freezer and placed them in four separate ovens. They were then heated from 0°C to 50°C. Which oven used the LEAST amount of energy to heat its sample?

    A. the oven containing the ice cube   C. the oven containing the lead cube

    B. the oven containing the copper cube   D. the oven containing the glass cube

2. How much heat is needed to raise the temperature of 2 kg of copper from 20°C to 30°C?

    A. 15,600 J   B. 23,400 J   C. 7,800 J   D. 1,950 J

3. The temperature of a 1 kg water sample drops by 1°C, resulting in a release of energy from the sample. In which phase will the greatest amount of energy be released?

    A. liquid water at 25°C

    B. ice at 0°C

    C. steam at 100°C

    D. This question cannot be answered unless the volume of the sample is given.

4. Aluminum has a lower specific heat capacity than liquid water. What is the result of this?

    A. It takes less energy to increase the temperature of a 1 kg water sample by 1°C than a 1 kg aluminum sample.

    B. It takes more energy to increase the temperature of a 1 kg water sample by 1°C than a 1 kg aluminum sample.

    C. It takes more energy to increase the temperature of a 1 kg aluminum sample by 1°C than a 1 kg water sample.

    D. This question cannot be answered unless the volume of the sample is given.

5. 450 J of heat are added to a 100 kg block of iron. What is the resulting temperature change?

    A. 10°C   B. 1°C   C. 0.1°C   D. 0.01°C

6. Which of the following correctly describes the relationship between thermal energy and heat?

    A. Thermal energy and heat mean the exact same thing.

    B. Heat is the measure of thermal energy in an object.

    C. Heat is the random motion of particles and thermal energy is the transfer of heat.

    D. Thermal energy is the random motion of particles and heat is the transfer of thermal energy.

7. Which of the following processes gives off energy?

    A. melting ice

    B. burning propane in a gas heater

    C. sublimation of carbon dioxide ice to carbon dioxide gas

    D. recharging a car battery

8. What is the primary function of a catalyst?

    A. to decrease energy of the product

    B. to increase energy of the reactants

    C. to decrease activation energy

    D. to increase activation energy

CHAPTER 7 REVIEW

A. Choose the best answer.

1. An object with a mass of 30 g and a volume of 6 cm³ has a density of

   A. 5 g/cm³.   B. 15 g/m³.   C. 180 g/cm³.   D. 180 g·cm³.

2. Which state(s) of matter does the term "fluid" describe?

   A. liquids   C. gases, liquids and plasmas

   B. gases and liquids   D. gases

3. Look at the two pictures at right. Both cylinders contain the same volume of the same gas at the same temperature. Which of the following statements is true?

   A. The position of the piston in cylinder R creates more pressure than the position of the piston in cylinder S.

   B. The position of the piston in cylinder S creates more pressure than the position of the piston in cylinder R.

   C. There is no way to compare the pressure in the cylinders with the information given in the problem.

   D. The position of the pistons does not affect the pressure within the cylinders.

4. When the temperature of a particle of matter rises, there is an increase in the

   A. size.   C. mass.

   B. potential energy.   D. kinetic energy.

5. Volatility is the tendency of a liquid to

   A. disappear.   B. vaporize.   C. burn.   D. explode.

6. When a substance condenses, it changes from

   A. a liquid to a solid.   C. a gas to a liquid.

   B. a liquid to a gas.   D. a gas to a solid.

7. Mixtures can be separated by physical means. Which is NOT a way to separate mixtures?

   A. evaporation   C. magnetic separation

   B. filtering   D. cooking

8. Two equivalent samples of argon gas are placed in two containers of equal and constant volume. The temperature of Sample A is increased by 10°C. The temperature of Sample B is kept constant. Which statement is true?

   A. The pressure of Sample A increases.

   B. The pressure of Sample A decreases.

   C. The pressure of Sample A is constant.

   D. The pressure of Sample B and Sample A are equal.

9. A 2 kg sample of lead has a specific heat of 130 J/kg°C. What change in temperature is required to generate an energy gain of 500J?

   A. temperature increase of 1°C

   B. temperature increase of more than 1°C but less than 2°C

   C. temperature decrease of 1.5°C

   D. temperature decrease of more than 1°C but less than 2°C

10. Which state of matter usually consists of molecules, rather than atoms?

   A. solid   B. liquid   C. gas   D. plasma

11. Which state of matter consists of ions, rather than atoms or molecules?

   A. solid   B. liquid   C. gas   D. plasma

12. A group of students boiled saltwater and condensed the vapor given off while the saltwater was boiling. They collected the condensate. Select the BEST description of that condensate.

   A. pure water   C. saltwater

   B. deionized water   D. salt

13. An 3 kg iron sample requires a 1°C change in temperature to gain 390 J of heat. What is its specific heat capacity?

   A. 1170 J   B. 1170 J/kg °C   C. 130 J   D. 130 J/kg °C

14. The reactants in an exothermic chemical reaction have an initial energy of 800 kJ. After the chemical reaction, what could be energy of the products?

   A. 600 kJ

   B. 800 kJ

   C. 810 kJ

   D. 1600 kJ

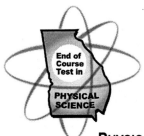

Chapter 8
Solutions

PHYSICAL SCIENCE STANDARDS COVERED IN THIS CHAPTER INCLUDE:

SPS6 a – e	Students will investigate the properties of solutions.

SOLUTION PROPERTIES

A **solution** is a homogenous mixture of one or more substances, called **solutes,** dissolved in another substance, called a **solvent**. A good example of a common solution is salt water. In that case, salt is the substance that dissolves and water is the substance that does the dissolving. Together, they make a uniform solution in which one part is the same as any another part.

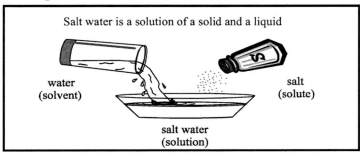

Salt water is a solution of a solid and a liquid

water (solvent)

salt (solute)

salt water (solution)

Figure 8.1 Salt Water as an Example of a Solution

You are probably very familiar with this kind of solution, where a solid solute dissolves in a liquid solvent. Keep in mind, though: *the solute and the solvent can be any phase of matter.* Let's look at a few examples.

Table 8.1 The Parts of a Solution

Solution	Solute(s)	Solute phase	Solvent	Solvent phase
air	oxygen	gas	nitrogen	gas
brass	copper	solid	zinc	solid
steel	carbon	solid	iron	solid
soda water	carbon dioxide	gas	water	liquid
humid air	oxygen, water	gas, liquid	nitrogen	gas

But wait— aren't all these just mixtures? Well, yes! Solutions are a particular kind of mixture, called a **homogeneous** mixture. Homogeneous means "of uniform composition — that is, the solution is the same throughout. Homogeneity is a property of all solutions. Another solution property is that they cannot be separated by filtering. A compound and a mixture are defined as follows:

- A compound is a chemical union that cannot be separated by physical means.
- A mixture is a physical union that can be separated by physical means.

Well, a solution is somewhere in between:

- A solution is a physical union that can be separated by *some* physical means.

As we said, a solution is a mixture that cannot be separated by filtering. It may, however, be separated by drying. As an example, allowing the water to evaporate from a salt water solution will leave behind the salt. Removing the water affected the **solubility** of the salt. There are several other factors that affect solubility, which are covered in the following sections. The bottom line is that solutions can often be separated by taking advantage of the physical properties of either the solute or the solvent...and sometimes both.

SOLUBILITY OF MATTER

A solution can contain dissolved molecules or ions or a combination of the two. The solubility of a substance is one property that is used to distinguish one substance from another. The solubility is measured by the **concentration** of the solute in the solvent. The concentration is a measure of the number of grams of solute dissolved per volume of solvent. Many factors affect the solubility of solutes in solvent, which we will look at in the next section.

IDENTITY OF SOLUTE AND SOLVENT

There is a saying among scientists that explains why a solute will dissolve in some solvents but not in others. The saying is: **Like Dissolves Like**. It means that solutes and solvents that have similar molecular polarity will interact. These molecules interact according to certain polarity rules, which are ultimately related to the electrical force fields surrounding each molecule. These forces are either attractive or repulsive. So, "like dissolves like" really is a description of the solvent and solute's electrical properties. Let's look at a few examples. Figure 8.2 shows the dissolution of $NaCl$ in water. $NaCl$ separates into the ions Na^+ and Cl^- when in water. Water molecules are polar, so they have a **dipole**—that is, they are neutral molecules that have an imbalance in the distribution of charge. Negative charge is distributed around the oxygen atom, and positive charge around the hydrogen atoms. Since opposite charges attract, the oxygen portion of the water will be attracted to the Na^+ ion, while the hydrogen portion of water will be attracted to the Cl^- ion. These attractions are the reason that $NaCl$ dissolves in water. If the interactions between the Na^+ and Cl^- were stronger than their interaction with water, it would not dissolve.

The following scenarios summarize solubility based on common substances of different polarity.

Polar/Polar: Water is a polar solvent and easily dissolves the polar NaC1 molecule, as in Figure 8.2.

Polar/Nonpolar: Water will not dissolve wax, a non-polar solute.

Nonpolar/Polar: The nonpolar solvent gasoline will not dissolve polar sugar molecules.

Nonpolar/Nonpolar: Gasoline will dissolve the nonpolar solute oil, like the oil stains on a driveway.

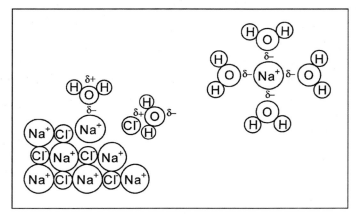

Figure 8.2 Salt Dissolving in Water

Keep in mind the following general rules:

- Most **organic** (carbon-based) compounds are nonpolar, and will not dissolve in water.

- Most ionic solids are polar, and will dissolve in water.

- Most importantly: LIKE DISSOLVES LIKE!

PRESSURE

Air pressure has no effect on solid or liquid solutes. However, an increase in pressure of a gaseous solute above the solvent pressure increases the solubility of the gas. For example, when a carbonated drink is placed in a can, pressure is added to keep the carbon dioxide in the liquid solution. However, when the tab is popped and the pressure is released, the carbon dioxide begins to escape the liquid solution.

The effect of pressure on gas solubility has important implications for scuba divers. Underwater, pressure increases rapidly with depth. The high pressure allows more nitrogen than usual to dissolve in blood and body tissues. If divers ascend too rapidly, the suddenly lower pressure causes the nitrogen gas to come out of solution, forming gas bubbles in the blood and tissues. The gas bubbles result in a condition called "the bends," which can cause severe pain, dizziness, convulsions, blindness and paralysis. Divers must ascend to the surface slowly in order to keep air bubbles from forming.

SURFACE AREA

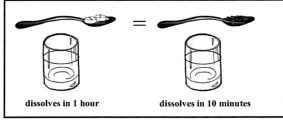

Figure 8.3 Effect of Surface Area on Solubility

The surface area of a solid solute also affects the rate of its solubility. The more surface area that is exposed to the solvent, the more readily the solute can interact with the solvent. This increased rate of reaction occurs because there is an increased chance of collisions between reactant particles. Since there are more collisions in any given time, the rate of reaction increases. For example, suppose you had a medicine which you can take in the form of a pill or a powder. Which substance would enter the body more quickly, the pill form or the powder? The answer is the powder, because there is more surface area available for interaction with the solvent — in this case, stomach acid.

AGITATION

To agitate something means to shake it up. In many cases, people agitate a solution in order to mix it. For instance, you may shake a salad dressing bottle before pouring it, to make sure that the dressing you pour is mixed and not separated.

In most cases, agitation will help to mix a solution. By increasing the motion of the solution particles, you increase their interaction with each other, and also the degree to which they will mix. There is one type of solution in which agitation decreases solubility. Can you guess it? Yes, any time a gas is the solute, agitation decreases solubility. Why? Because agitation gives the gas molecules more kinetic energy. The added kinetic energy gives the gaseous solute molecules enough energy to break the interactions with the solvent that are keeping them dissolved. So, the gas literally escapes the solvent and comes out of solution.

TEMPERATURE

Have you ever noticed that you can dissolve more sugar in hot tea than you can in cold? As you increase the temperature of a solvent, you usually increase the solubility of liquids and solids. Viewing the graph in Figure 8.4, you see how the solubility of the potassium nitrate increases with higher temperatures.

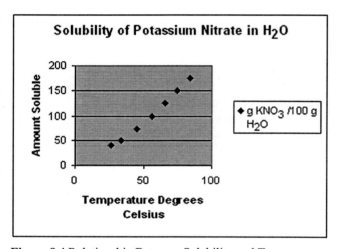

Figure 8.4 Relationship Between Solubility and Temperature

The solubility of gases, however, has the opposite relationship with temperature. As the temperature increases, the solubility of gases in solution decreases. Again, this is due to the fact that heat transfers thermal energy to the gaseous solute molecules. Added thermal energy increases their motion — that is, their kinetic energy. For example, an open carbonated beverage will lose its fizz quickly in a hot environment, while the fizz escapes slowly in a cool environment. A *decrease* in temperature gives gas a greater solubility.

DEGREE OF SOLUBILITY

As you have now seen, solubility depends on a number of factors. How those factors interact is different for different phases of matter, but it is also different for different compounds and under different conditions. Let's say that we want to dissolve a 50-gram cube of KNO_3 in 100 mL of water. We use a balance to mass our sample and pour it into the beaker of water. And nothing happens. Huh. Well, let's review what we know, and see how we can get the sample to dissolve more quickly – that is, have the fastest **rate of dissolution**.

Identity of the solute and solvent: KNO_3 dissolves very well in water, because the charge of the ions interacts with the polarity of the water molecule. Since the solute (KNO_3) matches the solvent (water), it should dissolve.

Pressure: This doesn't really play a role here, since we are examining a solid dissolved in a liquid.

Surface area: Granulated KNO_3 will dissolve more quickly than a block of KNO_3 of the same mass. So, perhaps we should use a stirring rod to break up the cube.

Agitation: KNO_3 will dissolve more quickly when it is stirred into the water, than if you simply pour it in and let it sit there. After breaking up the cube of salt we stir it into solution. But when we stop, there is still a lump of KNO_3 at the bottom of the beaker. What gives?

Well, at some point, the solution becomes **saturated**. This means that no more solute can be dissolved in a given solvent. If you continue to add solute after the point of saturation, it will simply settle to the bottom. It turns out that the solubility of KNO_3 in water is about 30 g/100 mL at 20°C, so we have surpassed the solubility limit for our solution.

Temperature: The solubility of the salt will increase with increased temperature…right? Well, take a look at Figure 8.5. Clearly, not all salts become more soluble when heated. NaCl doesn't seem to be affected much at all by heating. Copper sulfate becomes slightly more soluble. However, KNO_3 becomes markedly more soluble when heated. Based on this data, heating our salt will indeed increase its solubility. So let's get out the Bunsen burner.

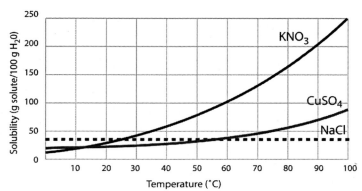

Figure 8.5 Solubility Curves of Three Salts

As you heat the solution, you will notice that the salt settled at the bottom disappears. Well, not really, it just becomes soluble, right? What happens if we turn off the heat and let the solution cool? Good question.

When the temperature of a saturated solution is changed such that the solute concentration is higher than its solubility value, the solution becomes **supersaturated**. The solution was homogeneous when it was warm and everything was dissolved. As it cools, the solution actually becomes heterogeneous as solute molecules start to fall out of solution and rest on the bottom of the beaker.

There is another way to get a supersaturated solution. At the beginning of the chapter, the process of separating a mixture by drying was mentioned. If you think about it, drying also creates supersaturated solutions. For instance, imagine you dissolve 33.0 g of NaCl in 100 mL of water and place it in a large dish on a warm day. The standard solubility of NaCl in water is 35.9 g/100 mL of water. This is usually stated as .0359 g/mL. At that concentration, the solution is saturated. Below that, it is not. So 33 g should easily dissolve, but then, the water begins to evaporate. After a period of time, 10 mL of water has evaporated. This means that there are now 33.0 g of NaCl in 90 mL of water. Well, now the concentration of NaCl is 0.367 g/ml. So the solution is supersaturated. Since it is supersaturated, crystals may begin to form. As more solvent dries, the solution will become increasingly **heterogeneous** (non-uniform). Eventually, the water and the NaCl can be completely separated: the salt will be left in the dish as a crystalline solid after the water has evaporated.

Section Review 1: Simple Solutions

A. Define the following terms.

solution	saturated	supersaturated	solubility curve
solute	Like Dissolves Like	rate of dissolution	homogeneous
solvent	polar	heterogeneous	organic

B. Choose the best answer.

1. In which of the following will sugar be hardest to dissolve?

    A. hot tea   B. warm milk   C. hot coffee   D. iced tea

2. The substance that dissolves the solute is called the

    A. solution.   B. solvent.   C. solid.   D. salt water.

3. What would be the best way to increase the solubility of carbon dioxide gas in water?

    A. heating the solution

    B. agitating the solution

    C. cooling the solution

    D. decreasing the pressure above the solution

4. Which form of matter increases its solubility as pressure is increased?

    A. solid   B. gas   C. liquid   D. powder

5. Which phase of matter does NOT become more soluble with increased agitation?

    A. solid   B. liquid   C. gas   D. ice

6. Which solid would be the MOST likely to dissolve in gasoline?

    A. motor oil   B. ice   C. salt   D. wood

7. Marisol mixes olive oil and red wine vinegar together with spices in a bottle. She closes the cap and agitates the mixture. What does she end up with?

    A. A solution of olive oil and vinegar and spices.

    B. A mixture of olive oil and vinegar and spices.

    C. A solution of olive oil and vinegar, with spices mixed in.

    D. A compound of olive oil and vinegar, with spices mixed in.

C. Answer the following questions.

1. Draw a water molecule. Label the hydrogen and oxygen atoms. Which part of a water molecule is partially negative δ^-? Partially positive δ^+? Draw KNO_3 molecules and show how they line up with the water molecules.

2. Name two ways to increase the solubility of a gas.

3. Which form of matter experiences increased solubility as a greater surface area is exposed to a solvent, and why?

4. Could you dissolve a plasma in a gas to form a solution?

ACIDS AND BASES

This particular area of solution chemistry deserves special attention. Acid-base reactions are very important to almost every chemical process on Earth.

ACID-BASE REACTIONS

According to the Arrhenius theory, an **acid** is a compound that contains hydrogen and dissociates in water to produce **hydronium ions** (H^+ or H_3O^+). To **dissociate,** means to break down into smaller parts. **Strong acids** are acids that almost completely dissociate in water. Hydrochloric acid (HCl) is a strong acid because the hydrogen ion separates to a great extent from the chloride ion in water. The list of strong acids is short. See Table 8.2 to the right. **Weak acids** are acids that partially dissociate in water. Most acids are weak. Examples of common acids are citric acid in a lemon, tannic acid in tea, lactic acid in sour milk and acetic acid in vinegar.

Table 8.2 Strong Acids

hydrochloric acid	HCl
nitric acid	HNO_3
sulfuric acid	H_2SO_4
hydrobromic acid	HBr
hydroiodic acid	HI
perchloric acid	$HClO_3$

Table 8.3 Examples of Bases

hydroxide ion	OH^-
silicate ion	SiO_3^{2-}
phosphate ion	PO_4^{3-}
carbonate ion	CO_3^{2-}
ammonia	NH_3

The **Arrhenius theory** states that a **base** is a compound that produces **hydroxide ions** (OH^-) in a water solution. Solutions containing a base are **alkaline**. Examples of common bases are sodium hydroxide in lye, ammonium hydroxide in ammonia, magnesium hydroxide in milk of magnesia, aluminum hydroxide in antiperspirant, and calcium hydroxide in limewater. Most bases do not dissolve in water. However, those that do dissolve in water are called alkalis.

A more inclusive theory of acids and bases is the Brønsted-Lowry theory. According to the **Brønsted-Lowry theory**, an acid is a proton donor, and a base is a proton acceptor. Remember that a proton is a hydrogen ion (H^+). This theory explains why substances like ammonia, NH_3, are bases even though they don't have a hydroxide (OH^-) group. The NH_3 compound becomes a proton acceptor.

A list of different Brønsted-Lowry bases is shown in Table 8.3.

What would happen if an acid and a base reacted together? When an acid reacts with a base, both substances neutralize, and the products are water and a **salt**. A salt is a compound composed of the positive ion of a base and the negative ion of an acid. For example, equal amounts of hydrochloric acid (HCl) and sodium hydroxide (NaOH) will react to form table salt (NaCl) and water (H_2O). In reality, this reaction can be quite dangerous because it produces a large amount of heat, which causes the HCl and NaOH to splatter everywhere. The chemical reaction is:

$$HCl\ (aq) + NaOH\ (aq) \rightarrow H_2O\ (l) + NaCl\ (aq) \qquad \textbf{Equation 8.1}$$

When there is an equivalent amount of acid and base reacted together, it is called a **neutralization reaction**. It is neutral because there is neither an excess of acid nor base in the product. Does this reaction look familiar to you? It should—it is a kind of double displacement reaction. Because water is always formed in a neutralization reaction, they are sometimes called "waterforming" reactions.

This is, of course, an ideal reaction. The real reaction gets very close, but never reaches 100% completion. It turns out that water, to a very small extent, dissociates into H^+ and OH^- on its own. To what extent, you may ask? Well, one water molecule out of half a billion will be dissociated! This may seem like a small amount, but it is a significant amount when it comes to acid/base chemistry.

pH SCALE

We measure acidity and alkalinity using the **pH scale**, pH being short for "potential of hydrogen." The pH scale ranges from 0 to 14. It is **logarithmic**, so that a difference of one pH unit represents a tenfold change in hydrogen (or rather, hydronium) ion concentration. While we are not concerned with how to calculate pH, it is important to know how pH changes with hydronium ion concentration: it is a **reciprocal scale**. This means that as the pH values decrease, the concentration of hydronium ions (H_3O^+) increases. For instance, a substance with a pH of 2 has 10 times the hydronium ion concentration as a substance with a pH of 3. As the pH values increase, concentration of hydroxide ions (OH^-) increases.

A substance with a pH of 11 has 100 times (10×10) the hydroxide ion concentration as a substance with a pH of 9. Although it may be confusing, remember that if you hear about a solution having a low pH, it actually means that it is quite acidic.

Water is a neutral compound, except for that very small amount—one in half a billion molecules—that is dissociated. When this is translated to the pH scale, water has a pH of 7. This is considered the neutral point. Acids have pHs lower than 7, and bases have pHs higher than 7. One way to think of this is that for every pH point lower than 7, the solution has 10 times more H^+ floating around than is present in regular water. Likewise, every pH point above 7 means that 10 times more OH^- is present than is in water.

For example, Figure 8.6 shows that pure vinegar, a weak acid, has a low pH of 2.8. Many soda drinks have acidic pHs lower than 3. These acidic drinks are known to damage the enamel of human teeth. Bleach has a pH of 10. Many consumer products have acidic pHs, which makes it difficult to maintain pH balance in the body. Foods containing baking soda, such as saltine crackers and pretzels, are good for restoring an acidic body stomach to a neutral pH.

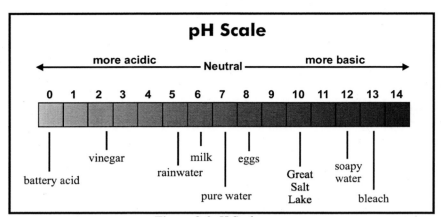

Figure 8.6 pH Scale

MEASURING PH

The pH of a substance can be determined by a pH meter or by an **indicator**, such as litmus. Indicators turn different colors, depending on the pH of a solution. You have probably heard of a **litmus test**. This involves placing a drop of solution onto litmus paper, which contains the indicator, and observing the color change, if any. For instance, acids will turn blue litmus paper red, and bases will turn red litmus paper blue. However, the range over which indicators change colors is small. Litmus will tell you whether something is acidic or basic, but not *how* acidic or basic it is. Therefore, chemists use many different indicators to test the pH of solutions across the entire pH scale.

Let's say that Shaquille has 100 mL of an HCl solution. Now, how does Shaquille know what the pH of his solution is? He can use litmus paper to determine whether it's acidic or basic, but that's no help here. After all, HCl is a strong acid, so he knows an HCl solution will be acidic, right? He wants an exact pH value. Well, to determine that, he will need to get a pH meter. A **pH meter** measures pH using a glass electrode.

The **glass electrode** contains a reference solution and reference electrode which holds a stable, measurable voltage. At the bottom, it has a small glass ball that interacts with solution. At the top, it has a wire that connects it to the pH meter itself. The pH meter measures the difference in voltage between the stable internal reference electrode solution and the external solution in the beaker. The whole set-up is shown in Figure 8.7.

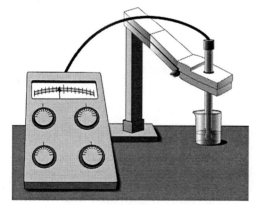

The voltage difference measured by the pH meter is then translated to a pH value. If Shaquille uses a pH meter, he will be able to tell the exact concentration of hydronium ions in his solution.

Figure 8.7 pH Meter Apparatus

A pH meter can be used in any pH range, but it must always be calibrated first. **Calibration** ensures that the pH meter gives accurate readings. Calibration is usually done by dipping the glass electrode in solutions of known pHs 2, 7 and 10. These are know as **buffer solutions**; they contain salt that resist pH change. The meter itself is adjusted to make sure that it measures those values.

ELECTRICAL CONDUCTIVITY

Some ionic solutions, such as salt water — where NaCl dissociates into Na^+ ions and Cl^- ions — can conduct electricity. These ions are **electrolytes** They are a special kind of conductor that transports electrons directly. Electrolytes — whether they are atomic or molecular — actually carry the electrons as part of their ionic structure within the solution. This is different than a conducting wire in a circuit. The wire transports the current — the flow of electrons — while the wire's atoms themselves remain fixed in place.

A measurable physical property of solutions then is their **electrical conductivity**, that is, the ability of a solution to conduct an electrical current. Some compounds cannot conduct a current, even though they are soluble in water. These compounds are called **nonelectrolytes**. Just as acids and bases are labeled as strong or weak depending on their degree of dissociation, water-soluble compounds can be **strong** or **weak electrolytes**.

A typical experiment testing the strength of electrical conductivity involves placing two **electrodes** that are connected to a power source into a solution (Figure 8.8). One electrode called the **anode** has a negative charge while the other electrode, the **cathode**, has a positive charge. When the power source is turned on, electricity will flow only when the electrodes are placed in a conductive solution. The electrolytes carry the electrons from the anode to the cathode. The more conductive the solution, the more electrons are able to flow.

If a light bulb is attached to the circuit, the light intensity can be used as a relative gauge of electrical conductivity. In a solution with a nonelectrolyte, the solution acts just like a resistor, in that it prohibits electron flow. So, the light bulb does not light up. In a weak electrolyte solution, some light is given off by the light bulb while a strong electrolyte allows more electricity to flow and therefore, the light bulb is much brighter.

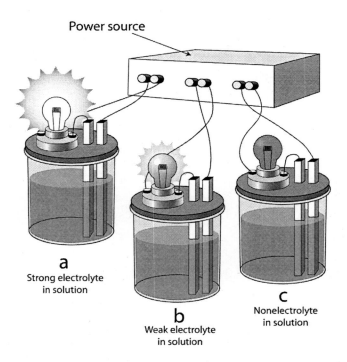

But what is different about a strong electrolyte? What makes it able to conduct electricity better than a weak electrolyte? The key property is the degree of dissociation. A strong electrolyte is almost completely dissociated in solution, meaning that the cation and anion are completely separated. Likewise, weak electrolytes dissociate to a much lesser extent. This means that there are very few ions in solution. Weak acids and bases are also weak electrolytes because they dissociate to a small degree. Nonelectrolytes do not dissociate at all, which means they are neutral species.

Figure 8.8 Electrical Conductivity of Various Solutions

Section Review 2: pH

A. Define the following terms.

acid	alkaline	salt	litmus	buffer solution
dissociate	weak acid	pH scale	pH meter	hydronium ions
strong acid	Arrhenius theory	indicator	calibration	hydroxide ions
Brønsted-Lowry theory	neutralization reactions	conductivity	glass electrode	logarithmic
		electrolyte	base	reciprocal scale

B. Choose the best answer.

1. Which of the following is a weak acid?
   - A. hydrochloric acid
   - B. sulfuric acid
   - C. nitric acid
   - D. acetic acid

2. Which of the following substances is alkaline?
   - A. milk
   - B. vinegar
   - C. bleach
   - D. rainwater

3. Orange juice has a pH of 3, and tomato juice has a pH of 4. Orange juice has a lower pH because
   - A. it is more basic than tomato juice.
   - B. it is a more concentrated acid than tomato juice.
   - C. it is a stronger acid than tomato juice.
   - D. it is a weaker acid than tomato juice.

4. All of the following are bases *except*
   - A. HBr
   - B. $Al(OH)_3$
   - C. NaOH
   - D. NH_3

5. The pH meter measures
   - A. pH, which it translates into voltage.
   - B. pH, which it translates into hydronium ion concentration.
   - C. voltage, which it translates to pH.
   - D. voltage, which it translates into an indicator range.

6. Which of the following ions is both an Arrhenius base and a Brønsted-Lowry base?
   - A. OH^-
   - B. NH_3
   - C. H^+
   - D. CO_3^{2-}

CHAPTER 8 REVIEW

A. Choose the best answer.

1. In the following reaction, what is $NaClO_3$?
$$HClO_3 + NaOH \rightarrow H_2O + NaClO_3$$
   A. strong acid
   B. salt
   C. element
   D. reactant

2. Sodium hydroxide completely dissociates into positive and negative ions. It is a
   A. strong acid.
   B. weak acid.
   C. strong base.
   D. weak base.

3. The pH of acid rain is
   A. less than 7.
   B. 7.
   C. greater than 7.
   D. not measurable by ordinary means.

4. A substance that causes red litmus paper to turn blue is
   A. an acid.
   B. a salt.
   C. a base.
   D. pure water.

5. A solution with a pH of 1 is how many more times acidic than a solution with a pH of 5?
   A. 5
   B. 4
   C. 1,000
   D. 10,000

6. Which of the following is a balanced neutralization equation?

   A. $2Al(OH)_3 + 3H_2SO_4 \rightarrow 6H_2O + Al(SO_4)_3$

   B. $2KOH + HNO_3 \rightarrow 3H_2O + KNO_3$

   C. $4Ca(OH)_2 + H_2SO_4 \rightarrow H_2O + 3CaSO_4$

   D. $NaOH + HCl \rightarrow H_2O + NaCl$

7. A student made a solution by dissolving sugar in tap water. She wanted to increase the concentration of her sugar solution. Select the best way for her to do that.

   A. add more sugar to the existing solution

   B. add more water to the existing solution

   C. warm the solution

   D. agitate the solution

8. Identify the liquid that is the best conductor of electricity.

    A. concentrated sugar solution
    C. pure water

    B. molten candle wax
    D. saltwater

9. Identify the property of water that makes water an excellent solvent for salts.

    A. low freezing point
    C. polar molecules

    B. high specific heat
    D. translucent

10. A given solid and a given gas both dissolve in a given liquid. Identify the result that vigorously shaking the liquid will have on the amount of the solid and the amount of gas that can dissolve in the liquid.

    A. More solid and more gas can dissolve.
    C. Less solid but more gas can dissolve.

    B. More solid but less gas can dissolve.
    D. Less solid and less gas can dissolve.

11. A given solid and a given gas both dissolve in a given liquid. Identify the result that cooling the liquid will have on the amount of the solid and the amount of gas that can dissolve in the liquid.

    A. More solid and more gas can dissolve.
    C. Less solid but more gas can dissolve.

    B. More solid but less gas can dissolve.
    D. Less solid and less gas can dissolve.

12. A group of students boiled saltwater and condensed the vapor given off while the saltwater was boiling. They collected the condensate. Select the best description of that condensate.

    A. pure water
    B. an acid
    C. saltwater
    D. salt

13. An electrode connected to a power source and a light bulb are both placed in a solution containing a weak electrolyte. When the power source is turned on,

    A. electricity will not flow.
    C. the light bulb will be somewhat bright.

    B. the light bulb will not light up.
    D. the light bulb will be very bright.

14. The solubility of NaCl is 36 grams in 100 mL of water. Which of the following saltwater solutions is supersaturated? (You may use a calculator to make sure.)

    A. 18.5 g of NaCl in 50 g H_2O
    C. 5.0 g of NaCl in 15 g H_2O

    B. 25.0 g of NaCl in 90 g H_2O
    D. 43.5 g of NaCl in 125 g H_2O

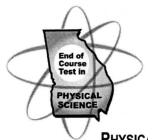

Chapter 9
Motion and Force

PHYSICAL SCIENCE STANDARDS COVERED IN THIS CHAPTER INCLUDE:

SPS8 a – d	Students will determine the relationships among force, mass and motion.

MOTION

MOVING IN SPACE

Everything in the universe moves. This may be hard to believe when you look out your window on a calm day and see no movement. But, this apparent lack of movement is an illusion. We only need to watch the Sun for a little while to see that it changes its location in the sky throughout the day. This is a simple observation that gives us qualitative data. But, if we want to accurately describe the movement of the Sun or any other object, we need to learn how to measure the movement and collect quantitative data. This requires a whole new vocabulary that will ensure accurate descriptions of movement.

An object's location in space is called its **position**. The **motion** of an object is defined as the change in its position during a specific amount of time. Motion is a **rate**. Before we concern ourselves with how much time it requires for an object to move, we will just focus on changing positions. We know that objects can change positions in a variety of ways. To make it very straightforward, let's consider **linear motion** where objects move along lines.

An object that moves from one position to another has traveled a **distance**, that is, a certain measure of length through space. **Displacement** is a term that describes the distance an object moves *in a specific direction*. The terms distance and displacement are similar, but displacement always includes a direction. For instance, "5 miles due north" is an example of a displacement value. The distance is 5 miles, but the direction of due north makes it a displacement value. Now, say a person walks 2 miles north and 3 miles east. The distance traveled is still 5 miles but there are two displacements. We can describe this person's movement as a path. A path is the overall course or track that an object travels along. So, to accurately describe the motion of any object, we need to consider its specific path, which consists of one or more displacements.

For example, imagine that you could have a satellite record your motion throughout a typical day. You would see a series of displacements that would follow a course beginning and ending at your home. Your motion would define a path that might look something like Figure 9.1.

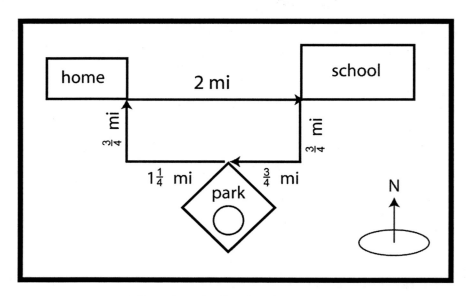

Figure 9.1 A Satellite View of Your Typical Day

Your motion defines a path from home to school to the park and back home again. This path involves a series of displacements that returns to the same position. Your overall displacement then at the end of the day is zero because you are back where you started. However, no one can say that you didn't go anywhere because the distance you traveled is 2 + ¾ + ¾ + 1 ¼ + ¾ = 5 ½ miles! And that only includes walking between places, not the moving around you did when you were actually there. Altogether, there are five displacements, each with a specific distance and direction. Notice that if we removed the arrowheads, you would lose information about the direction of motion. The fact that the arrowheads are shown means that you traveled exactly 2 miles east, then ¾ miles south, and so on. So, it is the distances and the directions that define the path of motion.

These quantities have specific mathematical names. The distance alone is called a **scalar quantity**. It can be completely described using only the magnitude (a number). Displacement is called a **vector quantity**. A vector quantity must be described by both a magnitude and a direction.

VELOCITY VS. SPEED

THE TIME OF MOTION

Remember that the motion of an object is defined as the change in position during a specific amount of time. So far, we talked about changing positions. Now we are ready to bring in the element of time. Imagine you are standing in line at a fast food restaurant. After a while, your might think, "It's taken ten minutes to move two feet! I'm never going to eat!" You notice that the other line is moving much faster because your friend, who chose the other equally long line, is already being served. He gets his food and comes up to you and says, "Man, that only took five minutes!"

While you have time to wait, you naturally begin to think about the difference in your motion versus your friend's. If the distance from the back of the line where you started and the register is ten feet, then you have only traveled 20% of the distance while your friend traveled 100%. But what about the time it has taken? If it took ten minutes to move two feet, how long will it take for you to get to the register if the line keeps moving in the same way? You calculate that it will take 50 minutes! Hardly the definition of *fast* food. Now, what if we wanted to describe how fast you were moving per minute? If it took ten minutes to move two feet, then you are traveling at 0.2 feet per minute. Your friend, on the other hand, moved ten feet in five minutes, or 2 feet per minute. No wonder he already has his food!

When motion is described as distance (feet) per unit time (min), it is called **speed**. We are most familiar with speed when driving in a car. A speedometer in a car that reads 55 mph or "miles per hour" means that if the car continues moving at the same rate for one hour, it will travel 55 miles. In general, any measurement that involves a change in something per unit time is referred to as a rate. Notice that the speed says nothing about the direction or the actual amount of time that the car is traveling for. It could be that the car is being driven for 15 minutes or 15 hours; either way, the speed is the same. Now, when someone typically drives a car, she starts at 0 mph and increase her speed while traveling to her destination. At a stop sign or traffic light, she returns to 0 mph. The pattern is continued until the final destination is reached. But at any given moment, the speedometer only gives the present speed. This is referred to as an **instantaneous rate** because it only gives information about exact points in time (that is, at a particular instance) and not how the rate may have changed over the path of motion. The car may have traveled 30 miles in an hour, in which case the **average rate** of the car is 30 mph. However, the instantaneous rate of travel changed constantly throughout the trip, and rarely had a value of 30 mph.

As you can see, we have used familiar units, like feet and minutes, to describe speed. That is OK as a thought exercise, but it is important to use SI units when making measurements. The box for Equation 9.1 shows the unit derivation or speed.

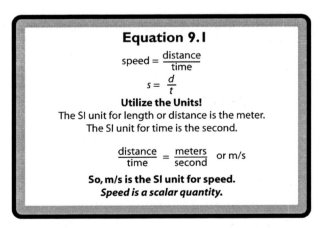

Equation 9.1

$$\text{speed} = \frac{\text{distance}}{\text{time}}$$

$$s = \frac{d}{t}$$

Utilize the Units!
The SI unit for length or distance is the meter.
The SI unit for time is the second.

$$\frac{\text{distance}}{\text{time}} = \frac{\text{meters}}{\text{second}} \quad \text{or m/s}$$

So, m/s is the SI unit for speed.
Speed is a scalar quantity.

Velocity differs from speed in much the same way as displacement differs from distance. The **velocity** is the speed plus the direction along the path. Another way to say this is that it is the displacement of an object over a period of time. The SI unit for velocity is meter per second (m/s). The numerical value of velocity and speed will be the same, but velocity implies that there is also information about the direction of motion. For example, what is the velocity of a car traveling 550 miles due south for 12 hours? Simply dividing 550 miles by 12 hours gives a rate of about 46 mph. This answer alone does not tell us direction nor does it reveal what the instantaneous rates were. It simply gives the average rate. If we wanted to know more information about the different rates the car traveled along the path, we would need more information. In order to avoid the confusion between instantaneous and average rates, many problems you will encounter deal with **uniform motion**, that is, motion that has a constant rate. Equation 9.2 is the equation used to calculate velocity between two positions.

Equation 9.2

$$\text{velocity} = \frac{\text{final position} - \text{initial position}}{\text{final time} - \text{initial time}}$$

$$v = \frac{\Delta x}{\Delta t}$$

Utilize the Units!

The Δ symbol means "change in." Change in position is a distance. The SI unit for length or distance is the meter. The SI unit for time is the second.

$$\frac{\text{distance}}{\text{time}} = \frac{\text{meters}}{\text{second}} \text{ or m/s}$$

So, m/s is the SI unit for velocity.

Velocity is a vector quantity.

Practice Exercise 1: Calculating Displacements and Rates

Find the displacement for the following problems. Use graph paper and a protractor when needed, and use a convenient scale.

1. Shawn runs 4 times around a 400-meter oval track and stops at the same point he started.

2. A truck driver travels 50 miles north, then turns west and drives another 50 miles.

3. Dupree Park has a perfectly circular walking track that has a circumference of 200 feet and a diameter of about 64 feet. Dale starts at the westernmost point and walks to the easternmost point.

4. A father runs errands with his children. He leaves his home, drives five miles south to the gas station, 10 miles southeast to the dry cleaners, 5 miles east to the grocery store, 10 miles northeast to the eye doctor, 5 miles north to the park, and 19 miles west to return home.

Calculate the rate of speed for the following problems.

1. James drives 400 km in 5 hours.

2. A man hang glides down a 3,048 m mountain in 20 minutes.

3. A turtle crawls 120 cm in 4 minutes.

4. Michelle swims 100 m in 50 seconds.

Velocity or speed can also be shown graphically with distance on the *y*-axis and time on the *x*-axis. Figure 9.2 shows the distance that two cars travel versus time. You can use a graph like this to determine speed. Remember, speed is distance divided by time.

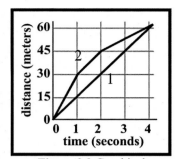

Figure 9.2 Graphical Representation of Car Speed

Since the line for car 1 is straight, the speed is constant. From the graph, you can see that car 1 travels 15 meters every second. Between any two points, the distance divided by the time is 15 meters per second. Therefore, the speed of the car is 15 m/s. The slope of the line (the change in distance divided by the change in time) represents the speed. Recall from math class that the slope of a line equals rise over run, or the difference in the *y*-value divided by the difference in the *x*-value. The graph for the second car is not a straight line. Therefore, the speed is not constant. Car 2 travels 30 meters in the first second, and then 15 m in the next second. Finally, the car only travels 15 meters in the last 2 seconds. The speed of the car is decreasing from 30 m/s initially, to 15 m/s, and finally to 7.5 m/s.

RATE CHANGES

How do you describe motion that does not have a uniform rate? **Acceleration** is the change in velocity over time. You are probably familiar with this term in the sense of a car "accelerating". For instance, car enthusiasts often compare the time it takes for different cars to go from 0 to 60 mph. Notice that this is describing the change in a rate over a period of time. So, one car may take 4.2 seconds to go from 0 to 60 mph, while another car may take 5.0 seconds. When acceleration is a positive number, the object is increasing its speed. Likewise, when acceleration is a negative number, the object is decreasing in speed. Negative acceleration is also called **deceleration**.

Equation 9.3

$$\text{acceleration} = \frac{\text{final velocity} - \text{initial velocity}}{\text{final time} - \text{initial time}}$$

$$a = \frac{\Delta v}{\Delta t}$$

Utilize the Units!

The Δ symbol means "change in." Change in velocity is a rate. The SI unit for rate is the meter per second. The SI unit for time is the second.

$$\frac{\text{velocity}}{\text{time}} = \frac{\text{m/s}}{\text{s}} = \frac{\text{m}}{\text{s}} \times \frac{1}{\text{s}} = \text{m/s}^2$$

So, m/s² is the SI unit for speed.
Acceleration is a vector quantity.

Example: A car accelerates from 10 m/s to 22 m/s in 6 seconds. What is the car's acceleration?

$$a = \frac{22 \text{ m/s} - 10 \text{ m/s}}{6 \text{ s}} = 2 \text{ m/s}^2$$

Notice that the units for acceleration are distance per time squared. In this example, the car accelerates 2 meters per second each second, or 2 m/s².

Practice Exercise 2: Calculating Acceleration

Calculate the acceleration in the following problems. Use a negative quantity to indicate deceleration.

1. A sky diver falls from an airplane and achieves a speed of 98 m/s after 10 seconds. (The starting speed is 0 m/s.)

2. A fifty-car train going 25 meters per second takes 150 seconds to stop.

3. A Boeing 747 was flying at 150 m/s and then slows to 110 m/s in 10 minutes as it circles the airport. (Note: Time is given in minutes. Convert minutes to seconds to make your units consistent.)

4. A runner speeds up from 4 m/s to 6 m/s in the last 10 seconds of a race.

5. A car traveling 24 m/s comes to a stop in 8 seconds.

Acceleration can also be shown graphically, with speed on the *y*-axis and time on the *x*-axis. Figure 9.3 shows the acceleration of a car by graphing speed versus time. The line in this graph is straight; therefore, the acceleration is constant. Since acceleration is the change in speed over time, the slope of this graph represents the acceleration of the car.

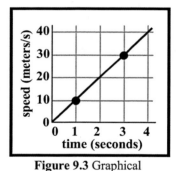

Figure 9.3 Graphical Representation of Car Acceleration

Example: Use the graph to determine the car's acceleration. Pick any two points to calculate the change in speed and the change in time. Using the two points marked on the graph;

$$a = \frac{30 \text{ m/s} - 10 \text{ m/s}}{3 \text{ s} - 1 \text{ s}} = \frac{20 \text{ m/s}}{2 \text{ s}} = 10 \text{ m/s}^2$$

The acceleration of the car is 10 m/s².

Now, look at Figure 9.4. Let's interpret the meaning of this graph. First, notice the plot is time versus velocity. The plot will show changes in velocity over the course of 60 seconds. At a time equal to zero(t=0), the car had no speed, meaning that it was at rest. Between 0 and 20 seconds, the speed changes from 0 m/s to 10 m/s. During this time interval, the car's speed is changing, which means that the car is accelerating. Between 20 and 30

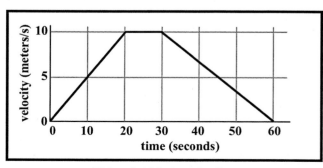

Figure 9.4 Motion of a Car

154

seconds, the speed remains at 10 m/s and does not increase or decrease during this time interval. Acceleration during this interval is zero, and the car travels at a constant speed of 10 m/s. From 30 seconds to 60 seconds, the car's speed changes again, but this time the speed decreases. Therefore, between 30 and 60 seconds, the car decelerates. At 60 seconds, the speed is zero, meaning the car has completely stopped.

Practice Exercise 3: Interpreting Graphs of Motion

Use Figure 9.4 to answer the following questions.

1. Calculate the acceleration of the car between 0 and 20 seconds.

2. At 25 seconds, what is the car's acceleration?

3. Calculate the acceleration of the car between 30 and 60 seconds.

4. At 45 seconds, what is the car's speed?

Section Review 1: Motion

A. Define the following terms.

position	speed	acceleration
motion	instantaneous rate	deceleration
linear motion	scalar	rate
distance	average rate	
displacement	velocity	
vector	uniform motion	

B. Choose the best answer.

1. Calculate the average speed of a bicyclist who travels 20 miles in 60 minutes.

   A. 0.33 miles per hour   C. 40 miles per hour

   B. 3 miles per hour   D. 20 miles per hour

2. Calculate the acceleration of a race car driver if he speeds up from 50 meters per second to 60 meters per second over a period of 5 seconds.

   A. 2 m/s^2 B. 5 m/s^2 C. 60 m/s^2 D. 50 m/s^2

3. Which of the following is a vector quantity?

   A. 0 mph   B. 55 mph   C. distance   D. acceleration

C. Use the graph to the right to answer the following questions.

1. What is the acceleration of the train between 0 and 20 seconds?

2. What is the acceleration of the train between 20 and 40 seconds?

3. What is the acceleration between 100 and 120 seconds?

4. At 80 seconds, what is the train's speed?

5. Calculate how far the train traveled during the period of time when its speed was 10 m/s. (Hint: speed = distance/time, so distance = speed × time.)

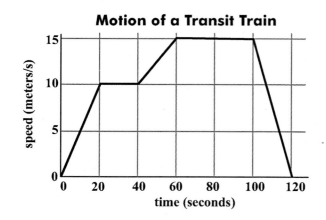

Motion of a Transit Train

FORCES AND MOTION

How do objects move? Well, if you think about it, there are really only two possibilities that could explain the mechanism of movement: either there is something inside the object that makes it move or there is something outside the object that influences its motion.

So, let's perform a test in our mind. Imagine that you have gathered a bunch of different kinds of rocks. You decide to drop them from a few feet off the ground. You know what will happen: they would all fall back to the ground, each demonstrating very similar motion. You could cut them open or smash them, but you would never isolate anything inside the rocks that made them behave this way. On the other hand, they all behaved similarly, right? There is no string or spring or anything dragging the rocks back to the ground, yet they all appear to be pulled in a similar way. Just from watching rocks fall, we can determine that something pulls objects down toward the Earth. Whatever that "something" is, it is undetectable to the human eye. If we examine more objects, we soon find that this phenomenon is not limited to rocks. All things seem to experience this phenomenon.

So, what is this invisible something that makes things move? It is a force. A **force** is a push or pull on matter. Forces act on objects and sometimes cause them to move. For example, you use force to pull a door open or to push a shopping cart. Force can cause matter to speed up, slow down, to stop or to change direction. For example, applying force to the brakes of a bicycle causes the bicycle to slow down. When a rock falls and hits the ground, the force of the ground against the rock stops the rock's motion. The force of a swung bat connecting with a baseball changes the direction of the baseball. Recall that a change in speed or direction of motion with time results in some change in acceleration of the object. Therefore, force can change the acceleration of an object.

Forces are pushing or pulling on matter in the world around us all the time, even when the matter appears to be at rest! For instance, the force of gravity pulled those dropped rocks toward the Earth. When they landed, they stopped moving — but NOT because the force of gravity stopped pushing. The motion of the rock ceased because the force of the Earth pushing UP on the rock was balanced by the force of gravity pushing DOWN on the rock. Overall, the rock doesn't move up or down, because the forces acting upon it are in balance. We can generalize this by saying that when the forces that act on an object at rest are in balance, the object remains at rest. When the forces that act on an object are unbalanced, the object moves in the direction determined by the sum of all forces acting on it.

Sir Isaac Newton (1642 – 1727) formulated three laws of motion that describe how forces affect the motion of objects. Newton's laws and their consequences are often referred to as **Newtonian**, or **classical mechanics**.

NEWTON'S FIRST LAW OF MOTION

Newton's first law of motion states that an object at rest will remain at rest, and an object in motion will remain in motion, unless acted on by an unbalanced force. The state of "rest" can occur in either of two ways. First, an object will be at rest if no forces are acting on it. Second, an object will be at rest if two or more forces are acting on the object in such a way that they all balance each other, so that the sum total of their push or pull on the object is zero.

Balance of forces can be illustrated by a classic tug-o-war competition. If the teams pulling on either end of the rope are not well-matched, the rope will move in the direction of the stronger team. The stronger team has the greater force. If the teams are well-matched, then they will be pulling with equal strength. In this case, the forces on the rope are balanced. The result: the rope will not move.

Newton's first law is also referred to as the **law of inertia**. The tendency of an object to remain at rest or in motion is called **inertia**. Another way to think about inertia is that it is an object's resistance to a change in its motion. It is not a measurable property of an object but more of a qualitative description. You feel inertia when you are in a car that starts suddenly, stops suddenly, or goes around a sharp curve. When a car starts suddenly, the inertia of your body keeps you at rest even though the car moves forward. The result is that you feel pushed back into the seat, even though, the seat is actually being pushed into you! The opposite occurs when you are in a car that stops suddenly. The inertia of your body is going forward, but the car is stopping. The result is that you feel like your body is being thrown forward. When you are riding in a car that goes around a sharp curve, the inertia of your body keeps you moving in a straight line, but the car's motion is in the opposite direction. You feel pushed in the opposite direction. These are the forces that seatbelts are designed to counteract. The seatbelt stops at the same rate as the vehicle, and because it surrounds your body, it exerts a stopping force on your body.

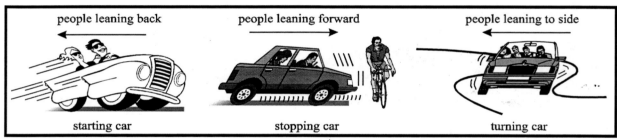

Figure 9.5 Newton's 1st Law: Examples of Inertia

FRICTION

So, if Newton's first law is true, why does a ball slow down — and eventually stop — when you roll it down a long hallway? It slows down and stops because **frictional forces** are acting on the object in the opposite direction of motion. The forces of friction occur because of the interaction of an object with matter it is in contact with. If the object is moving along a surface that is rough, frictional forces will be stronger and slow the object down more quickly than if the surface was smooth. You only need to think about roller skating to understand this. Roller skating on carpet or grass is much harder than skating on linoleum or tile. The frictional force exerted by a smooth surface inhibits motion less than that exerted by a rough surface.

Friction occurs between any two surfaces in contact because the irregularities on the surfaces interact with one another. These surfaces can be solids, liquids or gases. If you've ever skipped rocks on a lake, you know that the rock will slow down after a few skips and eventually, fall in. This occurs because the rock is slowed down by the frictional forces from the surface of the water. Frictional forces also apply when you bounce a ball across cement or if you throw a paper airplane through the air. In each case, frictional forces slow objects down — that is, they impede motion.

Let's take a closer look at types of friction.

1. **Static friction** is the force required to overcome inertia of a stationary object. In other words, it is the force required to start a stationary object in motion. This kind of friction is the hardest to overcome.

2. **Kinetic friction** is the force required to keep an object moving at a constant speed. Kinetic friction is less than static friction because the object is already in motion.

3. **Rolling friction** is the force required to keep an object rolling at a constant speed. Rolling friction is the easiest to overcome.

4. In all cases, friction is greater between rough surfaces than smooth surfaces. To further decrease friction, surfaces can be lubricated with a liquid such as oil or even water. Friction between a liquid and a solid is less than friction between two solids. Friction between a gas and a solid is even less.

NEWTON'S SECOND LAW OF MOTION

Newton's second law of motion states the mathematical relationship between force, mass and acceleration. Equation 9.4 relates force, mass and acceleration. The mass of an object multiplied by the acceleration of an object determines the force exerted by the object.

Equation 9.4

Force = mass × acceleration

$$F = ma$$

Utilize the Units!
The SI unit for mass is the kilogram (kg).
The SI unit for acceleration is the m/s².

$$kg \times \frac{m}{s^2} = \frac{kg \cdot m}{s^2} = a \text{ newton (N)}$$

So, the newton (N) is the SI unit for force.
Force is a vector quantity.

An important point about force is that it goes both ways. A force is the push or pull exerted *on* matter (it is a vector!), but it is also the push or pull exerted *by* matter. Newton's second law not only allows you to determine the amount of force that object can exert by its motion, but also the amount of force required to change the motion of the object.

A second point about the calculation of force is that mass and acceleration play equal roles. Look at Figure 9.6. A set of bowling pins at rest is experiencing balanced forces. In order to knock the pins down, a force must be applied to them that is unbalanced by another force. Obviously, the object applying this force will be a bowling ball. Is the mass of the bowling ball or the acceleration with which you throw it more important? They both are!

If you throw a bowling ball with a high acceleration, the bowling ball hits the pins with a large force, and you may get a strike. But, if a small child throws the same bowling ball with a low acceleration, then the ball will not hit the pins with as much force and only a few pins will be knocked down. Similarly, if you bowl with a basketball, which has a much lower mass than a bowling ball, the force it generates may not be enough to knock down many of the pins, even if you throw it quite hard.

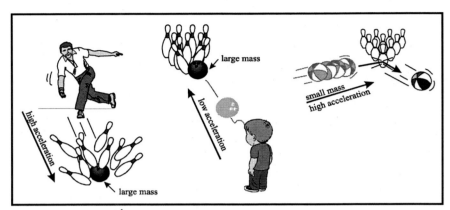

Figure 9.6 Newton's 2nd Law: The Relationship Between Force, Mass and Acceleration

Rearrange the terms of Equation 9.4 to see how mass and force affect acceleration. Writing F=ma as a=F/m shows that acceleration can be determined by dividing the force of an object by its mass.

Now, let's look briefly back to the point that force goes both ways. The bowling ball applied a force to the pins. But what applied force to the bowling ball? Well, the bowler did! The amount of force applied to the pins is directly related to (but not equal to) the amount of force applied by the bowler. Why aren't the forces equal? Because the motion of the bowling ball rolling down the alley was opposed by both the frictional force of the alley and the frictional force of air resistance. These frictional forces lowered the acceleration of the bowling ball, so that the force applied by the ball when it reached the pins was less than the initial force applied to the ball by the bowler.

Practice Exercise 4: Calculation with the Second Law

Use the force equation to solve each problem below.

1. Ryan hits a baseball with an acceleration of 40 m/s^2. The mass of the baseball is 0.5 kg. What is the force of the swing?

2. Richard hits a golf ball that has a mass of 0.45 kg. The acceleration of the ball is 41 m/s^2. What is the force of Richard's swing?

3. How much force is required to give an object with a mass of 20 kg an acceleration of 12 m/s^2?

4. What is the acceleration of a 500 kg crate when it hits a wall with a force of 1000N?

NEWTON'S THIRD LAW OF MOTION

Newton's third law of motion is the law of action and reaction. It states that for every force or action, there is an equal and opposite force or reaction. Your book lying on your desk exerts a force on the desk. The desk exerts an equal and opposite force on the book. The force of the desk on the book is called the **normal force**. The word "normal" is a mathematical term that means at a 90° angle, or perpendicular, to the object. You might

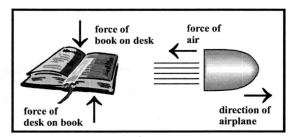

Figure 9.7 Newton's 3rd Law: Action and Reaction

recall from math class that when objects are perpendicular to each other, they are said to be normal to each other. The normal force is basically a resistance force of matter interacting with matter. It is actually an observable force because you don't ever see your book suddenly sink into the desk. The normal force of the desk onto the book has enough force to prevent this but not enough force to push the book into the air. Instead, they remain in contact.

In a jet engine, air is forced out in one direction, which then drives an airplane forward in the opposite direction. Although they are not shown in Figure 9.7, the plane also has forces exerted on it in the vertical direction. The weight of the plane acts as a downward force and air resistance acts as an upward, frictional force. When describing the motion of an object, it is helpful to visualize the motion by drawing a diagram of all the forces acting on the object. This type of diagram is called a **free body diagram**. Figure 9.7 shows some examples of free body diagrams for the motion of different objects.

Notice the arrows in Figure 9.7. They show the direction of the forces. Because force is a vector quantity, it can be described with vector diagrams, in which arrows show both direction and magnitude.

Take a look at the vector diagram in Figure 9.8 and see if you can figure out what it shows:

$$\underrightarrow{5} + \underrightarrow{5} = \underrightarrow{10}$$

Figure 9.8 Additive Vector Diagram

You have probably guessed that the diagram shows one force of 5 newtons (N) moving to the right, adding to another force of 5 N moving to the right. This equals a total force of 10 N moving to the right.

$$10\uparrow + -5\downarrow = 5\uparrow$$

Figure 9.9 Subtractive Vector Diagram

In Figure 9.9, we have something very different going on. There is a force of 10 N pushing up, and a force of 5 N pushing down, creating a net force of 5 N pushing up. A **net force** is the sum of all the forces acting on an object. Remember that forces have magnitude and direction (a vector) and if two forces are equally acting in opposite directions, they will cancel each other out! Give this a try on your own by working through the challenge activity on the next page.

Challenge Activity

This vector diagram corresponds to the discussion in the chapter. Use the diagram to answer the following questions.

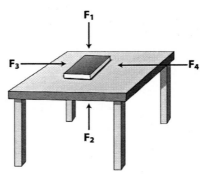

1. Define the four forces in the diagram, according to the discussion in the text.

_____

2. If F_1 equals 9.81 N, what does F_2 equal? _____

3. Describe what must happen to the forces, in order for the book to move to the left.

_____

4. Describe what must happen to the forces, in order for the book to move up.

_____

5. Tom applies a force F_3=12N to the book. Laura applies a force F_4 of 9N to the book. Draw a vector diagram that shows this in the space below. Indicate which direction the book will move.

Section Review 2: Forces and Motion

A. Define the following terms.

force	frictional forces	newton
Newtonian mechanics	static friction	Newton's third law
Newton's first law	kinetic friction	normal force
law of inertia	rolling friction	free body diagram
inertia	Newton's second law	

B. Choose the best answer.

1. Which of the following is a force that can oppose or change motion?

   A. gravity   B. air resistance   C. friction   D. all of the above

2. A passenger in a car that suddenly stops will

   A. lean forward.   C. lean to the right.

   B. lean backward.   D. feel no motion.

3. A book lying on your desk will only move if

   A. an unbalanced force acts on it.   C. a normal force acts on it.

   B. a downward force acts on it.   D. the frictional force on it is reduced.

4. Mariah and Charley each pull at opposite ends of a rope. Charley is stronger. Who will move backwards?

   A. The rope will move but Mariah and Charley won't.

   B. Both Mariah and Charley will move backwards.

   C. Mariah will move backwards.

   D. Charley will move backwards.

5. A car engine works harder to accelerate from zero to 10 km/hr than it does to maintain a 10 km/hr velocity. Why is this?

   A. Because static friction is harder to overcome than kinetic or rolling friction.

   B. Because static friction is easier to overcome than kinetic or rolling friction.

   C. Because static friction is harder to overcome than potential friction.

   D. Because static friction is easier to overcome than potential friction.

THE FUNDAMENTAL FORCES

Most of the observations that we make every day can be described with Newtonian mechanics…but not all of them. Scientists became increasingly aware of situations where Newtonian mechanics did not adequately explain a phenomenon. Physicists, chemists and theorists began to discuss, hypothesize, theorize and debate, heatedly looking for the solutions to these apparent mathematical anomalies. Among those involved were Albert Einstein, Niels Bohr, Max Plank, Erwin Schrödinger and Werner Heisenberg. The result was a 20th century revolution in physical science. Thanks to the contributions of many great minds, observations that could not be easily explained by Newtonian mechanics could now be explained by quantum and relativistic mechanics.

Quantum mechanics is the physics of the smallest pieces of matter. Without the powerful mathematical tools of quantum mechanics, the nature of matter in its most basic form cannot be explained. For instance, the behavior of the nucleus of an atom, and the orbit of electrons around that nucleus are both completely contrary to Newtonian mechanics but are easily explained in quantum mechanical terms.

Relativistic mechanics explains the physics of motion at speeds near the speed of light. It defines the speed of light ($c = 3.0 \times 10^8$ m/s) as a fundamental constant that plays a role in the way that space and time are tied together. Einstein's theory of special relativity also explains with the famous equation $E=mc^2$ that energy (E) and matter (m) are linked states.

Equation 9.5

Energy = mass × speed of light

$$E = mc^2$$

Utilize the Units!

The SI unit for mass is the kilogram.

The SI unit for speed is m/s.

$$kg \times \frac{m}{s} \times \frac{m}{s} = \frac{kg \cdot m^2}{s^2} = \text{a joule (J)}$$

The joule was named in honor of James Prescott Joule, as he discovered this quantity that related work to thermal energy. Note that a joule can also be described as a newton·meter (N·m)

So, the SI unit for energy is the joule (J).

Energy is a scalar quantity.

All forces can be divided into four **fundamental forces**. These are the gravitational force, the electromagnetic force, the weak nuclear force and the strong nuclear force. We will discuss each in turn and connect them to forces that are more familiar and directly observable. Of the four fundamental forces, you are probably most familiar with gravity.

Activity

Use an Internet search engine or wikipedia.com to search for information on one of the 20th century scientists mentioned above. Write an essay describing their contributions to modern physics.

GRAVITATIONAL FORCE

Sir Isaac Newton also formulated the **universal law of gravity**. This law states the following:

- Every object in the universe pulls on every other object;

- The more mass an object has, the greater its gravitational force (pull);

- The greater the distance between two objects, the less attraction they have for each other.

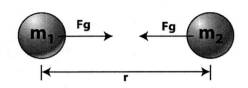

Figure 9.10 Attractive Gravitational Force Between Two Masses

Newton's law of gravitation is expressed in Equation 9.6.

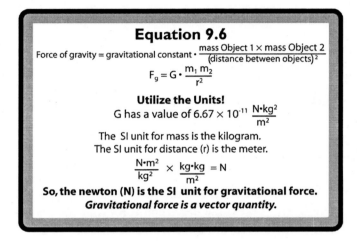

Equation 9.6

Force of gravity = gravitational constant $\cdot \dfrac{\text{mass Object 1} \times \text{mass Object 2}}{(\text{distance between objects})^2}$

$$F_g = G \cdot \frac{m_1 \, m_2}{r^2}$$

Utilize the Units!

G has a value of $6.67 \times 10^{-11} \, \dfrac{\text{N}\cdot\text{kg}^2}{\text{m}^2}$

The SI unit for mass is the kilogram.
The SI unit for distance (r) is the meter.

$$\frac{\text{N}\cdot\text{m}^2}{\text{kg}^2} \times \frac{\text{kg}\cdot\text{kg}}{\text{m}^2} = \text{N}$$

So, the newton (N) is the SI unit for gravitational force.
Gravitational force is a vector quantity.

The universal gravitational constant is necessary to correct the result of the equation (kg_2/m_2) to the correct unit for force (N). Even though the units of G look complicated, they are really just a way to translate the value obtained from the mass-distance infraction into units we are familiar with. This relationship is an example of the **inverse square law** in physical science: the gravitational force is proportional to the inverse square of the distance between the objects. So, gravitational force increases with increased mass and decreased distance.

Gravity gives the mass of an object its weight. Many confuse the terms "mass" and "weight." Mass is **not** the same as weight. As we know, mass measures the amount of matter an object consists of. **Weight** is a measure of the force of gravity exerted on an object by the Earth. Weight depends on the mass of the object and its distance from the earth. In the SI measurement system, weight is measured in newtons, the same unit as force. Weight is calculated by using the same equation as given in Equation 9.4, Newton's second law.

Gravity is a force that attracts objects to one another. In other words, it is a force that pulls. Objects are pulled or accelerate toward the Earth at a rate of about 9.81 m/s². This is referred to as the **free-fall acceleration,** or the acceleration due to gravity. If you drop a ball, the Earth's gravity will cause that ball to accelerate towards the Earth's surface at 9.81 meters per second, each second. This value is not actually the same everywhere on Earth. However, for our calculations, we will assume that it is a constant. This value for acceleration can be substituted into Equation 9.4 and multiplied by mass to calculate weight. Since acceleration due to gravity on the Earth is different than the gravity on the Moon, you do not weigh the same on the Earth as you would on the Moon. Your mass, however, is constant. Equation 9.7 is the formula to calculate weight. It replaces "force" with "weight," and "acceleration" with "acceleration due to gravity." Using Newton's second law, we can express weight with the following equation where w is the weight and g is the acceleration due to gravity.

Equation 9.7

Weight = mass × acceleration due to gravity

$$W = mg$$

Utilize the Units!
g is the free fall acceleration, with units of m/s^2
The SI unit for mass is the kilogram.

$$kg \times \frac{m}{s^2} = \frac{kg \cdot m}{s^2} = N$$

So, weight is a force, and its SI unit is the newton (N).
The force of weight is a vector quantity.

ELECTROMAGNETIC FORCE

The electromagnetic force should also be quite familiar to you, although you might think of it more naturally in terms of its component forces, the electrical force and the magnetic force. The **electrical force** causes static electricity and drives the flow of electric charge (electric current) in electrical conductors. The **magnetic force** is associated with magnets. These two forces are caused by their respective fields — in effect, the field produces the force.

The electric and magnetic fields are interconnected. For example, the presence of an electric field will actually produce a magnetic field. Similarly, a change in the magnetic field produces an electric field. Because the fields are so intimately linked, they are referred simply as the electromagnetic field. The **electromagnetic force** is the force exerted by the electromagnetic field on any charged particle.

We will discuss the everyday phenomena of electricity and magnetism in Chapter 12. For now, we will simply note how the electromagnetic force is different from the gravitational force. The gravitational force describes the push and pull of the components of the universe based on *mass and distance*. The electromagnetic force describes the push and pull of the components of the universe based on *charge and distance*. (Incidentally, the law describing electromagnetism is Coulomb's Law, and it is another example of the inverse square law.)

The electromagnetic force is powerful down to a very tiny scale — it is the primary cause for the bonding between molecules and atoms. Inside the nucleus, however, even more powerful forces actually reside.

NUCLEAR FORCES

The nucleus of an atom contains protons and neutrons. If you think about this arrangement for a moment, you will realize that it means that the nucleus of the atom is packed with positively charged material (protons). There are no negative charges to balance the positive charge because neutrons are neutral. That should seem unusual to you — opposites attract, right? Well, most of the time they do. In our everyday experience, opposite charges attract (and like charges repel) because of the electromagnetic force. However, the inside of a nucleus is not like any environment that we have ever seen.

In the nucleus, protons and neutrons are both referred to as **nucleons**, and they are held together by a force called the **nuclear force**. The nuclear force is *totally different* than the electromagnetic force — it has nothing at all to do with the charge of the nucleon. It is actually the result of the exchange of much smaller and more fundamental particles than the proton and neutron, particles called **mesons**. A full discussion of this subject is not merited at this stage — here, it is enough to understand that the nuclear force only operates between nucleons inside the nucleus, and only at very specific distances.

The typical separation of each nucleon from its nearest neighboring nucleon is about 1.3 femtometers (that is, 1.3×10^{-15} meters). That inter-nucleon distance is nearly constant because of the nuclear force. At 1.3 fm, the nuclear force is an *attractive* force of about 104 N, much stronger than the electrostatic force. At distances shorter than 1.3 fm, the nuclear force is very *repulsive,* forcing the protons and neutrons to keep that respectful 1.3 fm distance from one another. At distances farther than 1.3 fm, the nuclear force drops off quickly to zero. From that point outward, the electromagnetic force is dominant. For instance, two protons separated by 3 fm would exert powerful repulsive electromagnetic forces on one another but be totally unaffected by the nuclear force.

To be clear, the nuclear force is actually two different forces: the strong nuclear force and the weak nuclear force. Both are short range interactions that operate within the atomic nucleus. The **strong nuclear force** holds the atomic nuclei together, as described above. The much weaker but very distinct **weak nuclear force**, causes changes in the nucleus that result in radioactive decay, particularly beta decay.

Section Review 3: The Fundamental Forces

A. Define the following terms.

quantum mechanics	inverse square law	magnetic force	proton
relativistic mechanics	free fall acceleration	force field	neutron
fundamental forces	electromagnetic force	nucleus	strong nuclear force
universal law of gravity	electrical force	electron	weak nuclear force

B. Choose the best answer.

1. Which force is responsible for chemical bonding?
    A. gravitational force
    B. electromagnetic force
    C. strong nuclear force
    D. weak nuclear force

2. Which force is responsible for radioactive decay by beta emission?
    A. gravitational force
    B. electromagnetic force
    C. strong nuclear force
    D. weak nuclear force

3. Which force is responsible for static electricity?
    A. gravitational force
    B. electromagnetic force
    C. strong nuclear force
    D. weak nuclear force

4. Steve drops a marble from the top of the bleachers in the gym. What is the marble's acceleration just after he releases the marble (a_{drop}) and the moment before it hits the floor (a_{floor})?
    A. $a_{drop} = 9.81$ m/s^2, $a_{floor} = 9.81$ m/s^2
    B. $a_{drop} = 9.81$ m/s^2, $a_{floor} = 0$ m/s^2
    C. $a_{drop} = 0$ m/s^2, $a_{floor} = 9.81$ m/s^2
    D. $a_{drop} = 0$ m/s^2, $a_{floor} = 0$ m/s^2

5. If the mass of the marble is 20 grams, what is the force (F) with which the marble hits the floor?
    A. 196.2 kg m/s^2
    B. 19.62 kg m/s^2
    C. 1.962 kg m/s^2
    D. 0.196 kg m/s^2

C. Answer the following questions.

1. The gravitational pull of Mars is less than the gravitational pull of Earth. Would you weigh more or less on Mars than you do on Earth? Explain why you think so.

2. If an object weighs 49 N on Earth, how much does it weigh on the moon if the gravitational acceleration of the moon is approximately 1.63 m/s^2? HINT: Solve for mass first. Then calculate the weight on the moon.

CHAPTER 9 REVIEW

Choose the best answer.

1. A (n) _____ is a unit of force.
   A. newton   B. joule   C. Kelvin   D. ampere

2. Velocity includes both speed and
   A. distance.   C. time.
   B. rate of change.   D. direction.

The graph to the right shows the motion of a roller coaster from the beginning of the ride to the end. Use the graph to answer questions 3 and 4.

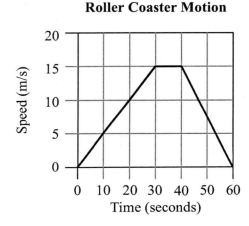

Roller Coaster Motion

3. Calculate the acceleration of the roller coaster for the first 30 seconds of the ride.

   A. 0 m/s^2

   B. 15 m/s^2

   C. 2 m/s^2

   D. 0.5 m/s^2

4. Identify the motion of the roller coaster during the first 30 seconds, the middle 10 seconds and the final 20 seconds of the ride.

   A. acceleration, constant speed, negative acceleration

   B. acceleration, stopped, acceleration back to starting point

   C. constant speed up hill, stopped at top of hill, acceleration down hill

   D. constant speed up hill, constant speed at top, constant speed down hill

5. Identify the changes in force and mass that together produce an increase in acceleration.
   A. increased force and increased mass   C. decreased force and increased mass
   B. increased force and decreased mass   D. decreased force and decreased mass

6. Identify the changes in mass and distance between two objects that act together to produce an increase in the gravitational force between those two objects.
   A. increased mass and increased distance   C. decreased mass and increased distance
   B. increased mass and decreased distance   D. decreased mass and increased distance

7. An unbalanced force acts on a body. Identify the change or changes in motion the unbalanced force can produce.

   A. increased speed only

   B. increased or decreased speed only

   C. increased speed and direction change only

   D. increased speed, decreased speed, or direction change

8. An object is taken from the Earth to the Moon. Identify the statement that describes the mass and weight of the object on the Moon compared to its mass and weight on Earth.

   A. Mass is the same and weight is the same on the moon.

   B. Mass is greater and weight is greater on the moon.

   C. Mass is the same and weight is less on the moon.

   D. Mass is less and weight is less on the moon.

9. Erin drops a ping-pong ball from the top of the bleachers in the auditorium. What is its acceleration just before it leaves her fingers (a_{drop}) and the moment after it hits the floor (a_{floor})?

   A. $a_{drop} = 9.81$ m/s^2, $a_{floor} = 9.81$ m/s^2

   B. $a_{drop} = 9.81$ m/s^2, $a_{floor} = 0$ m/s^2

   C. $a_{drop} = 0$ m/s^2, $a_{floor} = 9.81$ m/s^2

   D. $a_{drop} = 0$ m/s^2, $a_{floor} = 0$ m/s^2

10. Which surface will exert the most friction on a rolling ball?

    A. grass   B. concrete   C. glass   D. gravel

11. Which of the following describes the rules of motion for objects on a very small scale?

    A. Newtonian mechanics   C. quantum mechanics

    B. relativistic mechanics   D. classical mechanics

12. Two pinballs, each with a mass of 1.0 kilogram, are placed 0.50 meters apart from each other. What is the attractive gravitational force between the pinballs?

    A. 4.0G   B. 0.50G   C. 0.25G   D. 5.0G

13. Which force is responsible for holding the atomic nucleus together?

    A. gravitational force   C. strong nuclear force

    B. electromagnetic force   D. weak nuclear force

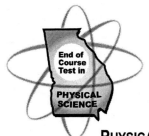

Chapter 10
Energy, Work and Power

PHYSICAL SCIENCE STANDARDS COVERED IN THIS CHAPTER INCLUDE:

SPS7 (a)	Students will relate transformation and flow of energy within a system.
SPS8 (e)	Students will determine the relationships among force, mass and motion.

TYPES OF ENERGY

All energy can be conceptually divided into two categories: kinetic energy and potential energy. To examine these two types of energy, let's think about riding a bike. Riding along, you see a hill in the distance. You decide to see if you can build up enough speed to get up the hill without pedalling. You start far away from the hill. Pedaling harder and harder to get enough speed, you finally reach the base of the hill. Then you stop pedalling. As you go up, your speed decreases and just as your bike comes to a stop, you reach the top. Then, *whoosh* down the hill as fast as you can psychologically (and legally) stand for your victory ride!

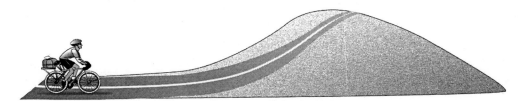

Figure 10.1 A Biking Scenario

In this scenario, we can identify three things about energy. First, changes in motion are related to energy. Whether going up or down the hill, energy is being transferred. Second, although there is no motion at the top of the hill, taking the bike in any direction will lead to downhill motion. Finally, the bike goes faster *down* the hill than *up* the hill.

How do we translate these observations into a scientific understanding of energy? We can do this by separating energy into two types. The first type is the energy of motion, known as **kinetic energy (KE)**. Any time the bike is moving, kinetic energy is responsible. The second type, called **potential energy (PE)**, is stored energy. At the top of the hill, you and your bike have potential energy because you have the potential of

171

motion any direction you turn. Your potential energy has to do with your position. Our final observation about the speed of the bike downhill versus uphill can be understood as the transfer of energy. At the base of the hill, you and your bike have a certain amount of kinetic energy. This kinetic energy was completely converted into potential energy when you came to rest at the top of the hill. This potential energy was then converted back to kinetic energy on the ride down. This scenario is illustrated in Figure 10.2.

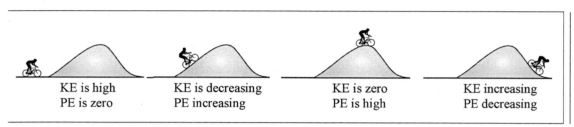

| KE is high | KE is decreasing | KE is zero | KE increasing |
| PE is zero | PE increasing | PE is high | PE decreasing |

Figure 10.2 Energy Transfer Up and Down a Hill

POTENTIAL ENERGY

Potential energy is the energy of *position*. Recall from the previous chapter that all objects exert a gravitational force on other objects. Objects on Earth have a potential energy related to the distance between the object and either the ground or a body of water. This gravitational potential energy is equal to the object's mass measured in kilograms × the acceleration due to gravity (9.8 m/s^2) × height from the ground in meters. This is summarized in Equation 10.1

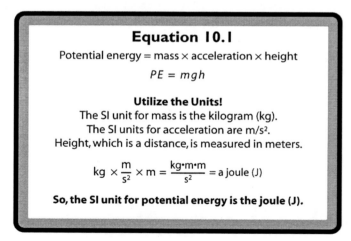

Equation 10.1

Potential energy = mass × acceleration × height

$$PE = mgh$$

Utilize the Units!
The SI unit for mass is the kilogram (kg).
The SI units for acceleration are m/s^2.
Height, which is a distance, is measured in meters.

$$kg \times \frac{m}{s^2} \times m = \frac{kg \cdot m \cdot m}{s^2} = a \text{ joule (J)}$$

So, the SI unit for potential energy is the joule (J).

The SI unit for potential energy is the **joule** (J), which is equivalent to a newton-meter.

Example: Suppose a rock weighing 2.2 kilograms is about to be dropped off a cliff that is 300 meters above the ground. What is the potential energy of this rock?

Step 1. Set up the equation: $PE = mgh$

Step 2. Insert the known information. In this problem, we know the mass of the rock (2.2 kg), the acceleration due to gravity (9.8 m/s^2), and the height above ground (300 m). The equation becomes: PE = (2.2 kg)(9.8 m/s^2)(300 m)

Step 3. Solve: PE = 6,468 joules = 6.5×10^3 J

KINETIC ENERGY

Moving objects also possess energy, related to the object's mass and velocity. Kinetic energy is the energy of *motion*. The formula for calculating kinetic energy is shown in Equation 10.2.

Equation 10.2

Kinetic energy = $\frac{1}{2}$(mass × velocity^2)

$$KE = \frac{1}{2}mv^2$$

Utilize the Units!
The SI unit for mass is the kilogram (kg).
The SI units for velocity are m/s.

$$kg \times \frac{m}{s} \times \frac{m}{s} = \frac{kg \cdot m \cdot m}{s \cdot s} = \frac{kg \cdot m^2}{s^2} = a \text{ joule (J)}$$

So, the SI unit for kinetic energy is the joule (J).

Example: Suppose that a bowling ball has a mass of 4.0 kg and travels at a speed of 5.0 meters/second in a southward direction. What is the kinetic energy of the bowling ball?

Step 1. Set up the equation: $KE = \frac{1}{2}mv^2$

Step 2. Insert the known information. In this problem, the mass is 4.0 kg and the velocity is 5.0 m/s.

The equation becomes: $KE = 1/2 \cdot (4.0 \text{ kg}) \cdot (5.0 \text{ m/s})^2$

Step 3. Solve: KE = 50 J

PUTTING IT TOGETHER

The fact that energy cannot be created or destroyed, only transferred, is reflected by the units of potential and kinetic energy: both forms of energy have the same SI unit, the joule. In fact, if we rearrange the equation for kinetic energy, we can see that it has a very similar form to the potential energy. Since velocity squared (m^2/s^2) and acceleration (m/s^2) differ only by a distance measurement (we'll call it x), we can rewrite the kinetic energy equation as $KE = \frac{m \times a \times x}{2}$. This shows that the gravitational potential energy is a specific situation where a = g and h = x/2. Because these two equations are of the same general form, and they have the same units, the total energy in any situation will be the sum of the potential and kinetic energy. Now we can calculate some really interesting things!

Example: A roller coaster car begins a ride at rest at the top of a 50 m hill. What is the velocity of the roller coaster car at the base of the hill?

Step 1. Set up the equations: $KE = \frac{1}{2}mv^2$ and $PE = mgh$

Step 2. To solve for velocity, we need to rearrange the equation: $v^2 = \frac{2KE}{m}$

Since the KE is the same as the PE, we can combine the equations: $v^2 = \dfrac{2mgh}{m}$

Since the mass is in both the numerator and denominator, it cancels out. The equation can then be written in terms of v as: $v = \sqrt{2gh}$

Now, insert the known information: $v = \sqrt{2(9.8 \text{ m/s})(50\text{m})}$

Step 3. Solve: $v = \sqrt{2(9.8 \text{ m/s})(50\text{m})}$

$v = 31.3$ m/s

It is interesting that this value is *independent of mass*. An object of any mass placed at the top of a 50 m hill will reach a velocity of 31.3 m/s at the base, assuming that the frictional force is negligible.

However, here on Earth, frictional forces are rarely negligible. That is why you will so often encounter questions that state that you should "ignore friction." If you include friction in the problem, it becomes difficult to solve.

Practice Exercise 1: Potential Energy

1. If a student drops a book having a gravitational potential energy of 5 joules from a height of 1.1 meters, what is the mass of the book?

2. What is the gravitational potential energy of a microscope with a mass of 0.49 kilograms on a shelf 1.6 meters from the floor?

3. What is the mass of a stereo sound system located on a shelf that is 1.7 meters above the floor and that has a gravitational potential energy of 83.3 joules?

4. A 3.1 kg cat sitting on a tree branch has a potential energy of 153.7 joules. How far above ground is the tree branch?

Practice Exercise 2: Kinetic Energy

1. A sport utility vehicle (SUV) with a mass of 2,450 kilograms is traveling at 21 meters/second south-east. What is the kinetic energy of the SUV?

2. A jet skier with a total mass (Jet Ski plus person) of 250 kilograms is traveling south with a kinetic energy of 40,500 J. What is the velocity of the jet skier?

3. A cat with a kinetic energy of 160 J is traveling up a tree at a velocity of 8 meters per second. What is the cat's mass?

4. A 173 gram baseball is thrown with a velocity of 21 m/s. What is the kinetic energy of the baseball?

Section Review 1: Potential and Kinetic Energy

A. Define the following terms.

potential energy   kinetic energy   joule

B. Choose the best answer.

1. On a construction site, cranes often hold expensive building materials up high in the air when the crew is off duty. This prevents the materials from getting stolen. A load of copper piping with a mass of 500 kg is suspended 25 meters from the ground. Which expression correctly assesses the potential energy of the load?

   A. PE= 20g   B. PE= 156,250g   C. PE= 12500g   D. PE=1250g

2. A bowling ball with a mass of 2 kg rolls down lane 15 at 0.5 m/s. What is its kinetic energy?

   A. 0.5 J   B. 0.25 J   C. 0.5 N   D. 0.25 N

3. A bowling ball with a mass of 2 kg rolls down lane 15 at 0.5 m/s. A second bowling ball of the same mass rolls down lane 16 at 1 m/s. Which has the greater kinetic energy?

   A. the first ball

   B. the second ball

   C. They have the same mass, so they have the same kinetic energy.

   D. The length of the lane is needed to answer this.

4. Will a feather or a rock reach the ground with a higher velocity if they are dropped from 2.0 m in a vacuum?

   A. the feather

   B. the rock

   C. They will have the same velocity.

   D. The mass of the objects is needed to answer this question.

5. A jewel thief is attempting to steal a famous diamond from a museum whose security includes a velocity detector. If anything in the room moves faster than 4.0 m/s, the detector will trigger an alarm. A tool weighing 150 g accidentally drops from his backpack at a height of 0.7 m. Does the alarm go off?

   A. Yes, but it wouldn't if the tool weighed 125 g.

   B. No, but a tool weighing 225 g would have set it off.

   C. No, but if would go off if it fell from 1.0 m

   D. Yes, but if it fell from 0.5 m the alarm wouldn't sound.

FORMS OF ENERGY

We now know that we can categorize energy into two types: the energy of motion (kinetic) and stored energy (potential). But these two categories are still somewhat vague in regards to our observations about energy. Often times, we look at our environment and see events but do not consider the energy that caused them to occur.

First, we know intuitively when energy is being transferred. Take a spring day, for example. The air is warm, there's a slight breeze and sunlight bathes everything. On the horizon, large clouds form into thunderstorms. Suddenly, lightning stretches out from the bottom of the clouds. A moment later, the thunder rolls past. The growing storm becomes more dangerous. If the lightning hits a tree, a fire could easily break out. Finally, the rain pours down. In each of these events, we can make observations about processes that involve energy transfer.

Second, for energy to transfer from one form to another there must be at least two, if not more, kinds of energy. In the example of the spring day, we can identify very distinct phenomena that most likely involve different forms of energy: wind, sunlight, lightning, thunder and fire. Each of these represents a distinct energy state because each can exist independently of the others.

Scientists have compared the different forms of energy that they have discovered. Table 10.1 shows the forms of energy that exist, organized as kinetic and potential energy. Do you see how the events of our spring day fit in?

Table 10.1 Forms of Energy

Kinetic Energy	
forms of energy	*examples*
motion energy	wind, bicycle
thermal energy	fire, friction
radiant energy	light, x-rays
electrical energy	lightning, electricity
sound energy	thunder, sonic booms

Potential Energy	
forms of energy	*examples*
gravitational energy	dam, skydiving
elastic energy	compressed spring, stretched rubber band
chemical energy	match, gasoline
nuclear energy	radioactive elements, stellar energy (Sun)

Let's revisit the example of riding a bike up a hill. There, we saw that kinetic energy can be converted to potential energy and back again. Now that we know the forms of energy, we can describe the bike ride more accurately. Chemical energy from the food you ate that morning fueled your trip up the hill. You used that chemical energy to generate motion and thermal energy. The thermal energy took the form of heat from your body and the heat resulting from the friction of the bike wheels on the pavement. Once you got to the top of the hill, you achieved a position that lent you gravitational energy, which you then expended during the victory ride down the hill.

There are many other examples of energy transfer between different forms of energy. A match, for example, has potential energy in the form of chemical energy. Once the match is struck, the chemical energy is converted to radiant and thermal energy as light and heat. Clearly, chemical potential energy cannot be described by Equation 10.1. This type of potential energy is based on the energy of the bonds broken and formed during the chemical reaction. Water behind a dam has potential energy due to the position of the water it blocks. Once the water is released from the dam, its potential energy is converted to kinetic energy. More specifically, gravitational energy is transferred to motion energy, just like a bike going downhill.

Figure 10.3 A Dam

If the dam is part of a hydroelectric plant, the falling water will turn the turbines of an electric generator. The motion energy of the turning turbine is converted to electrical energy by the generator. As the generator turns, thermal energy is created and dispersed into the environment. The main product of the generator is electrical energy.

Electrical energy may then be converted to radiant energy and thermal energy in a light bulb. Or into motion energy in a desktop fan. Or into chemical energy in a charging battery.

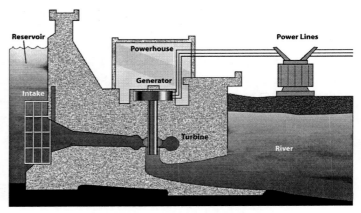

Figure 10.4 Hydroelectric Plant

Are you starting to see how this works? Energy is a commodity, a product that gets traded between every single thing in the universe, every single moment of the day. The **law of conservation of energy** states this clearly, by saying that energy cannot be created or destroyed. It can, however, be transferred from one form to another.

THERMAL ENERGY LOSS

Every energy transfer involves some formation of thermal energy as a side product. This is often referred to as energy loss because in any transfer some energy will be lost as thermal energy.

Table 10.2 Common Energy Changes

Use of Energy	Resultant Change in Energy	Energy Lost As
turning on a battery-powered flashlight	chemical to electrical to light	heat from flashlight bulb
turning the turbine in an electric generator	mechanical to electrical	heat from friction within the generator
turning on a light bulb	electrical to light	heat from bulb
using a nuclear reaction to produce heat	nuclear to thermal	heat from reaction
rock rolling down a hill	potential to kinetic	heat from friction of rock against earth

Thermal energy is a typical by-product of most energy transfers. To describe how well energy is transferred between two forms, we can gauge the efficiency of the transfer. **Efficiency** is the ratio of total energy output to total energy input. It is the amount of energy *actually* transferred divided by the amount that was *intended* to be transferred. The difference between these two quantities will often be the amount of thermal energy produced as a by-product. We can write the equation for efficiency as

$$\text{Efficiency} \quad \frac{\text{Energy in}}{\text{Energy out}}$$

Remember that efficiency can never be greater than one. This is because the energy output can never exceed the energy input.

Activity

Write the appropriate energy transition in the space provided.

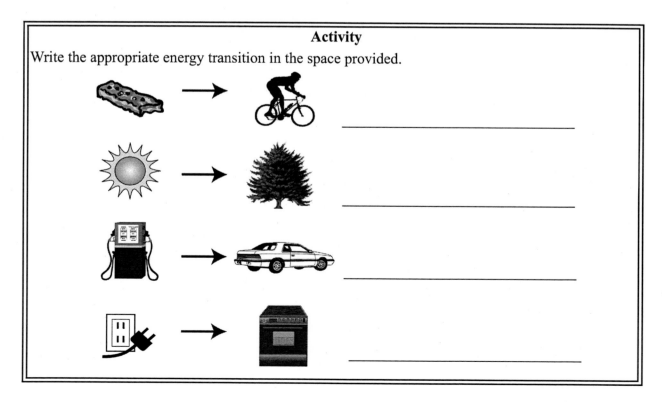

Section Review 2: The Law of Conservation of Energy

A. Define the following terms.

law of conservation of energy   efficiency

B. Choose the best answer.

1. Which of the following is true concerning the law of conservation of energy?

   A. Energy is conserved when converting from potential to kinetic energy but is destroyed by friction.

   B. Energy cannot be destroyed, but it can be transferred from one form to another.

   C. A tiny amount of energy is destroyed when converting from one form of energy to another.

   D. Energy is conserved as long as mass is also conserved, but when mass is destroyed, energy is also destroyed.

2. Which of the following does NOT describe the conversion of potential to kinetic energy?

   A. an avalanche

   B. a rocket leaving the Earth's atmosphere

   C. releasing a stretched rubber band

   D. the Sun emitting light

3. Which of the following is an example of the conversion of electromagnetic energy to electrical energy?

   A. chemical battery   C. light bulb

   B. nuclear fission   D. solar cell

4. Which of the following is an example of the conversion of thermal energy to nuclear energy?

   A. a generator turbine   C. nuclear fusion

   B. a light bulb   D. nuclear fission

5. Which of the following is an example of the conversion of electrical energy to electromagnetic energy?

   A. a generator turbine   C. nuclear fusion

   B. a light bulb   D. a solar cell

6. Which of the following would NOT be a source of sound energy?

   A. amplifier   B. thunder   C. light bulb   D. siren

WORK

We described how forces can change the motion of an object. A change in the motion of an object is a change in its kinetic energy. When a force is applied over a distance, it is called **work**. To calculate work, multiply the force applied to an object by the distance that the object moves, as shown in Equation 10.3. An object can have multiple forces applied to it at any given time, but unless it moves, no work is being done.

Equation 10.3

Work = force × distance

$$W = Fd$$

Utilize the Units!
The SI unit for force is the Newton (N).
The SI unit for distance is the meter (m).

$$N \times m = N{\cdot}m = a \text{ joule (J)}$$

So, the SI unit for work is the joule (J).

Example: Jason moved a chair 2 meters using 10 newtons of force. How much work did he do?

Step 1. Set up the equation: W = Fd

Step 2. Insert the known information. In this problem, the force is 10 N and the distance is 2 m.

Therefore, the equation becomes $W = (10 \text{ N}) \cdot (2 \text{ m})$

Step 3. Solve: W = 20 J

It's now time for a little mathematical analysis. Remember that a joule is also a newton-meter. Notice that work has the same units as potential and kinetic energy. If we substitute into the equation for work Newton's second law, F = ma, we can rewrite Equation 10.3 as W = m·a·d. Now, let's compare the three equations side-by-side but put the equation for kinetic energy in a slightly different form:

Potential energy	Work	Kinetic Energy
$PE = m{\cdot}g{\cdot}h$	$W = m{\cdot}a{\cdot}d$	$KE = \dfrac{m \cdot a \cdot x}{2}$

We already know that potential and kinetic energy are mathematically related. It should now be clear that the equation for work has the same general form as well. The total energy present in a system is related to its work. This relationship has in fact been used by scientists to define energy. After this entire discussion in this chapter, we are finally ready to define energy. **Energy** is the ability to do work. This definition derives completely from this mathematical analysis. It still doesn't tell us exactly what energy is, but it tells us what energy can do.

Practice Exercise 4: Work

Use the equation for work to answer the following problems.

1. How much work does Bill do if he uses 15 N of force to move a ladder 30 m?

2. How far was a box of books moved if Mike used a force of 50 N by expending 300 joules?

3. What force was applied by Cedrick if he moved a table 11 m by expending 990 joules?

4. How much work was done by Amy if she lifted her 12 N book bag 1.2 meters? (Remember, weight is a force.)

A **machine** is a device that does work. The six simple machines are shown in Figure 10.5.

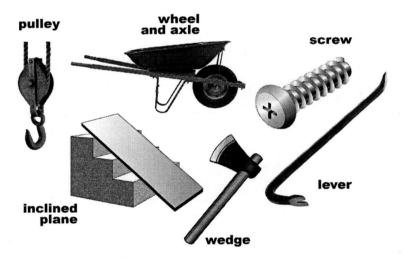

Figure 10.5 Examples of Machines

There may be no greater contribution to civilization's advancements than the machine. Why? The machines in our lives have made it possible for us to do more in less time. You may have heard or read about efforts to create machines like car engines that are incredibly efficient. Unfortunately, this dream has not yet been realized, because machines, in general, are inefficient. Much of their energy is lost as heat. With all this thermal energy being transferred around, you might wonder whether thermal energy can be used by a machine to do work. In fact, this is how steam and gasoline engines work. Heat is used to drive the internal parts which are used to create motion. Can an engine that is 100% efficient ever be built? The answer is no, it's physically impossible. Remember, one of the rules that we have is that thermal energy is also lost during energy transfer. So, even if we are transferring chemical energy (gasoline) to mechanical energy (the motion of the car), thermal energy will be a by-product.

Now let's look at the possibilities available to us if we use a simple machine. Why are they called "simple machines?" Well, because most of these ingenious devices don't have any moving parts! Each machine is used to change the amount of effort force needed to overcome the resistance force of the object. **Effort force** (F_e) is the force exerted by a person or machine to move the object. The **resistance force** (F_r) is the force exerted by the object that opposes movement. The resistance force is the weight of the object in Newtons: it may be augmented by inertia and friction. What the user of a simple machine gains is a **mechanical advantage** (MA) – a magnification of his applied effort force. In equation form, $MA = F_r / F_e$.

Example 1: The Inclined Plane

The inclined plane, or ramp, allows you to overcome a large resistance force by applying a smaller effort force over a longer distance. The mechanical advantage (MA) of the ramp comes from the ratio of the length of the ramp (L) to the height of the ramp (h), as in:

$$\frac{L}{h} = \frac{F_r}{F_e} \qquad \textbf{Equation 10.4}$$

To illustrate, let's look at two scenarios that confront Pete, who wants to lift a 100N box a vertical distance of 1 meter into the back of a moving van.

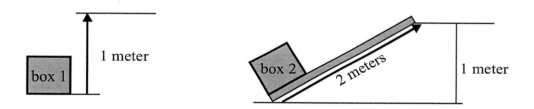

Figure 10.6 Mechanical Advantage of the Inclined Plane

In scenario A, Pete lifts the box straight up. The work that he does is:

$$W = F \times d = 100N \times 1m = 100 \text{ J}$$

In scenario B, Pete chooses to push the box up a 2 meter ramp to get it into the van. The work that he does is the same, 100J. The reason is that the weight is distributed by the angle of the ramp. Pete actually only has to push part of the weight of the box up the ramp. Let's find out how much MA he's gained.

From Equation 10.4, you can see that the mechanical advantage of the inclined plane equals the length of the plane divided by the height of the plane's terminal end. In our example, this is:

$$MA = \frac{L}{h} = \frac{2 \text{ meters}}{1 \text{ meter}} = 2$$

That means that Pete's effort force, when using the plane, is

$$F_e = \frac{F_r}{MA} = \frac{100\ N}{2} = 50\ N$$

So, the ramp made the work *easier*. You know it was easier because it required a lower effort force to move the box up the ramp than it did to lift it straight up.

In real life, an inclined plane will have friction that opposes motion. Remember, friction decreases mechanical advantage. What would be the mechanical advantage of the inclined plane if Pete had to apply an additional 10 N of force to overcome friction as he pushed the box up the inclined plane?

$$MA = \frac{F_r}{F_e} = \frac{100\ N}{50\ N + 10\ N} = \frac{100\ N}{60\ N} = 1\frac{2}{3}$$

The force necessary to move the box up the inclined plane is still less than lifting it vertically, but friction increases the effort force and, therefore, decreases the mechanical advantage.

*Test tip: The mechanical advantage of a frictionless inclined plane will always be the length of the plane (in our example, 2 meters) divided by the height of the plane's terminal end (in our example, 1 meter).

Example 2: The Lever

Another simple machine is the lever. The important parts of a lever are the **fulcrum** (which supports and distributes weight) the resistance arm and the effort arm. The mechanical advantage of a lever comes from manipulating the length of the arms: L_e is the length of the effort arm and L_r is the length of the resistance arm. The equation is:

$$\frac{L_e}{L_r} = \frac{F_r}{F_e}$$

A seesaw is a perfect example of a lever. On a seesaw, the fulcrum is placed in the center, between two equal length arms...which means that its mechanical advantage is one, right? Well, yes, that's because a seesaw is made for fun, not work.

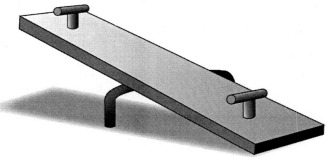

Figure 10.7 The Simplest Lever

So think about a modified seesaw, where one side (L_e) is 2 meters and the other (L_r) is 0.5 meters. The mechanical advantage of this lever is

$$MA = \frac{L_e}{L_r} = \frac{2 \text{ meters}}{0.5 \text{ meters}} = 4$$

Now, if Wanda puts her 6N bookbag at the end of the resistance arm (that is the short arm), what kind of effort force must be used to lift it 3 meters? That is:

$$F_e = \frac{F_r}{MA} = \frac{6 \text{ N}}{4} = 1.5 \text{ N}$$

So, Wanda needs to apply 6N of effort force to lift the bookbag by herself, but only 1.5N of effort force to lift it using the lever. Now *that* is a mechanical advantage!

Example 3: The Pulley

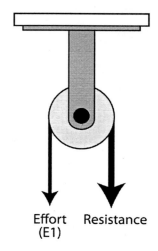

Effort
(E1)   Resistance

Figure 10.8 The Fixed Pulley

In the simplest arrangement, a pulley is **fixed** and **immovable** (Figure 10.8). In this arrangement, a 100 N load will require a 100 N of effort, that is, the mechanical advantage is 1 (100 N/100N).

$$MA = \frac{F_r}{F_e} = \frac{100N}{100N} = 1$$

Although this does not reduce the effort required to lift heavy loads, it does allow you to change the direction that you must lift. Instead of lifting an object up, you can pull down in order to lift up. This lets you use your body weight to help in the lifting.

A **moveable** pulley is more versatile. This type of pulley hangs from a rope attached at one end. The effort force is split, as shown in Figure 10.9.

A moveable pulley has a greater mechanical advantage than a fixed pulley because both sides of the rope exert an equal effort force on the load. That means that the man pulling on one side of the rope is only exerting half of the effort force.

$$MA = \frac{F_r}{F_e}$$

$$= \frac{100N}{50N} = 2$$

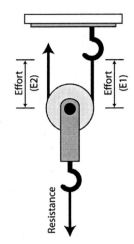

Figure 10.9 A Movable Pulley

More complex pulley systems can be designed by attaching pulley to one another. This is known as the "block and tackle." Figure 10.10 consists of a block and tackle that combines a fixed and moveable pulley. The MA of this set-up is the same as that of the movable pulley, that is MA=2. This is the same mechanical advantage as in a normal movable pulley, but the difference is that the addition of the fixed pulley allows the rope to be pulled downward, rather than upward, to lift the load.

Figure 10.10 shows a movable plus movable block and tackle system. Looping the rope through these pulleys gives a mechanical advantage of 4 because each length of rope carries an equal amount of force. This means that the final effort force is a quarter of what is would be without the two movable pulleys.

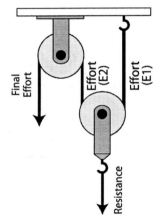

Figure 10.10 Fixed + Movable Block and Tackle System

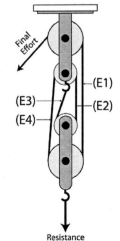

Figure 10.11 Movable + Movable Block and Tackle System

*Test Tip**: If you add up the number of rope segments that go both to and from a moveable pulley, you will have the mechanical advantage of that pulley. Remember not to add in the rope segment going from the fixed pulley; all it does is change the direction that the rope is pulled.

Section Review 3:   Work and Mechanical Advantage

A. Define the following terms.

work   energy   machine

lever pulley   effort force   fulcrum

inclined plane   resistance force   mechanical advantage

B. Choose the best answer.

1. What effort force must be applied to lift an 864 N load with a fixed pulley?

    A. 432 N   B. 864 N   C. 1728 N   D. 3456 N

2. A horse pulls a cart weighing 450 newtons for a distance of 100 meters. How much work did the horse do?

    A. 4,500 J   B. 45,000 J   C. 450,000 J   D. 4.5 J

3. The weight of a rock is 100 newtons. Using a lever, the rock was lifted using 80 newtons of force. What was the mechanical advantage of the lever?

    A. 1.25   B. 2   C. 0.8   D. 180

4. Which of the following decreases mechanical advantage?

    A. a fulcrum

    B. a fixed pulley

    C. friction

    D. heat

C. Use the picture to answer the following questions.

1. Describe this simple machine.

2. What is the mechanical advantage of this system?

3. The man is pulling at an odd angle. How could he improve his leverage?

4. In the picture, the man lifts a barrel weighing 40 newtons. What force must be exerted to lift the barrel?

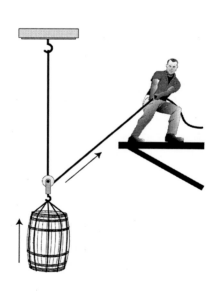

POWER AND EFFICIENCY

Power is the rate at which energy is transferred. It is also the rate at which work is performed. Power can also be calculated using a force or weight multiplied by a rate (distance divided by time). The formula for power is given in Equation 10.5.

$$\text{Power} = \frac{\text{Work}}{\text{time}} = \frac{\text{Force} \times \text{distance}}{\text{time}}$$

$$\text{or, } P = \frac{W}{t} = \frac{Fd}{t} \qquad \textbf{Equation 10.5}$$

Note: The W in this formula stands for work, while the unit for power is the **watt** (W). One watt equals one joule of work per second. W is work in joules, t is time in seconds, F is force in newtons, and d/t is the rate in meters per second.

$$P = \frac{W}{t} = \frac{F \cdot d}{t}$$

$$1 \text{ watt} = \frac{J}{s} = \frac{N \cdot m}{s}$$

Example: A forklift picks up a crate that weighs 400 N. It moves the crate 20 meters in 50 seconds. How much power is used?

Step 1. Set up the equation: $P = \frac{W}{t}$. Therefore, we need to calculate the amount of work done before we can solve for power.

Step 2. Set up and solve the equation for work: $W = F \cdot d$

$$W = (400 \text{ N}) \cdot (20 \text{ m})$$

$$W = 8000 \text{ J}$$

Step 3. Next, insert the values for work and time into the power equation.

$$P = \frac{8000 \text{ J}}{50 \text{ s}}$$

Step 4. Solve: $P = 160$ W (watts)

Efficiency can be calculated using power calculations.

$$\text{efficiency} = \frac{\text{Power out}}{\text{Power in}} \times 100\%$$

$$\text{or, efficiency} = \frac{P_{out}}{P_{in}} \times 100\% \qquad \textbf{Equation 10.6}$$

Example 2: An engine has a power input of 800 watts. It can move a 100 N object at a speed of 6 m/s. What is the efficiency of the engine?

Step 1. Set up the equation: $\text{efficiency} = \frac{P_{out}}{P_{in}} \times 100\%$. First, we need to calculate the power output.

Step 2. Set up and solve the equation for power output: $P = \frac{W}{t} = \frac{F \cdot d}{t}$

$$P_{out} = \frac{100 \text{ N} \cdot 6 \text{ m}}{1 \text{ s}}$$

$$P_{out} = 600 \text{ W}$$

Step 3. Next, insert the value for power output into the efficiency equation.

$$\text{efficiency} = \frac{600 \text{ W}}{800 \text{ W}} \times 100\%$$

Step 4. Solve: $\text{efficiency} = 75\%$ The engine is 75% efficient.

Section Review 4: Power and Efficiency

A. Define the following terms.

work   power   watt

B. Choose the best answer.

1. Which of the following is a true statement regarding the relationship between energy and work?

   A. Without energy, work could not occur.

   B. Work is calculated as the rate of energy input per unit of time.

   C. Work output is always greater than energy input.

   D. Without work, energy could not be produced.

2. A battery delivers 2400 joules of energy to an engine which is 20% efficient. How much energy will be lost as heat by the engine?

   A. 12,000 J   C. 1920 joules

   B. 480 J   D. 2400 joules

3. Tammy has a 100 N box to move to a shelf. The shelf is 0.5 m off the ground. If 25 watts of Tammy's power are used during the move, how long did it take her to move the box?

   A. 5 s   B. 2 s   C. 4 s   D. 40 s

4. Power can be described as a(n)

   A. constant.   B. rate.   C. acceleration.   D. force.

C. Answer the following questions.

1. A car accelerates from 0 to 60 miles/hr in 6.0 seconds. If the car has a mass of 1000 kg, how much power is needed during the acceleration? Ignore friction. (Hint: don't forget to convert mph to m/s; it may help to know that 1.6 km = 1 mile).

2. If 1 horsepower (hp) = 745.7 watts, how much horsepower did the engine need to perform the 0 to 60 acceleration?

3. It would actually take about 300 hp to accelerate a 1000kg car from 0 to 60 in 6 seconds. Explain why your answer in #2 is different than 300 hp.

CHAPTER 10 REVIEW

A. Choose the best answer.

1. Beating a drum represents what kind of energy conversion?
   A. electrical to mechanical
   B. mechanical to sound
   C. chemical to electrical
   D. sound to heat

2. Which of the following is true regarding the relationship between work and efficiency of a machine?
   A. Since energy output is always less than energy input, efficiency is always less than 100%.
   B. Since friction increases energy output, friction increases the efficiency of machines.
   C. Since energy input and energy output are always equal, efficiency is always 100%.
   D. Since efficiency of a machine is determined by the ratio of energy output to energy input, the greater difference in these numbers results in greater efficiency.

3. A box of textbooks poses a resistance force of 100 N. They need to be placed on a truck bed that is 2 meters high. The longest ramp is 10 meters, and it has a mechanical advantage of 5. How much MORE work (in J) will be done when pushing, rather than vertically lifting, the box?
   A. 100 J
   B. 400 J
   C. 500 J
   D. 800 J

4. Assume the acceleration due to gravity (g) equals $10 m/s^2$ (meters per second squared). What is the gravitational potential energy of a book that has a mass of 2.0kg (kilograms) that is sitting 1.5m (meters) above the floor on a table?
   A. 0.3 joules
   B. 20 joules
   C. 30 joules
   D. 200 joules

5. Calculate the kinetic energy of a football player if his mass is 100 kg and he is running at a speed of $10 m/s^2$.
   A. 5000 joules
   B. 500 joules
   C. 1000 joules
   D. 50,000 joules

6. A car uses gasoline for fuel. Which of the following describes the energy conversion from gasoline to the movement of the car?
   A. mechanical to electrical
   B. heat to light
   C. electrical to nuclear
   D. chemical to mechanical

7. Which of the following is an example of electrical energy being converted to light energy?
   A. ringing a doorbell
   B. striking a match
   C. turning on a computer monitor
   D. water falling over a dam

8. At the Bruce Family Auto Shop, a 2200 N engine must be loaded into a vehicle. The auto shop has four movable pulleys, each with different mechanical advantages (MA), and four mechanics, each able to exert a different force. Which of the following mechanic/pulley system combinations can lift the engine?

    A. "Little" Bruce can lift 720 N, and he likes the old pulley, which has a MA of 2.5.

    B. Bruce Jr. can lift 540 N and uses the cheap pulley with an MA of 3.8.

    C. Bruce Sr. can lift 450 N, and his favorite pulley has an MA of 4.9.

    D. Papa Bruce can lift 375 N and prefers the brand new pulley with an MA of 6.2.

9. How far did Charlie lift a dumbbell if he exerted a force of 10 N and expended 5 joules?

    A. 0.5 m　　　　B. 1.0 m　　　　C. 2.0 m　　　　D. 10.0 m

10. How far was a javelin thrown if 300 J was expended with a force of 30 N?

    A. 0.1 m　　　　B. 10 m　　　　C. 300 m　　　　D. 9000 m

11. How much time is required to do 30000 J of work at a rate of 100 watts?

    A. 0.30 sec　　　B. 10 sec　　　C. 100 sec　　　D. 300 sec

12. Which of the following involves the transfer of kinetic to potential energy?

    A. motion energy converted to elastic energy

    B. thermal energy converted to radiant energy

    C. gravitational energy converted to motion energy

    D. chemical energy converted to sound energy

13. If 1000 joules were transferred out of a motor with a 25% efficiency rating, how many joules went into the motor?

    A. 250 J　　　　B. 1000 J　　　　C. 2500 J　　　　D. 4000 J

14. A frictionless 5-meter ramp with a final height of 2 meters has a mechanical advantage of

    A. 0.40.　　　　B. 2.　　　　C. 2.5.　　　　D. 10.

15. The two inclined planes in the diagram come together to form what other simple machine?

    A. lever

    B. wedge

    C. pulley

    D. screw

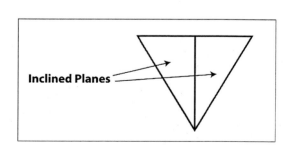

Inclined Planes

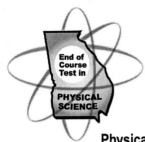

Chapter 11
Waves

Physical SCIENCE STANDARDS COVERED IN THIS CHAPTER INCLUDE:

SPS9 a – f	Students will investigate the properties of waves.

OBSERVING WAVES

Imagine you and your family go fishing in the mountains. You take a motorboat out onto a large lake nestled in a valley. As you cross the lake, you watch as the boat's wake spreads out in a V-shaped pattern behind the boat, moving across the water until it laps up on the shore. Finally, the fish finder

Figure 11.1 Find the Waves

beeps, indicating that the underwater radar has detected a school of fish is moving nearby. Your mom stops the boat, and you all cast out your lines. Ripples flow out from where your bob hits the water. You squint from the sunlight reflecting off the water. Suddenly, your bob dips underwater. You yell, "I got one!" and your voice echoes in the valley. You turn the reel as fast as you can. At the last minute, a huge fish jumps violently out of the water, and the fishing line ripples and goes slack. Then, flipping his large body around, he snaps the line and splashes back in. Your dinner has escaped.

This story describes the victory of a fish, certainly. But it also describes a few different kinds of waves. See if you can pick them out. Of course, it is easy to recognize waves in water, but many other types of waves exist in natural surroundings. You may simply not notice them because of their…well, "everyday-ness."

In fact, waves are literally everywhere. To identify them, we need to know what makes a wave a wave. Simply put, a **wave** is a disturbance caused by the mechanical motion of some particle of matter. The resulting wave may travel through either space or matter. It may be visible or invisible. How it travels and whether you can see it depends on the type of wave it is. In order to differentiate between the different kinds of waves, we need to ask two questions:

1. Does the wave require a medium in order to move?

A **medium** is any form of matter whose particles transport the wave's energy. Energy is transported as each particle moves and causes the adjacent particles to move. The matter that the wave travels through can be solid like earth (earthquakes), liquid like water (ocean waves) or gas like air (sound). These kinds of waves are known as **mechanical waves** because they are waves that **propagate** (travel) by the physical motion of particles. This means that mechanical waves require a medium.

A **sound wave** is a kind of mechanical wave.

There are other waves that do not require a medium. These **electromagnetic waves** can travel through a **vacuum**, that is, empty space. They involve both an electrical and magnetic component. These components are actually perpendicular (at right angles) to one another as they travel through space, as shown in Figure 11.2.

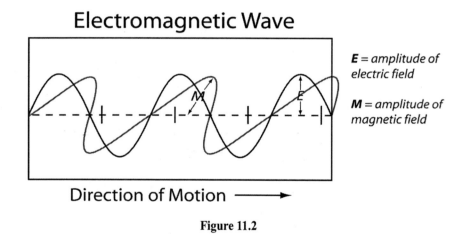

E = amplitude of electric field

M = amplitude of magnetic field

Figure 11.2

Notice that the electric field oscillates up and down, while the magnetic component appears to move into and out of the page. The two components of the waves are moving in different planes, at a 90° angle to each other. Though you cannot directly see them like waves on the ocean, electromagnetic waves are responsible for life on Earth. How? Because they are the means by which energy is transported from the Sun to the Earth.

Mechanical waves can also demonstrate this perpendicular motion, through the particles of matter that it disrupts as it passes. That brings us to our next question.

2. How do the particles of the medium move in response to the wave?

It is important to remember that waves do not transmit matter, they transmit energy. They may, however, move through matter to transmit energy. The direction that the wave travels, in relation to movement of the particles through which it moves, is another way to categorize the wave. A **transverse wave** oscillates in a direction that is perpendicular (at a right angle to) the direction in which the wave is traveling. A **longitudinal wave** oscillates parallel to (in the same direction as) the direction in which the wave is moving. That sounds hard, doesn't it? Let's look at it another way.

Lab Activity 1: Wave Motion in a Slinky

Obtain a long slinky. Get a friend to hold one end of the slinky on the floor about 5 –10 feet away from you. While holding the other end of the slinky, repeatedly move your hand to the right and left along the floor to introduce a wave into the slinky. Notice that the slinky is moving left and right with the movement of your hand. However, the slinky wave is traveling toward your friend. What type of wave is this?

Now, repeatedly move your hand holding the slinky toward and away from your friend. Notice that both the slinky and the slinky wave are moving toward your friend. What type of wave is this?

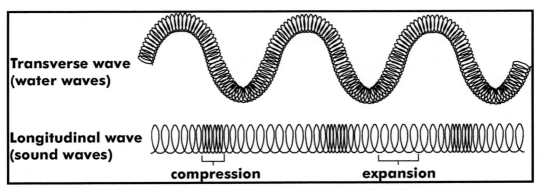

Figure 11.3 Examples of Transverse and Longitudinal Waves

PROPERTIES OF WAVES

The distance between any two identical points on a wave is called the **wavelength**. For example, the distance between two crests is the wavelength λ (pronounced lambda). Since wavelength is a measure of distance, its SI unit is the meter. However, wavelength is often given in nanometers (1 nm = 1×10^{-9} m) because visible light waves have wavelengths on that scale. The **amplitude (A)** is the maximum displacement of a wave particle from the midpoint between the crest and the trough. In other words, the amplitude is the height of the wave. The **period (T)** is the amount of time required for a wave particle to complete one full cycle of its motion, that is, from crest to crest. Period is measured in seconds.

Now, what if you were at the beach and you wanted to know how many waves were produced per hour? You could just count the number of wave crests over the course of an hour, right? The number of wave crests that occur in a unit of time is called the **frequency (f)**. Frequency is measured in hertz. One **hertz (Hz)** is equal to one peak (or cycle) per second, 1/sec. Now, with both the period and the frequency, you're concerned with wave crests and time. It turns out that they are related through an inverse relationship. Mathematically, this is known as a reciprocal relationship: in other words, f=1/T.

The velocity of a wave is the rate at which a wave moves through a medium, in meters/second (m/s). It is given by Equation 11.1. As wavelength increases, the wave frequency decreases (in the same medium). The frequency or wavelength of a wave can be determined by rearranging the terms of the equation.

Equation 11.1

velocity = frequency × wavelength

$$v = f\lambda$$

(λ is lambda)

Utilize the Units!

The SI unit for wavelength, which is a distance, is meters. The unit for frequency is the inverse second (Frequency is a measure of the number of times an event occurs *per length of time*.)

$$m \times \frac{1}{s} = m/s$$

So, m/s is the SI unit for velocity.
(But you already knew that, right?)

Move around the variables in Equation 11.1. If you shift the equation so that $f = v/\lambda$, you can see that a long wave (large λ) has a lower frequency than a short wave (small λ). You can see this graphically in Figure 11.4.

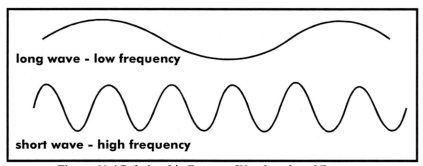

long wave - low frequency

short wave - high frequency

Figure 11.4 Relationship Between Wavelength and Frequency

As mentioned earlier, waves transport energy through a medium without transporting matter. The energy transported by a wave (wave energy) is proportional to the amplitude squared.

Section Review 1:   Types and Properties of Waves

A. Define the following terms.

wave	mechanical wave	transverse wave	period
medium	vacuum	longitudinal wave	frequency
propagate	electromagnetic wave	wavelength	hertz
	sound waves	amplitude	

B. Choose the best answer.

1. Which of the following is true regarding mechanical waves?

    A. Mechanical waves must travel through matter.

    B. Mechanical waves can travel through matter and space.

    C. Mechanical waves can only travel through a vacuum.

    D. Mechanical waves can change matter.

2. The height of a wave is its

    A. amplitude.   B. wavelength.   C. period.   D. crest.

3. Which of the following is NOT an example of a mechanical wave?

    A. sunlight   C. ocean waves

    B. vibrations of a guitar string   D. sound waves

4. The period (T) of an oscillating wave is 1/5s. What happens to the frequency (f) of the wave if T increases to 1/2s?

    A. It stays the same.   C. f decreases to 2 Hz.

    B. f increases to 2Hz.   D. f increases to 5 Hz.

5. The velocity of an electromagnetic wave in a vacuum is 3.0×10^8 m/s. If a visible light wave has a higher frequency than a radio wave, which will have the longer wavelength?

    A. the radio wave

    B. the visible light wave

    C. in a vacuum, both will be equal

    D. We need to know the amplitude in order to answer the question.

6. Name the type of wave that carries no energy.

    A. gamma rays   C. radio waves

    B. visible light   D. All waves carry energy.

BEHAVIOR OF WAVES

Whether you are aware of it or not, you have quite a bit of experience with waves. Let's see if we can clarify those experiences a little. In the story at the beginning of this chapter, your voice echoed off the hills as you yelled "I got one!" In terms of waves, what is an echo anyway? An echo is the sound waves bouncing off a surface. This same phenomenon is occurring when you look into a mirror: electromagnetic waves are bouncing off the mirror and hitting your eyes. This bouncing of waves off of a surface is called **reflection**.

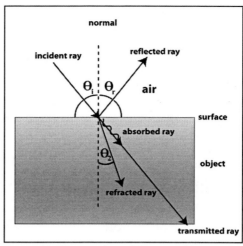

Figure 11.5 Interaction of Waves With a Surface

If the wave is only partially reflected, the leftover wave energy is **absorbed.** Think about being inside a quiet car when another car pulls up next playing loud music. If you roll up the windows of the car, the sound waves are partially absorbed and the sound becomes muffled. But let's say that you can still hear the bass beats, even with your windows rolled up. You can still hear the music because some sound waves were **transmitted** through the solid matter of the car. So, when a wave hits a surface, it can be reflected or transmitted.

The diagram in Figure 11.5 shows the waves as straight lines called **rays** for the sake of simplicity. The type of behavior the wave shows depends on the medium it is traveling in, the material it is entering and the energy of the wave itself. Table 11.1 describes the possible responses of a wave when it hits a surface. This table should serve as a helpful guide as you read over the next few pages.

Table 11.1 Possible Interactions of a Wave with an Object

Behavior	Description of Wave Motion
Reflection	bounces off the surface at the same angle it hit with
Transmission	travels through the material at the same angle it entered with
Refraction	travels through the material, but at an altered angle
Diffraction	travels through the material until it encounters an obstacle, which it then bends around
Absorption	cannot travel all the way through the material

REFLECTION

When you turn on a light bulb, the light travels through the room until it hits an object such as the wall. The light wave then bounces off the wall and continues to travel as reflected light. The **Law of Reflection** states that the angle of reflection (θ_r) equals the angle of incidence (θ_i). In other words, the angle at which the light hits the surface equals the angle at which it bounces off the surface. Figure 11.6 illustrates these angles. Notice that the **normal line** defines the angle of reflection (90°) for incident light that is exactly perpendicular to the mirror. Let's look at a few other features of the figure.

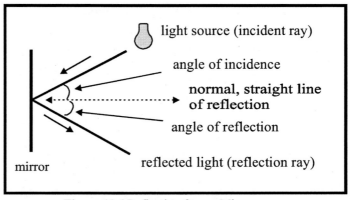

Figure 11.6 Reflection from a Mirror

- A flat mirror is a smooth, shiny surface that reflects light.
- Light travels in a straight line as it is reflected from a surface.
- The **incident ray** is the light ray that strikes the surface.
- The **reflection ray** is the light ray that reflects off the surface.

If a wave hits an object straight on, it will bounce back straight. If a wave approaches an object from the left, it will bounce off the object toward the right at the same angle.

REFRACTION

Refraction is the bending of a wave by the change in density of the medium. (Recall that density is a measure of the amount of matter in a particular volume. It has SI units of g/cm^3.) The bending of the wave is due to the reduced velocity of the wave as it enters a medium of higher density. This is often the case when light passes from the air to some liquid or solid. Figure 11.7 shows a pencil placed in a clear glass of water viewed through the glass. Since the water is more dense than the air, the light rays passing through the water will bend, causing the pencil to look broken and disconnected.

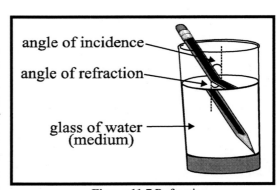

Figure 11.7 Refraction

The amount the wave bends is determined by the **index of refraction** (n) of the two materials. The amount the wave is bent, called the angle of refraction (θ_2), is determined using Snell's law ($n_1\sin\theta_1 = n_2\sin\theta_2$). A schematic representation of Snell's law is shown in Figure 11.8. Notice that, in the figure, the wave is bent toward the normal line (the dashed line perpendicular to the surface) as it moves from air into the glass. This occurs because the refractive index of glass is greater than the refractive index of air. The refractive index of a material is related to the density and atomic structure of the material. The higher the index of refraction, the more the material will bend the incoming wave. A wave moving from glass into air will bend away from the normal.

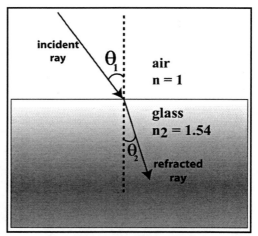

Figure 11.8 Refraction of a Wave

So far, we have only discussed the refraction of electromagnetic light waves. Refraction of sound waves also occurs. Sound travels in all directions from its source. The listener can usually only hear the sound that is directed toward him. However, refraction of the sound waves bends some of the waves downward, toward the listener, in effect amplifying the sound. Refraction of sound waves can occur if the air above the earth is warmer than the air at the surface. This effect can be observed over cool lakes early in the morning. The cold water of the lake keeps the air at the surface cool, but the rising sun starts to heat the air that is higher up. This effect is called **thermal inversion** and results in the refraction of sound. How would thermal inversion affect you if you were out fishing in the early morning? If another family was out on the lake but much further away than you would ordinarily be able to hear them, you could actually speak to one another. A pretty freaky phenomenon if you aren't expecting it!

ABSORPTION

Materials selectively absorb and transmit waves depending on the frequency of the wave and the atoms in the material. When a material absorbs a wave, the wave is no longer able to travel. The wave energy is completely transferred to the particles in the material themselves. When a material transmits a wave, the wave travels all the way through the material and eventually exits the material.

The absorption and transmission of electromagnetic waves has consequences in the color of visible light. **Visible light**, the light that humans can see with the naked eye, has wavelengths between 400 and 750 nm. Blue light has a wavelength of approximately 440 nm. (nm is the abbreviation for nanometer. 1 nm is one billionth of a meter.) What we see as the **color** of an object is actually a result of the light frequencies reflected, absorbed and transmitted by the object. Objects do not have color within themselves. For example, if a material strongly absorbs all wavelengths except those around 440 nm, the object appears to be blue, because it absorbs all wavelengths of visible light except the blue wavelengths. This means that the blue light will be reflected off of the material. Objects that reflect all wavelengths of visible light appear white, whereas objects that absorb all wavelengths of visible light are black. Chlorophyll is a pigment responsible for the green color of plants. The chlorophyll absorbs the wavelengths corresponding to red and blue, while it reflects the wavelengths corresponding to the color green.

DIFFRACTION

Another property of waves, called **diffraction**, relates to the ability of a wave to bend around obstacles or through small openings. Waves tend to spread out after going through an opening, which results in a shadow region. Diffraction depends on the size of the obstacle and the wavelength of the wave. The amount a wave bends, or diffracts, increases with increasing wavelength. Therefore, the diffraction angle is greater for waves with longer wavelengths. Waves with wavelengths smaller than the size of the obstacle or opening will not diffract.

Sound waves can diffract around objects or through very small holes. This is why we can hear someone speak even when they are around a corner, in a different room. Sound waves with long wavelengths are efficient at diffraction. Therefore, longer wavelength sounds can be heard at a greater distance from the source than shorter wavelength sounds. In addition, sound waves that have longer wavelengths become less distorted when they bend around objects. If a marching band were approaching, the first sounds that would be heard would be the long wavelength, low pitch, bass sounds. Elephants use this property of sound waves to communicate across the African plains using very long wavelength, low pitch sounds. Elephants travel in large herds, and it is easy for

Figure 11.9 Diffraction of Sound Waves

them to get separated from each other. Since they are sometimes out of visible range, they communicate using subsonic sound waves that are able to diffract around any obstacles present.

Light waves diffract differently than sound waves. The type of light diffraction that you are probably familiar with is called **scattering**. In order for scattering to occur, the obstacle must be on the *same order* of size as the wavelength of the wave. Light scattering is responsible for the corona we sometimes see around the sun or moon on cloudy days. The water droplets in the clouds act as obstacles to the light from these objects. The light is then bent and spread out. Therefore, the light from the object appears larger than the actual source and we see a "crown" around the object. *In light scattering, waves with a shorter wavelength are bent more than waves with a longer wavelength.* **Light diffraction** is a special case of light scattering that occurs when a light wave encounters an obstacle with a regularly repeating pattern resulting in a diffraction pattern. The amount of diffraction of a light wave depends on the size of the opening and the wavelength of the light.

INTERFERENCE

When waves coming from two different sources meet, they affect each other. This is known as **interference**. When two waves meet, and the high point (crest) of one wave meets the crest of the other wave, the resultant wave has the sum of the amplitude of the two waves. These waves are said to be **in phase** with one another. The interaction of waves that are in phase is called **constructive interference**. The two waves come together to *construct* a new wave, with a larger amplitude.

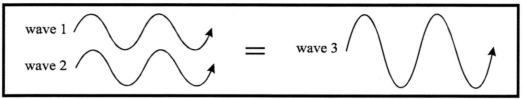

Figure 11.10 Constructive Interference

If, however, the low point (trough) of one wave meets the crest of another wave, then the waves cancel each other, and the wave becomes still. The waves are said to be **out of phase**. The interaction of out of phase waves is called **destructive interference**. The two waves meet and *destroy* each other.

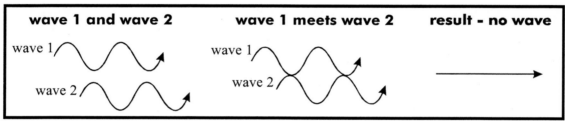

Figure 11.11 Destructive Interference

When waves interfere somewhere between these two extremes, there is some **distortion,** which results in a wave with an irregular pattern. To visualize distortion, think of what happens to the ripples made in a pond when two rocks are thrown into the water close to each other.

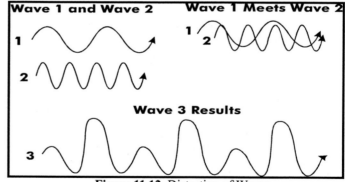

Figure 11.12 Distortion of Waves

Section Review 2:   Behavior of Waves

A. Define the following terms.

reflection	incident ray	visible light	in phase
absorbed	reflection ray	color	constructive interference
transmitted	refraction	diffraction	destructive interference
ray	index of refraction	scattering	out of phase
Law of Reflection	Snell's Law	light diffraction	distortion
normal line	thermal inversion	interference	

B. Choose the best answer.

1. The indices of refraction for four materials are listed below. Which material combination will bend incoming light the most?

   A. vacuum, (n=1.00) ➤ air (n=1.00)   C. ice, (n=1.31) ➤diamond (n=2.42)

   B. air, (n=1.00) ➤ ice (n=1.31)   D. diamond, (n=2.42) ➤ air (n=1.00)

2. A white sheet of paper appears to be white because it

   A. absorbs all wavelengths of visible light.   C. transmits all wavelengths of visible light.

   B. reflects all wavelengths of visible light.   D. refracts all wavelengths of visible light.

Use the diagram to answer questions 3 and 4.

3. If $\theta_i = 50°$, identify the value of the angles θ_{xi}, θ_{xr}, and θ_r.

   A. $\theta_{xi} = 50°$, $\theta_{xr} = 50°$ and $\theta_r = 50°$

   B. $\theta_{xi} = 40°$, $\theta_{xr} = 40°$ and $\theta_r = 90°$

   C. $\theta_{xi} = 45°$, $\theta_{xr} = 45°$ and $\theta_r = 50°$

   D. $\theta_{xi} = 45°$, $\theta_{xr} = 45°$ and $\theta_r = 90°$

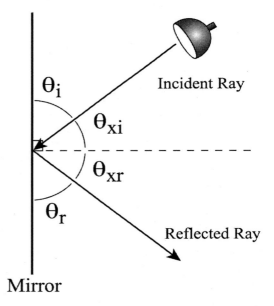

4. How would you move the light source to make the reflected ray move back toward the mirror (i.e. to increase the angle θ_{xr})?

   A. Move the light source down.

   B. Move the light source to the right.

   C. Move the light source up.

   D. Replace it with a light source that emits longer wavelengths.

SOUND WAVES

A **sound wave** is a mechanical wave produced by a vibrating object. The wave results from the compression and expansion of the molecules surrounding the vibrating object. For this reason, they are sometimes referred to as **compression waves**. Sound cannot travel through empty space or a vacuum. Sound travels faster through solids than through liquids and gases because the molecules are packed together more tightly in solids. When temperature increases, the speed of sound increases. The speed of sound also increases when the air becomes more humid (or moist).

Most people hear compression waves of the frequency 20 Hz to 20,000 Hz.

Example: A dog whistle is higher than 20,000 Hz. Elephants make a sound lower than 20 Hz. Therefore, humans cannot hear these sounds.

Sound waves of different frequencies have different wavelengths in the same medium. As frequency increases, wavelength decreases. Frequency of sound waves determines pitch. **Pitch** describes how high or low a sound is. Sounds with higher pitch have higher frequencies.

Example: A police siren has a high pitch. The growl of a large dog has a low pitch.

The intensity or volume of the sound is measured in **decibels**. The amplitude of the sound wave determines the volume. The higher the amplitude, the louder the sound and the higher the decibel value. Lower amplitudes produce softer sounds with lower decibel values.

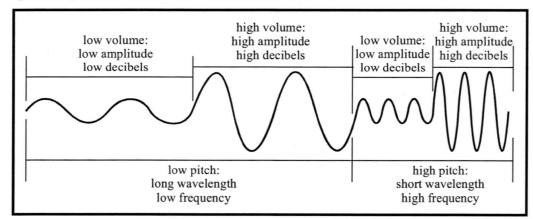

Figure 11.13 Relationship Between Volume and Pitch

THE DOPPLER EFFECT

When a sound source moves toward a listener, the pitch of the sound appears to increase. This is due to the **Doppler effect**. The reason is this: the movement of the sound emitter has the effect of increasing the frequency of the sound waves that the listener hears. It is important to realize that the frequency of the sounds that the source *emits* does not actually change. Next time you hear a siren while out walking, stop and listen to how the sound changes as it moves past you.

Section Review 3:   Sound Waves

A. Define the following terms.

      sound wave   pitch   decibel   compression waves
      Doppler effect

B. Choose the best answer.

1. Increasing the frequency of a sound wave has which of the following effects?
    A. increases wavelength
    B. increases amplitude
    C. increases pitch
    D. increases decibel level

2. Through which of the following would sound travel the fastest?
    A. a vacuum
    B. warm, humid air
    C. warm, dry air
    D. cold, dry air

3. The Doppler effect describes the following scenario: As a source of sound moves closer, the sound wave appears to
    A. increase in amplitude.
    B. increase in pitch.
    C. decrease in amplitude.
    D. decrease in pitch.

4. What determines the volume of a sound?
    A. the amplitude of the sound wave
    B. the frequency of the sound wave
    C. the Doppler effect
    D. the wavelength of the sound wave

C. Answer the following question.

1. Relate the speed of sound waves to temperature and medium. Through what type of medium does sound travel fastest? How is the speed of sound affected by temperature?

2. Examine the following four figures. Describe the movement of the sound source (•), relative to the sound it emits. When would a stationary observer to the right of the sound source hear the sound: before, after or just as the sound source reaches him?

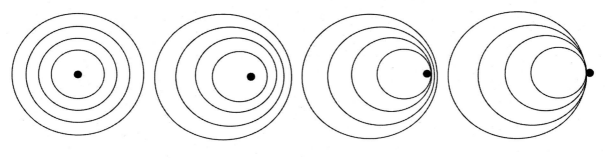

ELECTROMAGNETIC WAVES

Electromagnetic waves are transverse waves that do not need a medium through which to travel. Electromagnetic waves are produced by the acceleration or deceleration of electrons or other charged particles. The **electromagnetic spectrum** is made up of invisible and visible waves, ranging from low frequency to very high frequency, which travel at the speed of light in a vacuum.

The wave equation given in Equation 11.1 can be rewritten for electromagnetic waves by substituting c, the speed of light, for the velocity, v. The **speed of light** in a vacuum is 3×10^8 m/s.

As stated earlier, as the length of the wave increases, frequency decreases; as the length of the wave decreases, frequency increases. Notice in Figure 11.14 that radio waves have very long wavelengths, and gamma waves have very short wavelengths. Therefore, radio waves will have low frequencies, and gamma waves will have high frequencies.

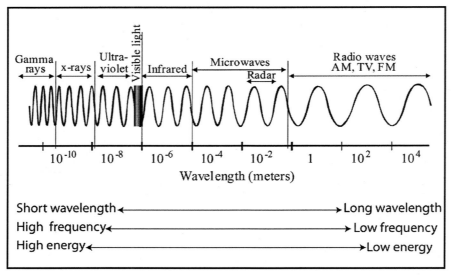

Figure 11.14 The Electromagnetic Spectrum

The energy of the wave is based on its frequency, as shown in Equation 11.2. Each type of electromagnetic wave has a different energy and is used for different purposes.

Equation 11.2

Energy = Plank's constant × frequency

$$E = hf$$

$$(h = 6.63 \times 10^{-34} \text{ J·s})$$

Utilize the Units!
The unit for Plank's constant is the joule-second.
The unit for frequency is the inverse second.

$$\text{J·s} \times \frac{1}{s} = J$$

So, the joule is the SI unit for energy.
(Look back to Eq. 9.5 for the first derivation)

Figure 11.15 Radio

Radio Waves: These wavelengths of light are invisible to us, and can range from a few centimeters to more than six football fields long. Radio stations code the sound into radio waves that your radio receives, unscrambles and translates back into sound again.

Microwaves: These invisible waves have a wavelength of only a few millimeters. The microwaves generated by a microwave oven cause the water molecules in the food to vibrate and rotate. It is the thermal energy generated by the movement of the water molecules that heats the food!

Figure 11.16 A Microwave

Figure 11.17 TV Remote

Infrared Waves: These wavelengths are up to a few micrometers in length. Your television's remote control uses a beam of infrared light to change the channel. The electronics in the TV respond to the infrared beam. Your body also radiates infrared light, but of a slightly different wavelength. That is how night vision goggles can see living things moving in the dark.

Figure 11.18 Sunscreen Blocks UV Light

Visible Light Waves: This is the only part of the electromagnetic spectrum that our eyes can see. It's the kind of waves we are most familiar with, but in the grand scheme of the electromagnetic spectrum, it is only a very narrow band of wavelengths, from about 0.35 micrometer to 0.9 micrometer. Our eyes sense the different wavelengths in this band as color. A great way to remember in what order the colors are arranged is **Roy G Biv**. Each letter of this silly name is the first letter of a color in the visible light range, arranged from longest wavelength (red -R) to shortest (violet-V).

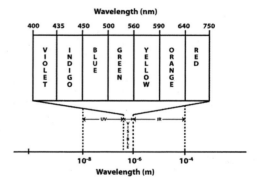
Figure 11.19 Roy G Biv

Ultraviolet Waves: The ozone layer in our Earth's atmosphere helps to protect us from most of the harmful effects of these short wavelength waves. Only some of the Sun's ultraviolet light reaches the ground, and those waves can cause sunburn or even worse, skin cancer. Ultraviolet light penetrates the skin, interacts with molecules and can tear them apart. Use sunscreen!

X-rays: These waves have wavelengths in the nanometer range. They are often used to image bones in a doctor's office. X-rays can be dangerous, so it is best to minimize your exposure to them. That is why the X-ray technician or radiographer covers the parts of your body that are not being X-rayed with a lead apron. This absorbs the radiation.

Figure 11.20 X-ray

Gamma Ray Waves: These are the most energetic wavelengths in the electromagnetic spectrum, and they have the shortest wavelengths. Gamma rays are generated by the breaking apart of atomic nuclei. This happens here on Earth, but the majority of gamma rays are produced in space. Gamma radiation is increasingly used by doctors for treating cancer. The "gamma knife" uses the powerful rays to destroy cancerous cells that they are aimed at.

Section Review 4:   Electromagnetic Waves

A. Define the following terms.

photon	speed of light	microwaves	X-rays
electromagnetic spectrum	Roy G. Biv	infrared waves	gamma rays
	radio waves	ultraviolet waves	visible light

B. Choose the best answer.

1. Energy from the Sun is transported by
    A. mechanical waves.   C. sound waves.
    B. electromagnetic waves.   D. compression waves.

2. How are microwaves different from gamma ray waves?
    A. Gamma rays have a higher frequency than microwaves.
    B. Gamma rays have a higher amplitude than microwaves.
    C. Gamma rays have a longer wavelength than microwaves.
    D. Gamma rays are electromagnetic, but microwaves are mechanical.

3. Which of the following color groups correctly shows increasing wavelength?
    A. green, blue, red   C. yellow, orange, red
    B. blue, yellow, violet   D. orange, yellow, green

4. What is the MOST likely reason why gamma rays are used in internal medicine?
    A. Because they can explode in the body.
    B. Because they have long wavelengths and low frequencies.
    C. Because they carry little energy and won't hurt anything.
    D. Because they have very short wavelengths, and they can be aimed to very short, specific distances.

5. What are the units of frequency?
    A. seconds (s)   C. joules (J)
    B. inverse seconds (s^{-1})   D. meters (m)

C. Answer the following questions.

1. How are electromagnetic waves different from mechanical waves? How are they similar?

2. Name the colors of the visible light spectrum, beginning with the shortest wavelength.

CHAPTER 11 REVIEW

CHAPTER
REVIEW

A. Choose the best answer.

1. What are mechanical waves?

    A. the means by which energy moves through a medium

    B. photons of energy transported through space

    C. anything that moves energy from one place to another

    D. the way that matter moves

2. Identify the property of electromagnetic waves that is NOT also a property of mechanical waves.

    A. can be reflected

    B. can cause matter to vibrate

    C. can travel through a vacuum

    D. can transfer energy but not matter

3. Which of the following types of electromagnetic waves has the shortest wavelength?

    A. radio wave

    B. visible light wave

    C. ultraviolet wave

    D. gamma ray wave

4. Identify the combination of frequency and amplitude that would maximize the energy transferred by a wave.

    A. high frequency and high amplitude

    B. high frequency and low amplitude

    C. low frequency and high amplitude

    D. low frequency and low amplitude

5. Identify the statement that correctly identifies the units of frequency or wavelength and the relationship between frequency and wavelength.

    A. Frequency, measured in hertz, increases as wavelength increases.

    B. Frequency, measured in hertz, decreases as wavelength increases.

    C. Wavelength, measured in hertz, increases as frequency increases.

    D. Wavelength, measured in hertz, decreases as frequency increases.

6. Identify which of the following relies on refraction.

    A. using echoes to measure distance

    B. using a mirror to see what is behind you

    C. using contact lenses to improve eyesight

    D. using soundproofing to create a quiet room

7. Which of the following is NOT a transverse wave?

    A. sound

    B. X-rays

    C. vibrations of a violin string

    D. rippling water

8. Which of the following lists electromagnetic radiations from lowest to highest energies?

    A. radio waves, microwaves, ultraviolet radiation, visible light

    B. microwaves, radio waves, visible light, X-rays

    C. radio waves, infrared radiation, visible light, ultraviolet radiation

    D. gamma radiation, infrared radiation, visible light, X-rays

9. The speed of sound in air at sea level and a temperature of 20 degrees Celsius is 343 meters per second. The musical note A has a frequency of 440 Hz. What would be its wavelength?

    A. 0.78 meters   B. 1.3 meters   C. 1.00 meters   D. 0.5 meters

10. Which statement is true about electromagnetic radiation?

    A. Electromagnetic waves require a medium to travel through.

    B. Electromagnetic waves are produced by vibrating matter.

    C. Electromagnetic waves travel through matter as compression waves.

    D. Electromagnetic waves travel faster through a vacuum than through matter.

11. The diagram below represents the motion of two mechanical waves. The waves have equal amplitude and frequency and are moving through the same medium. Choose the statement that BEST describes the motion of the medium at point P.

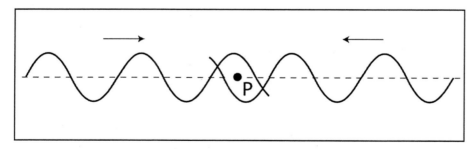

    A. The medium at point P will vibrate up and down.

    B. The medium at point P will vibrate left and right.

    C. The medium at point P will vibrate into and out of the page.

    D. The medium at point P will not move.

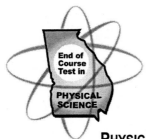

Chapter 12
Electricity and Magnetism

PHYSICAL SCIENCE STANDARDS COVERED IN THIS CHAPTER INCLUDE:

SPS10 a – c	Students will investigate the properties of electricity and magnetism.

ELECTRIC FORCE AND ELECTRICITY

ELECTROSTATIC FORCE AND FIELD

The **electrostatic force** between two charged particles is described by **Coulomb's law**, which is expressed mathematically in Equation 12.1. The important points to remember are:

- Charged particles exert forces on each other;
- Like charges repel, opposite charges attract;
- The greater the distance between charges, the less force they will exert on each other.

Coulomb's law states:

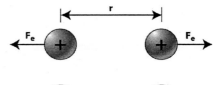

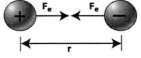

Figure 12.1 Electrostatic Force Between Two Charged Particles

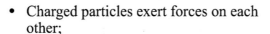

Equation 12.1

Electrostatic force $= k_e \times \dfrac{\text{(charge particle 1} \cdot \text{charge particle 2)}}{\text{(distance between particles)}^2}$

$$F_e = k_e \frac{q_1 \cdot q_2}{r^2}$$

Utilize the Units!

k_e is the Coulomb constant, equal to 8.998×10^9 Nm^2/C^2.
The SI unit for charge is the Coulomb (C).
The SI unit for distance is the meter (m).

$$\frac{N \cdot m^2}{C^2} \times \frac{C \cdot C}{m^2} = \text{the newton (N)}$$

So, the SI unit for electrostatic force is the Newton (N).

Notice that the equation for electrostatic force has the same form as the equation for gravitational force, but charge replaces mass, and the constants are different. While the electrostatic force can be attractive or repulsive, the gravitational force can only be attractive.

When the two charges have the same sign, they repel one another. When they have opposite signs, they attract each other. Recall that atoms are made of a positively charged nucleus surrounded by negatively charged electrons. The attractive electrical force between these charges is what holds the atom together.

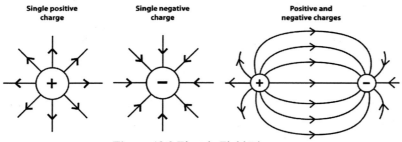

Figure 12.2 Electric Field Lines

An **electric field** surrounds every electric charge. If a test charge (a small, charged particle) were placed in the electric field of a charged particle, a force would be exerted upon it. The **electric field lines** point in the direction that a positive charge would move when in the presence of an electric field. A positively charged particle would be repelled by a positive charge and attracted by a negative charge. Thus, electric field lines always point away from positive source charges and towards negative source charges. Electric field lines do not actually exist in the physical world; they are simply used to illustrate the direction of the electric force exerted on charged particles. The strength of the field surrounding a charged particle is dependent on how charged the particle generating the field is and separation distance between the charged objects.

Practice Exercise 1: Electric Force

Let's calculate the attractive force between the nucleus and an electron in an atom. The charges of the particles and the distance between the particles is indicated in Figure 13.3 to the right.

$$F_e = k_e \cdot \frac{(1.60 \times 10^{-19} \text{ C}) \cdot (1.60 \times 10^{-19} \text{ C})}{(1.0 \times 10^{-10} \text{ m})^2}$$

$$F_e = 2.3 \times 10^{-8} \text{ N}$$

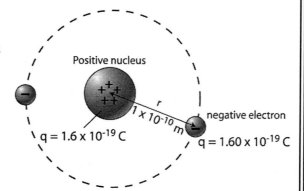

Figure 12.3 Distance Between Nucleus and Electron

Now, let's calculate the gravitational force between these particles given that the mass of a proton is 1.6726×10^{-27} kg and the mass of an electron is 9.11×10^{-31} kg.

$$F_g = G \cdot \frac{(1.6726 \times 10^{-27} \text{ kg}) \cdot (9.11 \times 10^{-31} \text{ kg})}{(1.0 \times 10^{-10} \text{ m})^2}$$

$$F_g = 1.0 \times 10^{-47} \text{ N}$$

Although the electrical force may seem like a very small force, if you compare it to the gravitational force between these particles, you will see it is 39 times greater than the force of gravity.

ELECTRICAL CONDUCTORS AND INSULATORS

Electricity involves the movement of electrons. Electricity results when electrons flow through a material. When this happens, the material is referred to as an **electrical conductor**, meaning that it can conduct electricity. Materials that cannot conduct electricity are **electrical insulators**. **Conductivity** is an intrinsic material property that is a measure of how easily electricity flows through a material. **Resistivity** is the inverse of conductivity and is also an intrinsic material property. In other words, it is the measure of how difficult it is for electricity to travel through a material.

Conductors typically have free electrons that can easily move about in the material. The charge is distributed uniformly in a conductor because the electrons are so mobile. Metals, such as copper and aluminum, are good conductors of electricity because the metallic bonding in most metals results in a sea of electrons that are easily able to move about. However, pure metals are not the only class of materials that conduct electricity! Some oxides of transition metals, such as Ti and Cr, are also good conductors. This is surprising, as most oxides are not conductive — they have very strong ionic bonds that greatly slow the movement of

Figure 12.4 Examples of Conductors

electrons. Even some special plastics are good conductors. In addition, water, electrolytes and the human body are good conductors. This is why it is important to keep electrical devices like radios and televisions away from water.

Figure 12.5 Examples of Insulators

In an **insulator,** there are almost no free electrons available to transfer current. The atoms in insulators have very tightly bound electrons. So, if charge is transferred to an insulator at a given location, it will stay at that location. The electrons are not able to move in order to distribute the charge evenly throughout the insulator. Many ionic solids are insulators because the ionic bonds are hard to break and electrons are not free to move about. Some covalent solids are also insulators. Examples of insulators are nonmetals, diamond, wood, glass, rubber, porcelain, dry air and most

plastics and oxides. If you've ever seen a broken electrical cord, then you know that it consists of a conductive wire surrounded by a plastic material. The plastic material is an insulator, thus current cannot flow, and you won't be electrocuted if you touch the electrical cord. This is why it is dangerous to handle equipment with broken electrical cords.

Semiconductors are a third group of materials. These materials have few electrons with which to conduct electricity, however if enough energy (thermal or otherwise) is provided, electrons can be freed and allowed to flow. Some elemental semiconductors are silicon and germanium, which are in Group 4 of the Periodic Table. There are many compound semiconductors formed by elements from Groups 3 and 5 or Groups 2 and 6 of the Periodic Table. GaAs (gallium arsenide) and CdTe (cadmium telluride) are examples of 3-5 and 2-6 compound semiconductors, respectively. Semiconductors are often used in the computer and optics industries. A semiconducting material forms the base wafer that most computer memory chips are made of.

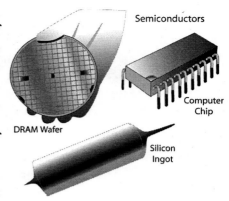

Figure 12.6 Examples of Semiconductors

Electrical resistivity is a measure of how much a material opposes the flow of electric current. A low resistivity means that current flows easily. In metals, resistivity decreases as temperature decreases. For most materials, there is a limit to how low resistivity values will go. Some materials, like aluminum and tin are superconductors.

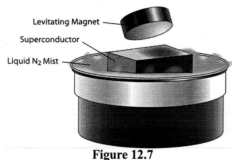

Figure 12.7
Superconducting Material with Permanent Magnetic Field

Superconductors are conductive materials whose the resistivity abruptly decreases to zero as the temperature decreases below a critical value, called the **critical temperature**. The value of the critical temperature depends on the chemical composition, pressure and structure of the material. Mercury was the first material to demonstrate superconductivity below the critical temperature of 4.15K. Recall that the temperature in Celsius equals the temperature in Kelvin minus 273.15. Therefore, the critical temperature for mercury is –269°C, which is *really* cold! Other superconductive elements include niobium, lead and zinc. Some compounds, such as the copper-oxides, exhibit superconductivity at temperatures as high as 134K; however, that is still well below room temperature (22°C).

STATIC ELECTRICITY

As you learned in a previous section, **electricity** involves the movement of electrons. Let's talk about two types of electricity: **static** electricity and **current** electricity. We experience static electricity in everyday life in the form of a shock when we touch a metallic object after dragging our feet along the carpet, or the standing up of our hair when we take off a winter hat. **Static electricity** occurs as a result of excess positive or negative charges on an object's surface. Static electricity is built up in three ways: friction, induction and conduction.

Figure 12.8 Static Electricity

Rubbing two objects together will often generate static electricity through **friction**. Some electrons are held more loosely than others in an atom. The loosely held electrons can be rubbed off and transferred to the other object. Static electricity occurs when an object gains electrons giving the object a negative charge, or an object loses electrons giving it a positive charge. Rubbing a balloon on carpet or combing your hair with a hard plastic comb on a dry day causes static electricity to build up. Like charges repel, and unlike charges attract. Rub two balloons on the carpet and then slowly move the balloons together. Both balloons will have the same negative charge, and you should be able to feel the mild repulsive force. The charged balloon or comb, however, will attract small pieces of paper or other small, light objects having an opposite positive charge. These attractive or repulsive forces are weak forces, but they can overcome the force of gravity for very light objects.

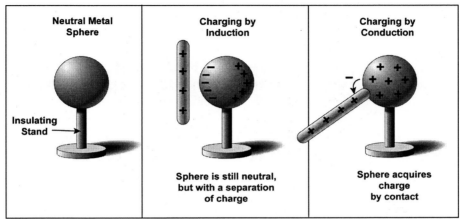

Figure 12.9 Generation of Static Electricity

Electrical charge generated by **induction** occurs when a charged object is brought near to, but not touching an insulator. Molecules within the uncharged object begin to shift with the negative side of the molecule moving closer to the positively charged object.

Electrical charge can also be generated by **conduction**. Conduction occurs when two objects, one charged and one neutral, are brought into contact with one another. The excess charge from the charged object will flow into the neutral object, until the charge of both objects is balanced.

Lightning is another example of static electricity. The actual lightning bolt that we see is a result of electric discharge from clouds that have built up too much excess charge.

CURRENT ELECTRICITY

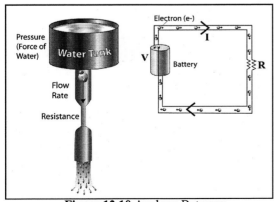

Figure 12.10 Analogy Between Flowing Water and Electric Current

To understand **current electricity**, let's compare electricity to the water flowing through a pipe. The flow rate of water in a pipe might be given in units of gallons per minute. In an electrical circuit, electrons flow through the circuit like water flows through a pipe. **Current (I)** is the flow rate of electrons through the circuit and is measured in **amperes**. As water flowing through a pipe rubs against the walls of the pipe, the water slows down. In the same way, electrons slow down as they move through a circuit. This slowing down of the electrons is called resistance. **Resistance (R)** is the measure of how difficult it is to move electrons through a circuit. Why does water flow through a pipe? A force like gravity or the force of a pump causes water to flow. **Voltage (V)** is the force that moves electrons through a circuit and is measured in **volts**. In other words, voltage drives the current in a circuit. In an electrical circuit, a battery commonly produces this force.

Electrical forces (voltage) found in nature can be very small, or they can be very large. Static electricity that builds up from our shoes as we walk across the carpet is small, and the discharge of that electrical force causes a small spark or shock. Static electricity that builds up in clouds is much larger, and the discharge of that buildup can result in high-voltage lightning.

OHM'S LAW

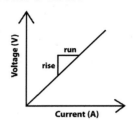

$$\frac{\text{rise}}{\text{run}} = \frac{\text{voltage}}{\text{current}} = \text{resistance}$$

Figure 12.11 Current - Voltage Relationship

Ohm's Law states that the resistance is equal to the voltage divided by the current as shown in Equation 12.2 where resistance has units of **ohms (Ω)**. You may notice that Ohm's law reveals a linear relationship between voltage and current. Given a linear graph of voltage versus current, the slope of the line (i.e. rise over run) is equal to the resistance. Thus, the resistance of a device can be determined experimentally by taking several voltage and current measurements, then plotting the data on a graph. Not all electronic devices have this linear relationship between voltage and current. Those that do have a linear relationship are called ohmic devices.

Ohm's law is more frequently written in the form shown in Equation 12.2. Ohm's law can be used to calculate either resistance, voltage, or current when two of the three quantities are known.

Example: A flashlight bulb with an operating resistance of 50 ohms is connected to a 9.0 V battery. What is the current through the light bulb?

Step 1. Set up the equation: $V = I \cdot R$

Step 2. Insert the known information: $9.0\ V = I \cdot 50\ \Omega$

Step 3. Solve: $I = \dfrac{9.0\ V}{50\ \Omega} = 0.18\ A$

Equation 12.2
Ohm's Law

Voltage = Current × Resistance

$$V = IR$$

Utilize the Units!

The SI unit for voltage is the volt (V).

$$1\ \text{volt} = \frac{1\ \text{joule}}{1\ \text{coulomb}}$$

The SI unit for current is the ampere (A).

$$1\ \text{ampere} = \frac{1\ \text{coulomb}}{\text{second}}$$

The SI unit for resistance is the ohm (Ω).

$$1\ \text{ohm}\ \Omega = \frac{1\ \text{volt}}{\text{amp}}$$

The volt was named for Italian physicist Alessandro Volta, who invented the voltaic pile (the first chemical battery). The ampere is named in honor of the French physicist André-Marie Ampère for his contributions to the discovery of electromagnetism. The ohm is named in honor of German physicist George Ohm, who established the fundamental relationship between voltage, current and resistance that today we call Ohm's Law.

Section Review 1: Electric Force and Electricity

A. Define the following terms.

electric force	electrical insulator	conduction	coulomb
Coulomb's law	semiconductor	current electricity	potential difference
electric field	superconductor	current	volt
electric field lines	static electricity	resistance	Ohm's Law
electricity	friction	voltage	ohms
electrical conductor	induction	ampere	resistivity

B. Choose the best answer.

1. What is the force that moves the electrons in an electrical circuit?

    A. ampere   B. coulomb   C. voltage   D. resistance

2. The flow of electricity through a circuit can be compared to the flow of water through a pipe. Using this comparison, the friction caused by the pipe wall would be similar to

    A. the resistance in the circuit.   C. the voltage of the circuit.

    B. the amperage of the circuit.   D. the coulombs in the circuit.

3. What is the resistance of a lamp that allows a current of 10 amps with 120 volts?

    A. 12Ω   B. 110Ω   C. 130Ω   D. 1200Ω

4. A low resistivity material will do which of the following?

    A. become a semiconductor

    B. allow electron flow easily

    C. block electron flow completely

    D. allow electron flow at low temperatures

C. Fill in the blanks.

1. The amount of electric current in a circuit is measured in _____.

2. The volt is a unit of electrical _____.

3. The opposition of a conductor to the flow of electrons is called _____.

D. Answer the following questions.

1. Explain the difference between an electrical conductor and an insulator.

2. Compare and contrast semiconductors and superconductors.

ELECTRICAL CIRCUITS

Electricity is a form of energy caused by moving electrons called electric current. The path through which the electricity is conducted is called a **circuit**. When we draw electrical circuits, we use the symbols shown in Figure 12.12 to represent voltage sources, resistors and wires. **Batteries** are commonly used as voltage sources. Devices such as radios and televisions draw current from the circuit, and so provide resistance to the flow of electricity. These

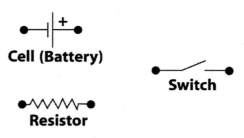

Figure 12.12 Symbols for Circuit Elements

devices, or **loads**, are usually represented as a simple resistor in circuit diagrams. There are two types of circuits: series and parallel circuits.

Ohm's law (Equation 12.2) can be used to determine the voltage, current or resistance in simple circuits, provided enough information is given.

SERIES CIRCUITS

In a **series circuit**, all current is the same through each part or load. If a resistor is broken or damaged, current will no longer be able to flow through a series circuit.

Figure 12.13 Series Circuit

We can use the symbols from Figure 12.12 to represent the series circuit as a **circuit diagram**. The three resistors represent the resistance provided by each light bulb. In a series circuit, you can determine the total equivalent resistance of the circuit by adding the individual resistance values. Equation 12.3 illustrates this relationship.

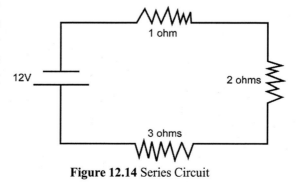

Figure 12.14 Series Circuit

$$R_{eq} = R_1 + R_2 + R_3 \qquad \textbf{Equation 12.3}$$

Thus, adding a resistor in series increases the overall resistance of the circuit. All resistors in a series have the same amount of current, or amperage.

A **switch** may be used to open and close the circuit. When the switch is open, electricity will not flow through a series circuit.

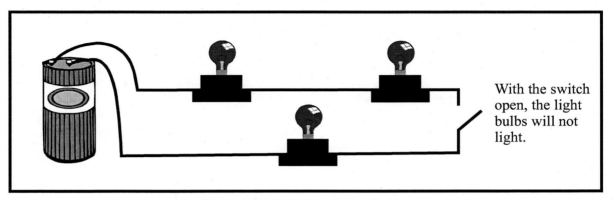

With the switch open, the light bulbs will not light.

Figure 12.15 Switch in a Series Circuit

Figure 12.15 is shown as a circuit diagram in Figure 12.16.

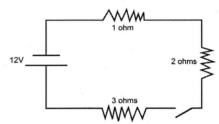

Figure 12.16 Series Circuit with Switch

Challenge Question 1

Determine the equivalent resistance of the circuits shown in Figures 12.14 and 12.16.

Just as the loads in a circuit can be connected in series, multiple batteries can be connected in series. This is done by connecting the positive end of one terminal with the negative terminal of another battery. This is shown in Figure 12.17.

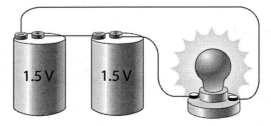

Figure 12.17 Batteries in Series

In this case, the voltage of the circuit is increased. To find the voltage of a circuit in series, add the voltages of the individual batteries together. For the circuit illustrated in Figure 12.17, you get:

$$V_{eq} = V_1 + V_2 \qquad \text{Equation 12.4}$$

Challenge Question 2

What is the total voltage of the circuit in Figure 12.17?

PARALLEL CIRCUITS

A **parallel circuit** has more than one path for the electricity to flow. The voltage is the same through all of the resistors in the circuit. If one path is removed or broken, current will still be able to flow in a parallel circuit. Most households are wired with parallel circuits, so that when you turn off a light, the television doesn't turn off as well.

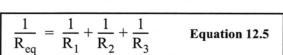

Figure 12.18 Parallel Circuit

We can also represent a parallel circuit with a circuit diagram using the symbols shown in Figure 12.19. The overall resistance of a parallel circuit is reduced as more resistors are added. Thus, more current flows through the circuit. The equivalent resistance of a parallel circuit is expressed by Equation 12.5 below.

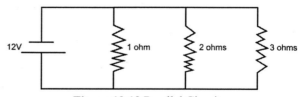

Figure 12.19 Parallel Circuit

$$\frac{1}{R_{eq}} = \frac{1}{R_1} + \frac{1}{R_2} + \frac{1}{R_3} \qquad \text{Equation 12.5}$$

The batteries of a circuit may also be connected in parallel. This is done by connecting the positive terminal of one battery to the positive terminal of the next battery. A parallel connection is shown in Figure 12.20.

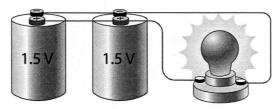

Figure 12.20

Connecting batteries in parallel does not increase the voltage of the circuit. The voltage of two batteries connected in parallel will equal the voltage of the lowest-voltage battery.

$$V_{eq} = V_1 = V_2 \quad \textbf{Equation 12.6}$$

Challenge Question 3

What is the total resistance for the circuit shown in Figure 12.19? What is the total voltage for the circuit shown in Figure 12.20?

Even though the voltage of the circuit is not increased by connecting batteries in parallel, the capacity of the circuit is increased. This means that the circuit has more charge to draw from, and the loads connected to it will last longer.

Practice Exercise 2: Series and Parallel Circuits

Draw the appropriate circuit diagram based on the descriptions given. Determine the equivalent resistance (R_{eq}) in each circuit. For #1 and #2, determine the current (I) running through the circuit also.

1. Two light bulbs, one with a resistance of 100 ohms and one with a resistance of 150 ohms, are connected in series to a 25-V battery.

2. Three resistors, all with a resistance of 50 ohms, are connected in parallel to a 9-V battery.

3. A strand of lights with five bulbs are connected to a 120-V voltage source. When one bulb goes out, the other four bulbs go out as well.

4. A strand of lights with four bulbs are connected to a 210-V voltage source. When one bulb goes out, the remaining bulbs stay lit.

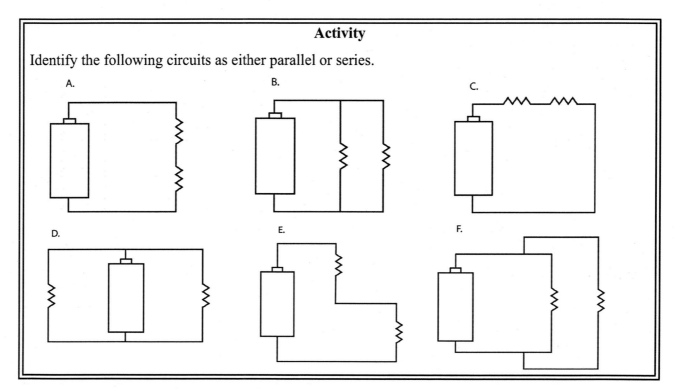

Activity

Identify the following circuits as either parallel or series.

COMPARISON OF SERIES AND PARALLEL CIRCUITS

Let's say that you have a single 1.5 V battery as the voltage source for a circuit. You connect one load, a light bulb, to the circuit, and the light bulb lights up. Now add a second light bulb to the circuit. Both light bulbs will still light, but they will be dimmer than the single light bulb. You can continue to connect light bulbs to the circuit, and eventually there will not be enough electrical force (voltage) to light them all. This is shown in Figure 12.21.

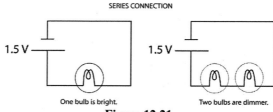

Figure 12.21

Note that the light bulb is drawn as a loop; this is only to distinguish the light bulb that we are talking about from other loads. Remember that a light bulb is still a resistor, a device that offers resistance to current flow in the circuit.

The situation is different if you connect your second bulb in parallel (Figure 12.22). Now both bulbs will burn equally brightly, because there is less overall resistance when two loads are connected than when one is connected.

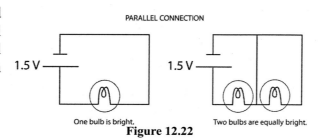

Figure 12.22

Section Review 2: Electrical Circuits

A. Define the following terms.

circuit	circuit diagram	parallel circuit
series circuit	switch	circuit breaker
surge protector	fuse	

B. Choose the best answer.

1. A switch is inserted into a series circuit of Christmas lights. During the night, the switch is left open. The lights will

   A. continue to burn.

   B. be turned off.

   C. become a parallel circuit.

   D. burn brighter.

2. A series and a parallel circuit each have two resistors of 2Ω each. A third 2Ω resistor is then added. The overall resistance of the _____ circuit _____.

   A. parallel, increases

   B. series, increases

   C. parallel, decreases

   D. B and C only

3. A series circuit has three resistors. R1 = 2 ohms, R2 = 2 ohms and R3 = 3 ohms. What is the total resistance of the circuit, and what will happen if R3 fails?

   A. The total resistance of 0.75 ohms will increase to 2 ohms when R3 fails.

   B. The total resistance of 7 ohms will decrease to 4 ohms if R3 fails.

   C. The total resistance of 0.75 ohms will decrease to 0 ohms of R3 fails.

   D. The total resistance of 7 ohms will increase infinitely; current will not flow if R3 fails.

Use the figure to answer questions 4 and 5.

4. The batteries in this flashlight

   A. are connected in series.

   B. have a voltage equal to 3 Ω.

   C. are connected in parallel.

   D. have a voltage equal to 1.5V.

5. Turning one battery around

   A. makes it a parallel circuit.

   B. allows the flashlight to burn brighter.

   C. opens a switch, so electricity will not flow.

   D. closes a switch, so electricity will not flow.

Use the following figure to answer questions 6 and 7.

6. The total voltage of this circuit
    A. is 1.5V.
    B. is 4.5V.
    C. is $(1 \setminus 1.5) + (1 \setminus 1.5) + (1 \setminus 1.5) = 2V$.
    D. cannot be determined from the figure.

7. The total resistance in this circuit
    A. is 1.5Ω.
    B. is 4.5Ω.
    C. is $(1 \setminus 1.5) + (1 \setminus 1.5) + (1 \setminus 1.5) = 2Ω$
    D. cannot be determined from the figure.

8. A standard transistor radio battery is 9V. If the local store was out of 9V batteries, how could you construct an equivalent power source?

    A. Securely connect 3 1.5V batteries in series.

    B. Securely connect 6 1.5V batteries in series.

    C. Securely connect 6 1.5V batteries in parallel.

    D. Securely connect 9 1.5V batteries in parallel.

Use the following figure to answer questions 9 and 10.

9. Describe the circuit.

    A. One 3V battery connected in series to three loads.

    B. Two 1.5 V batteries connected in series to three loads.

    C. One 3V battery connected in parallel to three loads.

    D. An open circuit where no current will flow.

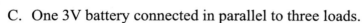

10. Which bulbs will be lit in the following circuit?
    A. 1 only
    B. 1 and 2 only
    C. 1, 2 and 3
    D. None will be lit.

MAGNETISM AND MAGNETIC FORCE

A **magnet** is a metallic substance capable of attracting iron and certain other metals. It has a north and south pole which creates a **magnetic field** consisting of invisible lines of force around the magnet between the two poles. These invisible lines, called **magnetic field lines**, always point from the north pole to the south pole of a magnet. The Earth acts as a giant magnet having a North Pole and a South Pole, and the magnetic field circles the Earth longitudinally.

A **compass** contains a small, thin magnet mounted on a pivot point. The end of the magnet that points toward the Earth's geographic North Pole is labeled as the north pole of the magnet; correspondingly, the end that points south is the south pole of the magnet.

The Earth's current g*eographic north* is thus actually its *magnetic south.*

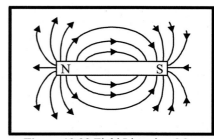
Figure 12.23 Field Lines in a Magnet

To avoid confusion between geographic and magnetic north and south poles, the terms *positive* and *negative* are sometimes used for the poles of a magnet. The positive pole is that which seeks geographical north.

The like poles on two magnets exhibit a repulsive (magnetic) force, but two unlike poles exhibit an attractive force. For example, the north pole of one magnet will repel the north pole of another magnet, but the north pole of one magnet will attract the south pole of another magnet.

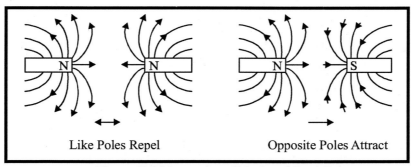

Like Poles Repel   Opposite Poles Attract

Figure 12.24 Interaction of North and South Poles

Natural occurring magnets are found as the mineral **magnetite**, Fe_3O_4 (s). Discovery of this mineral led to the ancient use of the **lodestone,** a primitive compass. In modern times, most magnets are man-made from a mixture of iron and other metals. A **bar magnet** is a man-made magnet, commonly used to illustrate the properties of magnetism.

Let's look inside a bar magnet to find out what makes it magnetic. Using a powerful microscope to look into a magnetic material, you would see that its atoms are aligned in a regular pattern, a series of tiny poles arranged end on end, as in Figure 12.25.

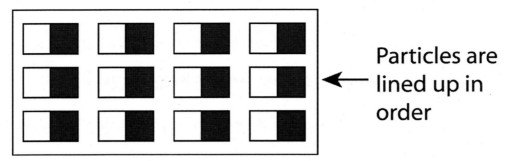

Figure 12.25 A Bar Magnet

So there is no *one* north or south pole in a magnet, but many. The accumulation of these poles creates the magnetic field, resulting in a magnet with an overall north and south pole.

Think of a line of people, each facing the back of the person in front of them. There is no one place where all the faces or the backs are, but the line as a whole has a beginning (the face of the first person) and an end (the back of the last person). What happens if you ask the two people in the middle of the line to separate? Now you have two lines, each with a beginning and an end. The same thing happens if you break a magnet in half. You create two new magnets, each with its own north and south pole.

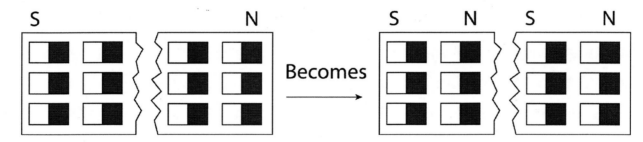

Figure 12.26 Breaking a Bar Magnet

The magnet can be subdivided again and again, but at some point (depending on its original size) the divisions become too small to maintain a magnetic field. The magnet has no long-term internal order and is now just a piece of de-magnetized metal. To see this, think of the line of people again. You can keep dividing the line of people, creating more and smaller lines, until you just have a bunch of individual people standing around.

This is one way to **de-magnetize** a magnet, or remove its magnetic quality. Other ways include heating it to a high temperature or dropping it. Both physical actions will upset the internal order of the magnet, and destroy its field.

Section Review 3:   Magnetism and Magnetic Force

A. Define the following terms.

bar magnet	magnetic field	magnetic field lines	compass
de-magnetize	magnetite		lodestone

B. Chose the best answer.

1. Which of the following will attract one another?

    A. the north pole of a magnet and the south pole of another magnet

    B. the north pole of a magnet and the north pole of another magnet

    C. the south pole of a magnet and the south pole of another magnet

    D. the north and south poles of the same magnet

2. The diagram below shows a powerful bar magnet. A strong magnetic field can be detected at point P.

P

N (+)   (–) S

Permanent Magnet

Identify the arrow that shows the direction of the magnetic field at point P.

A.   B.   C.   D.

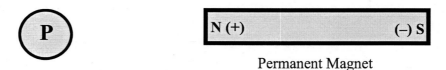

3. The magnetic field lines of a magnet always point from the magnet's

    A. north pole to its south pole.

    B. south pole to its north pole.

    C. south pole to the north pole of another magnet.

    D. south pole to the south pole of another magnet.

C. Answer the following questions.

1. In a magnetic compass, explain why the needle points north. What characteristics of Earth cause a magnetic compass to work? What material(s) must the needle be made of?

2. Why do like poles on magnets repel? Draw a diagram to show the magnetic forces around two magnets and use the diagram to explain your answer.

3. Name two ways to de-magnetize a material, and describe why the material loses its magnetic character.

ELECTROMAGNETIC FORCE AND FIELDS

ELECTROMAGNETS

Electricity and magnetism are actually related forces. You may recall that one of the fundamental forces in nature is the **electromagnetic force** – the electrical part of this force is responsible for electric charge and the flow of electrons while the magnetic part of the force produces magnetic properties in certain metals.

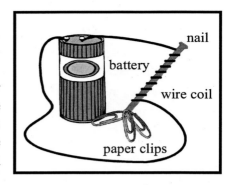

Figure 12.27 Electromagnet

Since both are actually components of the same force, electricity and magnetism are dependent on one another and can influence each other. One example of this interdependence occurs when electrons move or flow. This is an electrical current or electricity and it creates a magnetic field. Let's take the simplest example first: let's say that you connect a loop of wire to a battery, as shown in Figure 12.28A. In this arrangement, electrons (e) flow through the wire, from the negative (-) terminal of the battery, to the positive (+) terminal of the battery. If you were to view the magnetic field, it would be circling around the outside of the wire, perpendicular to the direction of electron flow. What if you change the direction of electron flow? Well, in order to do that, you switch the battery terminals, right? The result is a change in direction of the magnetic field (Figure 12.28B).

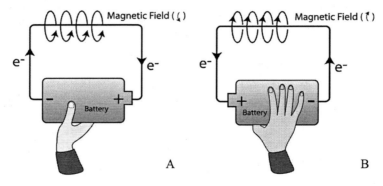

Figure 12.28 Generating a Magnetic Field with Simple Electrical Circuit

If you want to make the magnetic field stronger, coil the wire. Upon doing this, the magnetic field at every segment of the wire will add to the field of the segment next to it, because the magnetic field will be going in the same direction in both places. The more coils that you create, the stronger the field becomes.

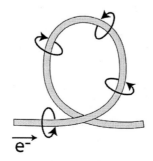

Figure 12.29 Coiling the Wire

But why is this useful? What can you do with a magnetic field? You can make an electromagnet! As the name implies, an **electromagnet** is a device that becomes magnetic when electricity flows through it.

Let's take the basic set-up from Figure 12.28A, add coils to the wire as in Figure 12.29 and, finally, add the *piece de resistance*...a nail! What will happen? Each individual magnetic fields adds together to create a strong, cumulative magnetic field. This turns your everyday nail into a magnet, with north and poles, as shown in Figure 12.30.

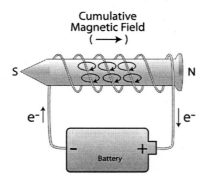

Figure 12.30 A Simple Electromagnet

You might be wondering what the purpose of the nail is. The nail actually does two things. First, iron is a **ferromagnetic** material, which means it is easy to magnetize in the presence of an external magnetic field. That is, the magnetic field from the coil causes the electrons in the nail's iron (Fe) atoms to become aligned with the field. If we removed the nail and the core of the coil was just air, a magnetic field would still be generated, but it would not be as strong. The second purpose of the nail is to serve as a solid cylinder to wrap the wire around. This keeps the wire coiling in a uniform direction, so that the magnetic fields are aligned properly.

The magnetic field will last as long as the battery continues to deliver electrons (a current). This means that an electromagnet will only work when the circuit is closed and electrons can flow. Also, when the battery "dies," no more magnetic field can be generated.

Figure 12.31 shows our electromagnet without its battery attachments. This is just a schematic to show you the full effect of the magnetic field (remember, no battery current, no field!). The field is strongest when close to the coils, and gets weaker as you move farther away.

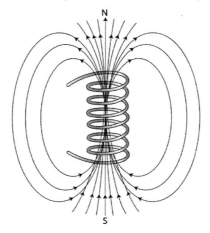

Figure 12.31 The Magnetic Field of an Electromagnet

ELECTROMAGNETS VS. BAR MAGNETS

So, how is an electromagnet different than a bar magnet? As you know, a bar magnet is a magnet that produces a permanent magnetic field. In other words, there is no current in the bar magnet creating the magnetism. Instead, the flow of electrons in each atom of the magnet is aligned in such a way that their magnetic fields add up to one large field. This means that every atom is a tiny magnet by itself. Aligning these atoms is similar to aligning a bunch of bar magnets together. On the other hand, an electromagnet produces a "temporary" magnetic field from the flow of electrons in the wire. There is no permanent change in the atoms of the wire for them to "hold" the magnetism, so the magnetic field disappears when the current stops. This can be useful for certain applications, such as a magnetic lock that can be turned off by switching off the electricity to the electromagnet in the lock.

A few basic design features of electromagnets should be fairly easy to surmise, if you think about it. One way, for instance, to control the strength of the magnetic field would be to increase or decrease the current through the wire. Also, one can increase the magnetic field strength by increasing the number of coils wrapping around the nail. Very large magnetic fields can be generated by designing the electromagnet correctly, much larger than would be possible by using bar magnets. In 2006, the world's largest electromagnet was built in Switzerland with 20,000 amps flowing through it – that's the same amount of current in a lightning bolt!

Because of the ability to control magnetic field presence and strength, electromagnets have found many uses in technology. One of the best examples is the electric motor, which is a common way to convert electrical energy into mechanical energy.

SIMPLE MOTORS

One of the most important types of machines is the **simple** or **electric motor**. Whether large or small, simple motors use an electromagnet (shown in Figure 12.30) and turn it into a electric motor. The very first thing that we need to do is to add a horseshoe magnet. The **horseshoe magnet** is a permanent magnet. Second, we will drive an **axle** through the nail to allow it to spin.

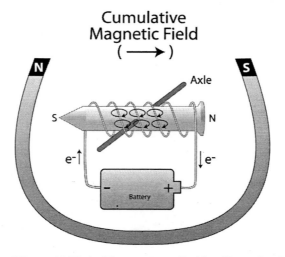

Figure 12.32 An Electromagnet Inside a Horseshoe Magnet

As it stands in Figure 12.32, the flow of electrons from the battery through the coiled wire has created a polarity that conveniently matches with that of the external permanent magnet (N-S-N-S). But what if we flip the battery? Here is what happens, in order:

1. The direction of the current changes, meaning that electrons are now moving through the wire in a direction opposite that shown in Figure 12.32.

2. The change in direction of electrical movement causes the direction of the magnetic field to change also.

3. The poles of the electromagnet (the nail) flip. Now the head is South and the tail is North.

4. The poles of the permanent magnet (the horseshoe) stay the same.

5. However, now the North pole of the horseshoe magnet is next to the North pole of the electromagnet. Likewise with the South poles. Now the arrangement of the poles is N-N-S-S.

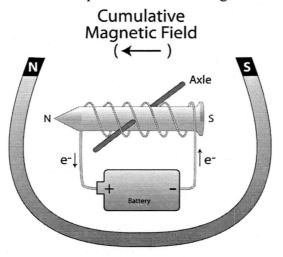

Figure 12.33 An Electromagnet Inside a Horseshoe Magnet, Reversed Polarity

6. These like poles repel each other. The South pole of the electromagnet (the nail head) goes up, and the North pole goes down. The nail goes vertical and then completes the half turn that brings it back to the desired N-S-N-S position. Now, the electromagnet stops rotating due to the attractive forces.

Well, OK. But what good is that? We have to take one final step to see the benefit. Flip the battery again. Steps 1–6 occur again, and the nail makes another half turn. The beauty of the electric motor is that is continuously flips the electromagnetic field, so that the electromagnet spins freely on its axle. In a real motor, the electromagnet is not a nail, as you may have guessed. It is a cylinder of iron called an **armature**. The whole spinning electromagnet part of the motor is called the **rotor**. The stationary permanent magnet part is called the **stator**.

With this simple design, electric motors have found great functionality because of the degree of control that is possible. The speed of the axle's rotation can be controlled by the amount of current that is passed through the loop. Furthermore, the direction of rotation can easily be adjusted by reversing the current.

Electric motors have many uses – in fact, you probably use simple motors all the time without realizing it. Just think about a typical day in your life and see how many simple motors you can identify.

GENERATORS

Not only can an electrical current create a magnetic field, but a magnet can produce an electric current by moving the magnet through a coil. Creating an electric current using a magnet is called **electromagnetic induction**. **Electric generators** are devices that use electromagnetic induction to create electricity. Figure 12.34 is a simple diagram of electromagnetic induction. Note that the magnet or the coils must be in motion in order for an electric current be generated. The direction that the electrons travel depends on the direction that the magnet travels.

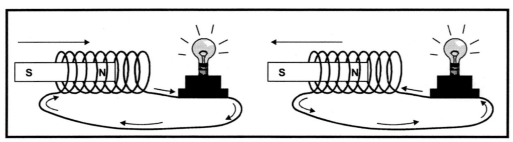

Figure 12.34 Electromagnet Induction

In the United States, electric power generators produce electricity by turning a coil between north and south poles of a magnet. Each time the coil switches from north pole to south pole, the direction of the current changes direction. This type of current is called **alternating current** or **AC**. Some countries use **direct current** or **DC**, which is the kind of current produced by a battery. Direct current flows in only one direction.

Challenge Activity

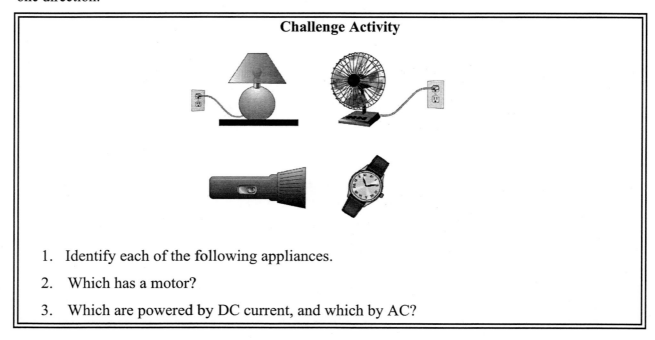

1. Identify each of the following appliances.

2. Which has a motor?

3. Which are powered by DC current, and which by AC?

Section Review 4: Electromagnetic Force and Fields

A. Define the following terms.

electromagnetic force   alternating current

electromagnet   direct current

B. Choose the best answer.

1. Which of the following would strengthen an electromagnet?

   A. increasing the electric current   C. increasing the voltage of the circuit

   B. increasing the number of coils   D. all of the above

2. How can a magnet produce an electric current?

   A. by wrapping a wire around the magnet

   B. by moving a magnet through a wire coil

   C. by placing a magnet next to a battery

   D. all of the above

3. Look at the diagram below, and then answer the following question.

What would happen if the poles of the magnet were reversed?

   A. The direction of the current would be reversed.

   B. The light bulb would not light.

   C. No current would be produced.

   D. The current would increase.

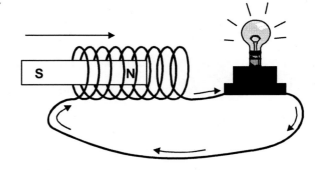

C. Answer the following questions.

1. In physics class, two groups of students experimented with making an electromagnet using a 9-volt battery, an iron nail, and copper wire. The first group made an electromagnet that would pick up 5 paper clips. The second group of students was able to make an electromagnet that picked up 7 paper clips. If the paper clips were all the same size, what other factor could have accounted for the difference? How would you suggest making an electromagnet that would pick up even more paper clips?

2. What is the difference between direct current and alternating current? How is alternating current produced?

CHAPTER 12 REVIEW

A. Choose the best answer.

1. A current of 0.5 amps flows in a circuit that is powered by a cell that produces 9.0 volts. Identify the resistance of the circuit.

   A. 18.0 ohms   B. 9.5 ohms   C. 8.5 ohms   D. 4.5 ohms

2. A voltage (V) is applied to a circuit with a resistance (R) producing a current (I). Identify the current when a voltage (5V) is applied to a circuit of resistance (R).

   A. 0.2 I   B. I   C. 5 I   D. 10 I

3. A 125 volt battery delivers a current of 2.0 amperes to a portable radio. What is the resistance of the radio?

   A. 0.02 ohms   B. 2.0 ohms   C. 63 ohms   D. 250 ohms

4. A 120 volt line supplies the electricity to a light bulb with an operating resistance of 60 ohms. How many amperes of current will it take to burn the lamp?

   A. 720 amperes   C. 20 amperes

   B. 0.5 amperes   D. 2 amperes

5. Which of the following statements is NOT true?

   A. A magnet can produce an electric field.

   B. The flow of electricity can produce a magnetic field.

   C. An electromagnet can be strengthened by decreasing the number of wire coils.

   D. An electromagnet can be strengthened by increasing the number of wire coils.

6. The diagram below shows two bodies, X and Y, that are distance, d, apart. Each body carries a charge of +q. The electrical force exerted on Y by X is equal to F.

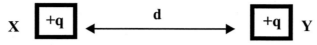

   Identify the change that would result in the biggest increase in the force exerted on Y by X.

   A. Change the charge on Y from +q to –q.

   B. Increase the charge on Y from +q to +3q.

   C. Increase the distance between X and Y from d to 2d.

   D. Decrease the distance between X and Y from d to 0.5d.

7. Identify the best description of an electric current.

   A. a flow of protons

   B. a flow of electrons

   C. a build-up of positive charge

   D. a build-up of negative charge

8. Identify the type of current used in battery-powered flashlights.

   A. static current

   B. direct current

   C. potential current

   D. alternating current

9. Identify the graph that shows the relationship between the voltage (V) applied across a given resister and the current (I) flowing through that resistor in an ohmic device.

A.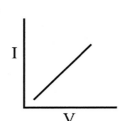

C.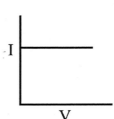

B.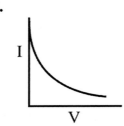

D.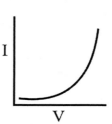

10. Renee has built a circuit with a single 1.5V battery connected in series to three light bulbs. The light bulbs are not as bright as she would like. What can she do to make them burn more brightly?

   A. Add a fourth light bulb in series.

   B. Connect a second battery in parallel.

   C. Connect a second battery in series.

   D. A and C only.

Use the figure to answer questions 13 and 14.

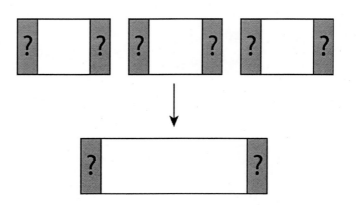

11. Correctly arrange the poles of the magnets in the following diagram so that each magnet is attracted to the next, forming one continuous bar magnet.

   A. N-S-N-S-N-S

   B. S-N-S-N-S-N

   C. N-S-S-N-N-S

   D. Arrangements A and B will both form a continuous attraction.

12. Once formed, what is the net polarity of the continuous magnet?

   A. N-S

   B. S-N

   C. Either N-S or S-N, depending on the original arrangement.

   D. The continuous magnet will be demagnetized, with no net polarity.

13. Identify the diagram that best represents the electrical field between two positively charged bodies.

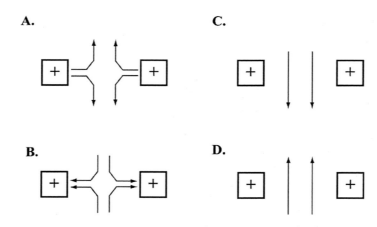

14. An analogy can be drawn between the work done by an electric current flowing through an electrical appliance and the work done by water flowing over a waterfall. In such an analogy, identify the property of the waterfall that is analogous to the potential difference (voltage) across the electrical appliance.

   A. width of the waterfall

   C. rate of flow of the water

   B. height of the waterfall

   D. temperature of the water

Section I

1 Ron measures the dimensions of a block of vanadium, and determines that his 300 gram block measures 2 cm × 5 cm × 6 cm. What is the density of vanadium?

SPS2a

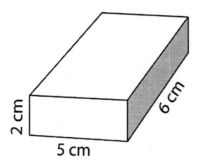

A 5 g/cm^3 **B** 0.2 g/cm^3 **C** 6 g/cm^3 **D** 30 cm^3

2 Lamar needs to measure the sliding friction of a cement block. How should he go about this?

SPS10a

A Roll the brick down a frictionless surface and calculate the acceleration of the brick.

B Attach a spring scale to the block with a string. Drag the scale and the block across the lab bench at a constant speed and read the force from the scale.

C Attach a spring scale to the block with a string. Gently lift the spring scale up and measure the vertical distance reached before the block begins to exert force on the scale.

D Place one cement block on top of another. Attach a spring scale to the one on top. Quickly pull the top block off the bottom block, and read the force required.

Go On

3 A recently-used hot ceramic tea-pot is placed on a cold trivet, as shown below. Which statement is correct about the sequence of thermal energy transfers? SPS7b

Trivet

A The air transfers energy to the teapot and trivet, and they become cool.

B The teapot transfers all of its energy to the air and becomes cool.

C The teapot transfers some energy to the trivet and some energy to the air and becomes cool.

D The trivet transfers energy to the teapot and the teapot becomes cool.

4 Laine's teacher tells her to do some research and identify her liquid sample. Laine conducts an experiment to determine the temperature at which the sample undergoes phase changes. She also looks up boiling point data for several liquid substances. SPS7d

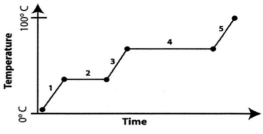

Substance	Boiling Point
bromine	58.8°C
benzene	80.1°C
water	100°C
octane	125.5°C

Which of the following could be the identity of her sample?

A bromine   **C** water

B benzene   **D** ethanol

5 "Smart glass" technologies have become increasingly popular. British scientists recently developed a window glass that helps buildings stay cool. At regular temperatures, the glass allows in both infrared (IR) and ultraviolet (UV) light. But above 29°C, the coating on the glass undergoes a chemical change, causing it to block IR light. What happens to the IR light? SPS9a

A It is absorbed by the glass.

B It is refracted by the glass.

C It is reflected by the coating on the glass.

D It is refracted by the coating on the glass.

Go On

6 A neon light is placed in one SPS9c, e evacuated (airless) chamber. A battery-powered radio is placed in a second evacuated chamber. Both devices are switched on at the same time by remote control. What observation could be made?

A An observer would only see the neon light

B An observer would only hear the radio.

C An observer would see the neon light and hear the radio.

D An observer would not see the neon light or hear the radio.

Use the graph below to answer question 7.

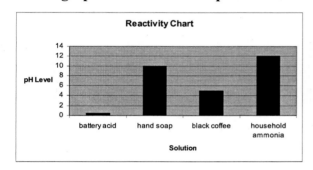

7 Which of the following substances, if combined together in equal amounts, would MOST closely approximate the pH of rain water? SPS6e

A hand soap and black coffee

B battery acid and hand soap

C black coffee and household ammonia

D battery acid and household ammonia

8 Trisha is cold and puts on a sweater. In a few minutes, she feels warmer. Why? SPS7b

A The sweater added heat to Trisha's body.

B The sweater took heat from the air around Trisha's body.

C The sweater slowed the loss of heat from Trisha's body.

D The sweater increased the loss of cold from Trisha's body.

9 Electromagnets are used in a rotary electric motor to produce a rotating magnetic field that turns the rotor. What energy conversion takes place in an electromagnet? SPS10c

A electrical to mechanical

B mechanical to electrical

C chemical to mechanical

D electrical to chemical

Go On

Use the graph below to answer question 10.

Work vs Distance

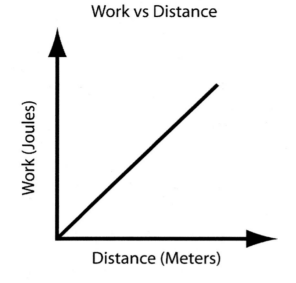

10 **What does the slope of this graph represent?**   SPS8b, e

A   speed

B   acceleration

C   force

D   energy

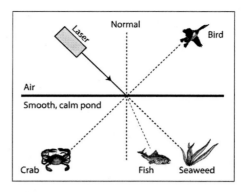

11 **A laser beam is directed at the surface of a smooth, calm pond. Which organisms will be illuminated by the beam?**   SPS9d

A   crab and fish

B   fish and bird

C   bird and crab

D   seaweed and bird

Go On

Use the following information to answer questions 12 and 13.

Rita obtains an unknown liquid sample from her teacher. It has a mass of 7 grams, and it fills a graduated cylinder to Level A on the graduated cylinder. She is given the densities of the following four liquids to help her identify the sample.

12 Which one is it?

SPS2a

	g/cc
water	1.00
vegetable oil	0.93
honey	1.42
gasoline	0.70

    ← A

   A   water

   B   vegetable oil

   C   honey

   D   gasoline

13 What additional volume of the sample should be added to reach Level B?

SCSh4a

   A   8 mL

   B   7 mL

   C   6 mL

   D   9 mL

14 Four unknown liquid samples were placed on four different hot plates, and labeled A – D. A thermometer with a maximum temperature of 110°C was placed in each sample. Students were instructed to observe and record the behavior of the samples as they were heated. This data is summarized in the following diagram. Based on the diagram, which sample has the highest boiling point?

SPS7b

   A   Sample A

   B   Sample B

   C   Sample C

   D   Sample D

15 Uranium-238 is the most abundant form of uranium. Which of the following processes is NOT available to uranium?

SPS3b

   A   fusion with another uranium atom

   B   fission to form two smaller atoms

   C   ionization to form an ion

   D   chemical reaction with another atom or molecule

Go On

16 The nucleus of an atom emits a particle. The particle is equal in size to a helium nucleus. What is this particle?   SPS3a

A   an alpha particle

B   a beta particle

C   a newton

D   a gamma ray

17 On the speed v. time graph to the right, identify the line or curve that represents the motion of a car driven from one stop sign to a second stop sign.   SPS8a

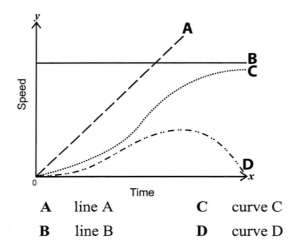

A   line A   C   curve C

B   line B   D   curve D

18 Identify the force needed to accelerate a car from 0m/s to 30m/s in 10s if the mass of the car is 2000kg.   SPS8b

A   6.7N

B   667N

C   6,000N

D   600,000N

19 Ross was riding his bike down a hill, and he ran straight into a mailbox. Identify the statement that most closely describes Ross's motion immediately following his collision with the mailbox.   SPS8b

A   He is thrown forward over the handlebars.

B   He is thrown backwards off the bike.

C   He is thrown sideways off the bike.

D   He is thrown upward into the air.

20 Gravity is the force of attraction between any two objects that have mass. The gravitational force that a body exerts depends, in part, on its mass. Which of the following factors also affects the amount of gravitational force experienced between two bodies?   SPS8c

A   the distance between the bodies

B   the relative speed of the bodies

C   the altitude of the bodies

D   the angle of the bodies

21 In a parallel circuit, the current has more than one path to follow through the circuit. In the circuit below, what is the total resistance?   SPS10b

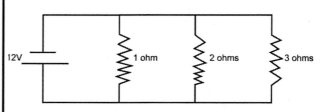

A   less than 1 ohm

B   less than 2 ohms

C   6 ohms

D   more than 6 ohms

Go On

22 Identify the result, if any, of moving a conducting wire loop through a magnetic field. *SPS10c*

A The wire loop will exert greater gravitational force on metal objects.

B Electromagnetic radiation will be emitted by the wire loop.

C An electric current will flow in the wire loop.

D There will be no detectable result.

23 Identify the property that would make a wire suitable for use as a 20-amp fuse in a 110-volt circuit. *SPS10b*

A The wire can conduct at least 2200 amps without overheating.

B The wire can conduct at least 20 amps without overheating.

C A 20 amp current will cause the wire to melt.

D A 2200 amp current will cause the wire to melt.

24 Which of the following statements is true concerning the motion of satellites around the Earth? *SPS8c*

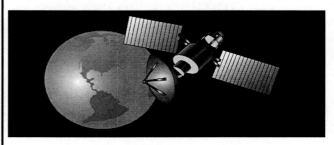

A Satellites fall toward the Earth due to the force of magnetism.

B Satellites fall toward the Earth due to the force of gravity.

C When a satellite's supply of energy is depleted, the satellite will fall to the Earth.

D Satellites experience no acceleration.

25 An electric iron operating at 120 volts draws 6.0 amps of current. What is the resistance of the iron? *SPS10b*

A 0.05 ohms

B 6 ohms

C 20 ohms

D 40 ohms

26 *Kinetic* and *potential* are terms that describe the expression of the energy of an object. Which of the following statements is true? *SPS7a*

A All potential energy becomes kinetic energy.

B Potential energy is expressed as motion.

C All kinetic energy becomes potential energy.

D Potential energy is stored.

Go On

27 A steel ball is released and allowed to roll down a steep, smooth ramp. Identify the statement that correctly describes the changes in potential energy (PE) and kinetic energy (KE) of the ball.   SPS7a

    A   PE and KE are both greatest mid-way down the ramp.

    B   PE and KE are both remain constant as the ball rolls down the ramp.

    C   PE is greatest at the top of the ramp; KE is greatest at the bottom.

    D   PE is greatest at the bottom of the ramp; KE is greatest at the top.

28 Which form of electromagnetic radiation is used to image bones?   SPS9b

    A   ultraviolet

    B   nuclear

    C   infrared

    D   x-ray

29 Identify the three elements that have valence electrons in the *s* orbital.   SPS4a, b

    A   magnesium, manganese, and molybdenum

    B   calcium, barium, and sodium

    C   aluminum, silicon, and sulfur

    D   rubidium, strontium, xenon

30 Tritium is the form of hydrogen that contains two neutrons and one proton. What is the relationship between tritium and hydrogen?   SPS1a

    A   Tritium is an isotope of hydrogen.

    B   Hydrogen is an isotope of tritium.

    C   Tritium is an ion of hydrogen.

    D   Hydrogen is ionized tritium.

31 All of the elements in the halogen family   SPS4a, b

    A   need to give up one electron to become stable.

    B   need to gain one electron to become stable.

    C   do not react at all with other elements.

    D   are metals.

32 The Arrhenius concept of acids and bases is limited in that it   SPS6d

    A   does not consider aqueous reactions.

    B   considers H+ the only source of basic character.

    C   considers OH– the only source of basic character.

    D   considers H_2O the only source of basic character

Go On

33 Which of the following types of elements have both ductility and malleability?   SPS5a

   A   metals

   B   non metals

   C   metalloids

   D   gases

34 Sodium chlorate ($NaClO_3$) and potassium nitrate (KNO_3) are solids at room temperature. The solubility curves for sodium chlorate and potassium nitrate in water are presented in the graph. Based on the data provided, identify the valid conclusion.   SPS6c

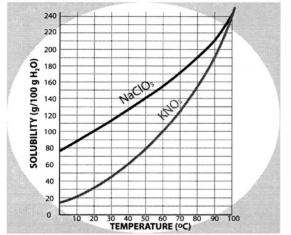

   A   The solubility of these solids in water decreases as water temperature increases.

   B   The solubility of these solids in water increases as water temperature increases.

   C   Nitrate ions are more soluble in water than are chlorate ions.

   D   Potassium nitrate is nearly insoluble at room temperature.

35 By mass, about 80% of the human body is water. Water's ability to surround ions is essential to the proper functioning of many biological processes. Identify the property of water that allows it to surround ions.   SPS6a

   A   density

   B   volatility

   C   buoyancy

   D   polarity

36 Rust forms by the reaction of iron with oxygen to produce iron oxide. An 88 g iron nail rusted. The rusted nail (iron oxide) had a mass of 102 g. Identify the mass of oxygen that reacted in the rusting of the nail.   SPS2d

   A   14 g

   B   88 g

   C   102 g

   D   200 g

37 The rusting of iron is represented by the following chemical equation.   SPS2b

$$4Fe(s) + 3O_2(g) \rightarrow 2Fe_2O_3(s)$$

The oxidation states of iron and oxygen are as follows:

- Elemental iron: 0
- Elemental oxygen: 0
- Iron in iron (III) oxide: +3
- Oxygen in iron (III) oxide: −2

Identify the number of electrons lost by each iron atom that rusts.

   A   2   **C**   5

   B   3   **D**   12

Go On

38 The following reaction is propane burning in oxygen to produce carbon dioxide and steam.

SPS2e

$$\underline{}C_3H_8 + \underline{}O_2 \rightarrow \underline{}CO_2 + \underline{}H_2O$$

Which of the following sets of numbers will balance this equation?

A 1, 5, 3, 4

B 1, 3, 4, 5

C 5, 4, 3, 1

D 4, 5, 1, 3

39 Which force exists between the nucleus and the electrons of an atom?

SPS1a

A gravitational

B nuclear

C electrostatic

D centripetal

40 Consider the portion of the Periodic Table of the Elements shown below. Which of the following elements is the MOST easily ionized?

SPS4b

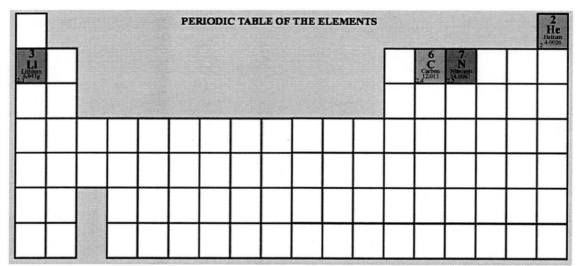

A nitrogen

B helium

C carbon

D lithium

Section II

41 What is the danger of an uncontrolled chain reaction within the core of a nuclear fission reactor?   SPS3d

A An uncontrolled chain reaction will use up all of the fuel in the reactor and force the fission of the metals that make up the core casing.

B An uncontrolled chain reaction will produce enough heat to crack the reactor core open, possibly releasing radioactive material.

C An uncontrolled chain reaction will produce enough electrons to electrically charge the reactor core.

D An uncontrolled chain reaction will produce enough heat to induce fusion in the reactor core, which will result in an explosion.

42 A carbon atom is single-bonded to other atoms to form a molecule. Which of the following expresses the correct number and type of bonds formed by a carbon atom?   SPS1b

A 2 covalent bonds

B 4 ionic bonds

C 4 covalent bonds

D 3 ionic bonds

43 A negatively charged plastic comb is brought close to, but does not touch, a small piece of paper. The comb and the paper are attracted to each other. Describe the charge on the paper.   SPS10a

A It may be negative or neutral.

B It may be positive or neutral.

C It must be negative.

D It must be positive.

44 Two spheres, *X* and *Y*, each have a charge of Q. The spheres are a distance, *d*, apart. The electrostatic force between the spheres is *F*. If the spheres are separated to a distance of 3*d*, identify the electrostatic force between the spheres.   SPS10a

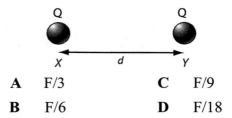

A F/3   **C** F/9

B F/6   **D** F/18

45 The air we breath is made up of 78% nitrogen, 21% oxygen and 1 % argon and other gases. Which of the following correctly lists the solutes in this gaseous solution?   SPS6a

A oxygen and other gases

B nitrogen

C oxygen, argon and other gases

D nitrogen and oxygen

46 Which of these elements is the BEST conductor of electricity?   SPS4a, b

A nitrogen

B chlorine

C sulfur

D copper

Go On

47 What is the total number of electrons found in an atom of phosphorus? *SPS4b*

   A   3

   B   5

   C   15

   D   31

48 Which particle diagram could represent a gaseous sample of carbon monoxide (CO)? *SPS2c*

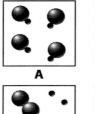

49 Which sample contains particles in a rigid, fixed, geometric pattern? *SPS5a*

   A $CO_2(aq)$

   B $HF(g)$

   C $H_2O_2(l)$

   D $SiO_2(s)$

50 What does the process of distillation accomplish? *SPS5b*

   A   Liquids are mixed.

   B   Liquids are purified.

   C   Gases are mixed.

   D   Gases are purified.

51 At standard temperature and pressure, a 5 gram sample of powdered iron will react more quickly with dilute hydrochloric acid than a 5 gram sheet of hammered iron. Why is this? *SPS6b*

   A   Because the iron sheet is denser than the iron powder.

   B   Because the iron powder has more surface area exposed to the acid than the iron sheet.

   C   Because the iron sheet has more surface area exposed to the acid than the iron powder.

   D   Because the iron sheet is less dense than the iron powder.

52 A gas has a volume of 16 liters at a pressure of 200 kilopascals. If the temperature of the gas is kept constant, identify the volume the gas will have at a pressure of 100 kilopascals. *SPS5b*

   A   4 liters

   B   8 liters

   C   32 liters

   D   256 liters

53 A 2 kg sample of silver (Ag) requires 2400 J of added energy to achieve a 5°C increase in temperature. What is the heat capacity of Ag? *SPS7c*

   A   1200 J/kg

   B   240 J/kg°C

   C   24,000 J/kg°C

   D   120 J/kg°C

Go On

54 The diagram below shows two neutral metal spheres, *x* and *y*, that are in contact and on insulating stands.

SPS10a

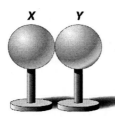

Which diagram BEST represents the charge distribution on the spheres when a positively charged rod is brought near sphere *x*, but does NOT touch it?

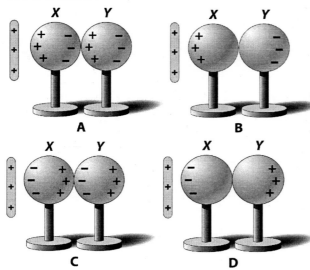

55 Electrons oscillating with a frequency of 1.5×10^8 hertz produce electromagnetic waves. Use the diagram below to classify these waves.

SPS9b

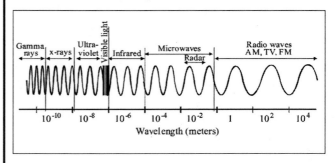

A   ultraviolet

B   visible

C   microwave

D   radio

56 A student heats a beaker full of water over a low flame. While heating, the student adds 3 grams of salt that has been measured out on a tared beam balance. He allows the solution to boil until its volume has been reduced by 50%. Then he uses metal tongs to transfer the beaker from the flame to an ice bath. What is the likely result of this series of actions?

SPS7b

A   The tongs will melt.

B   The beaker will melt.

C   The beaker will crack.

D   The tongs will crack.

Go On

57 Which pair of elements is MOST SPS1b
likely to form an ionic bond?

A   K and H

B   N and C

C   K and Cl

D   C and H

58 This figure shows SPS1a, b

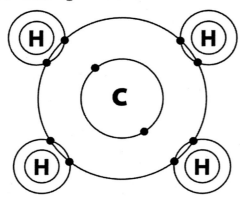

A   5 atoms and 10 electrons.

B   1 molecule and four ionic bonds.

C   5 molecules and 10 electrons.

D   1 atom and four covalent bonds.

59 Which of the following elements SPS4b
forms the MOST polar bonds?

A   F

B   Cl

C   Br

D   I

60 Which of the following radioac- SPS3a
tive emissions is the largest in
size?

A   alpha particle

B   beta particle

C   gamma

D   X-ray

61 What process does the following SPS7d
description refer to: "a block of
dry ice sitting on a laboratory benchtop
has a cloud of gas around it?"

A   melting

B   sublimation

C   evaporation

D   fumigation

62 If carbon dioxide is produced SPS2d
when fuel is burned, which of
the following atoms had to have been in
the fuel?

A   oxygen

B   nitrogen

C   helium

D   carbon

63 A radioactive isotope, Pu-241, SPS3c
has a half-life of 14.4 years. If
you start with 10 g of pure Pu-241, how
much will be left in 28.8 years?

A   14.4 g

B   5 g

C   20 g

D   2.5 g

Go On

64 Which of the following is a correct statement about a periodic trend?   SPS4a. b

  A In general, the atomic radius of elements decreases going down the Periodic Table.

  B In general, a valence electron is more tightly bound to its atom going from left to right across the Periodic Table.

  C The reactivity of metals decreases going down the Periodic Table.

  D In general, the atomic radius of elements increases going from left to right on the Periodic Table.

65 Three chemistry lab students in three different cities simultaneously bring water to boil in a beaker. Student 1 is in Norden, CA, a city that is about 6,900 feet above sea level. Student 2 is in San Francisco, CA, just at sea level. Student 3 is in Forrum, CA at 205 feet below sea level. Which student's results will indicate that the water boiled at a temperature below 100 degrees Centigrade?   SPS5a, b

  A Student 1

  B Student 2

  C Student 3

  D None of the students will get that result.

66 Four boys were working out with free weights in gym class.   SPS8e

  • Brett was holding 150 pound barbell above his head.

  • Philip was spotting for Brett.

  • Bryan was walking toward the teacher carrying a box full of weights.

  • Doug was holding a squat with a 30 pound barbell in each hand.

The physical science teacher came by and said only one boy was actually doing any work! Who was it?

  A Brett

  B Philip

  C Bryan

  D Doug

67 Lucas threw a softball up in the air to a height of 10 meters. Greg threw a softball up 12 meters. Greg threw the ball higher because   SPS8e

  A the pull of gravity on the ball was less.

  B he threw with greater force.

  C there was less air friction when he threw it.

  D gravity pulled the ball higher.

68 Which of the following weighs about 1 kilogram?   SPS2a

  A a cup of water

  B a liter of water

  C a milliliter of water

  D a kiloliter of water

Go On

69 A 200 N force, (F_1), and a 250 N, (F_2), force are applied to the same point at the same time to a large trunk on a frictionless level surface. Which diagram below shows the position of the forces that will give the greatest acceleration to the trunk? SPS8b

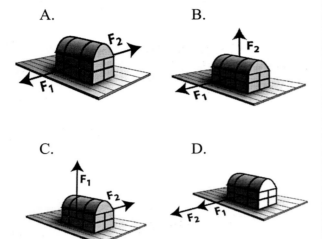

A.   B.

C.   D.

70 Which two molecules contain an equal number of atoms? SPS1a

C_2H_6 $KMnO_4$ H_2SO_4 C_2H_3OH

   A H_2SO_4 and C_2H_3OH
   B C_2H_6 and $KMnO_4$
   C $KMnO_4$ and H_2SO_4
   D C_2H_6 and C_2H_3OH

71 Select the BEST description of a solvent. SPS6a

   A   substance in which other substances dissolve
   B   a substance that dissolves in other substances
   C   a liquid that has a high boiling point
   D   a liquid that has a low boiling point

72 The diagram shows an electric circuit that uses a 120V source. It has a current of 10 amps. A toaster (R_1) and a blender (R_2) are plugged into the circuit. If the toaster creates a resistance of 5Ω, what is the resistance of the blender? SPS10b

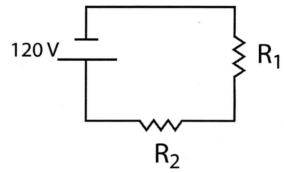

   A $12\ \Omega$
   B $17\ \Omega$
   C $7\ \Omega$
   D $60/59\ \Omega$

73 In order to determine the velocity of an object, what measurements must be made? SPS8a

   A   time and distance
   B   time and distance and mass
   C   time and distance and direction
   D   time, distance and volume

Go On

74 The following table shows the abundance and half-life of 4 of the 15 known carbon isotopes. Which is the MOST common stable isotope of carbon?   SPS3c

Isotope	Natural Abundance	Half-life
^8C	~0%	$1.99 \times 10^{-21}s$
^{12}C	98.89%	Infinite
^{13}C	1.11%	Infinite
^{14}C	1×10^{-10} %	5730 years

A ^8C

B ^{12}C

C ^{13}C

D ^{14}C

75 Rita wants to move a load of pumpkins from the garden to the barn. The pumpkins weigh 500 N. If Rita uses a wheelbarrow with a mechanical advantage of 5, how much effort force does she need to exert to move the pumpkins?   SPS8e

A   1 N

B   10 N

C   100 N

D   1000 N

76 An analogy can be drawn between the work done by an electric current flowing through an electrical appliance and the work done by water flowing over a waterfall. In such an analogy, identify the property of the electric current that is analogous to the rate of flow of water over the fall.   SPS10b

A   power

B   voltage

C   amperage

D   resistance

77 Identify the types of fields that interact to produce motion in an electric motor.   SPS10c

A   an electrical field and a gravitational field

B   a magnetic field and an electrical field

C   two electrical fields

D   two magnetic fields

78 On which surface will the force of static friction be easiest to overcome?   SPS10a

A   carpet

B   hardwood floor

C   grass

D   gravel

79 Complete the following reaction.   SPS2e

$NaOH\ (aq) + HCl\ (aq) \rightarrow \underline{\hspace{1cm}} + H_2O\ (l)$

A $2NaCl\ (s)$

B $NaCl\ (g)$

C $NaCl\ (aq)$

D $2NaCl\ (aq)$

80 Which of the following will have the lowest pH?   SPS6e

A   rainwater

B   distilled water

C   soapy water

D   bleach

Section I

1   The angle of the stirring rod in the beaker appears to change at the surface of the water. This phenomenon is explained by which property of light?   SPS9d

   A   scattering

   B   diffraction

   C   reflection

   D   refraction

2   Clara wants to determine the volume of an ice cube. She places the cube into a graduated cylinder and waits for it to melt. Is this an accurate way of determining the volume of the ice cube?   SPS2a

   A   Yes. The melted ice cube will be the same volume as the frozen ice cube.

   B   No. The melted ice cube has a smaller volume than the frozen ice cube, because liquid water is denser than solid water.

   C   No. Water vapor will be lost to the air during melting, which will change the measured volume of the two states.

   D   Yes. Even though the volume of water in ice and liquid form is different, it is not enough to be measureable.

Go On

3 Sound waves cause molecules to SPS9b
vibrate and bump into one
another. For sound to travel, there must
be molecules which can be made to
vibrate. The closer together the molecules are, the faster the sound is able to
travel. This explains why

A sound travels faster in steel than in
water.

B sound travels faster in outer space
than in air.

C sound travels faster in air than in
water.

D sound travels faster in water than in
steel.

4 Water is often called the universal SPS6e
solvent. The pH of pure water is
about 7. Adding bleach to pure water
would make the pH

A go down.

B go up.

C stay the same.

D more temperature dependent.

5 Lara navigates her kayak down a SPS8a
stretch of the Chattahoochee
River in 15 minutes. Her rate of speed
over the course of the trip is 8 km/hr.
How far has she traveled?

A 0.12 km

B 1.2 km

C 2 km

D 120 km

6 Which of the following examples SPS7a
represents potential energy but
NOT kinetic energy?

A an avalanche

B a coiled spring

C a hot air balloon in flight

D the pistons in a working engine

7 A science class is conducting a SCSh2a, b, c
laboratory activity that
involves observing a chemical reaction.
Each pair of students is given a flask
closed with a rubber stopper and containing an unknown liquid. The students
are told that the stopper needs to stay on
the flask because the liquid inside will
burn skin. Students are also told to keep
their aprons and goggles on throughout
the lab. Students will observe the chemical reaction that takes place when, after
shaking the flask, the liquid is mixed
with the air sitting above it. Which of
the following actions displays safe laboratory procedures?

A Instead of shaking the flask, Adam
and Shalandra turn the flask upside
down and balance it on the rubber
stopper to ensure that the liquid
mixes sufficiently with the air.

B After completing the experiment,
Mandy and Raul carefully remove
the stopper and waft the fumes produced by the liquid to try and determine its identity.

C Alka and Travis take turns shaking
the flask throughout the experiment.
They return the flask to a location
designated by the teacher at the end
of the lab.

D Since the rubber stopper is going to
remain in the flask throughout the
experiment, Matias and Tara take
their goggles off so that they can see
the reaction more clearly.

Go On

Use the graph below to answer question 8.

Changing the States of Water

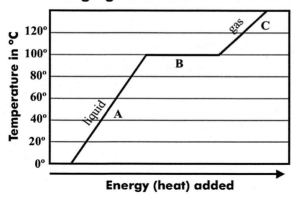

8   **Why does the temperature remain constant during section B of the graph?**   SPS7d

A   During section B, the temperature of the liquid phase cancels out the temperature of the gas phase.

B   During section B, energy is neither added nor removed.

C   During section B, the energy added is being used to change from a liquid phase to a gas phase.

D   During section B, a solid of constant temperature is formed as an intermediate phase between liquid and gas.

9   **Deuterium (^{2}H) is a common product of the fusion process. Often called "heavy hydrogen", deuterium consists of one proton and one neutron. Which of the following atoms could undergo fusion to become deuterium?**   SPS3b

A   U and an alpha particle

B   He and H

C   H and H

D   H and a neutron

10   **Find the amount of work done when 30 N of force is used to lift a box 400 cm.**   SPS8e

A   370 Joules

B   12 Joules

C   120 Joules

D   12,000 Joules

Go On

11 Which of the following BEST explains the difference between melting and boiling points? · SPS7d

    A The melting point is the temperature at which a gas becomes plasma. The boiling point is the temperature at which a gas becomes a liquid.

    B The boiling point is the temperature at which a liquid becomes a gas. The melting point is the temperature at which a solid becomes a liquid.

    C The melting point is the temperature at which a liquid becomes a gas. The boiling point is the temperature at which a solid becomes a liquid.

    D The boiling point is the temperature at which a solid becomes a gas. The melting point is the temperature at which a gas becomes a liquid.

12 Which of the following pieces of equipment would you use to heat a liquid on a hot plate? · SCSh2a, b, c

    A graduated cylinder

    B Petri dish

    C beaker

    D watch glass

Use the following passage to answer question 13.

When two light nuclei are forced to fuse, they form a heavier nucleus. During this process, a large amount of energy is produced. When the process is conducted at room temperatures and standard pressures, it is called cold fusion.

In 1989, Stanley Pons and Martin Fleischmann announced at a press conference that they had produced cold fusion one time in their laboratory. All over the world, scientists rushed to their labs to try and duplicate the experiment. In the end, no one was successful. Pons and Fleischmann were harshly criticized in the science community for their premature announcement.

13 What would have been the appropriate media form for Pons and Fleischmann to share how they performed the experiment and the results they achieved? · SPS3b, SCSh8a, b, c, d, e, f

    A newspaper and television

    B high school textbooks and workbooks

    C scientific journals

    D a podcast

Go On

14 Consider the graph shown SPS6b, 5b
below. X, Y, and Z each repre-
sent a different solute, and the curves
represent solubility of the solute in
water. Which of the following statements is MOST likely to be correct?

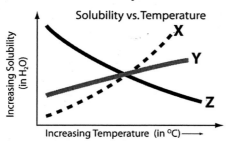

Solubility vs. Temperature

A   X, Y, and Z are gases

B   X and Y are gases; Z is a solid

C   X, Y and Z are solids

D   X and Y are solids; Z is a gas

15 Nuclear fission is a powerful SPS3b
energy source, used in both
nuclear power plants and atomic
bombs. Which statement is a possible
description of the nuclear fission of an
atom of U-235?

A   U-235 absorbs one neutron and splits
into an atom of krypton-94 and an
atom of barium-139.

B   U-235 absorbs one neutron and splits
into an atom of krypton-94, an atom
of barium-139 and three neutrons.

C   U-235 absorbs one neutron and splits
into an atom of krypton-94, an atom
of barium-139 and two neutrons.

D   U-235 absorbs one neutron and splits
into an atom of krypton-94, an atom
of barium-139 and one neutron.

16 Mark adds liquid water to an ice SPS7b
tray and places it in the freezer.
What happens?

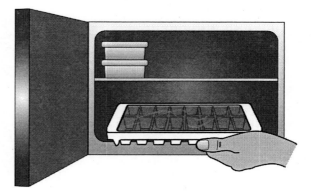

A   Thermal energy flows from the
higher-energy phase (water) to the
lower-energy phase (cold air).

B   Thermal energy flows from the
higher-energy phase (cold air) to the
lower-energy phase (water).

C   Cold radiates from the cold air into
the warm water.

D   The insulation of the ice tray keeps
the temperature from changing
much.

Go On

17 A collision between two billiard   SPS8a, 8b
balls is described below. Ball 1
has a mass of 0.5 kg and a velocity of 6
m/s – north. It collides with Ball 2,
which has a mass of 0.5 kg and is stationary prior to the collision. After the
collision Ball 2 achieves a velocity of 5
m/s – north. If ball 1 continues to move
north, what will be its speed?

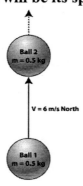

A   0 m/s

B   1 m/s

C   0.5 m/s

D   1.5 m/s

18 The circuit below represents the   SPS10b
wiring in a power strip. Identify
the way the circuit is wired and, if one
device breaks, the effect on the other
devices.

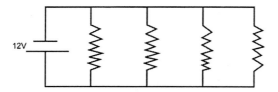

A   wired in parallel; other devices
remain on

B   wired in parallel; other devices turn
off

C   wired in series; other devices remain
on

D   wired in series; other devices turn off

19 A bowling ball with a mass of   SPS8c
5.44 kg and a soccer ball with a
mass of 0.43 kg are dropped from a 15
m platform in an evacuated chamber.
Identify the correct description of the
acceleration of the bowling ball and the
force with which it hits the ground, with
respect to the soccer ball.

A   The force of the bowling ball is
greater, and its acceleration is greater.

B   The force of the bowling ball is
greater, and its acceleration is the
same.

C   The force of the bowling ball is the
same, and its acceleration is greater.

D   The force of the bowling ball is the
same, and its acceleration is the
same.

20 X-rays are representative of   SPS7a, 9a
what type of energy?

A   thermal

B   nuclear

C   electromagnetic

D   chemical

21 A 12 N force is required to move a   SPS8e
box 6 meters across a gravel
driveway. How much work has been
done?

A   exactly 72 J

B   exactly 2 J

C   more than 72 J

D   between 2 and 72 J

Go On

22 When liquids of different densities are mixed together, they will sometimes separate and form layers. Based on the phases indicated below, what can you correctly infer about the density of these liquids? SPS2a

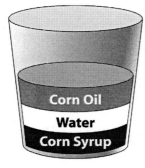 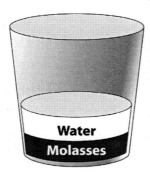

A Water is less dense than corn oil.

B Water is more dense than molasses.

C Corn oil is less dense than molasses.

D Corn syrup is more dense than molasses.

23 Select the electromagnetic wave with the largest wavelength. SPS9b

A infrared radiation

B radio waves

C visible light waves

D microwaves

24 Two waves of equivalent wavelength meet. Each travels in the same direction., but at an angle to one another. What must you know to classify their interference pattern? SPS9d

A whether they are electromagnetic waves or mechanical waves

B whether they are in phase or out of phase

C whether they have equivalent pitch

D what medium the travel in

25 Where are the halogens in the diagram below? SPS4a

PERIODIC TABLE OF THE ELEMENTS

A
B
C
D

A A

B B

C C

D D

Go On

26 Which of the following diagrams shows an ion with a positive charge?   SPS2b

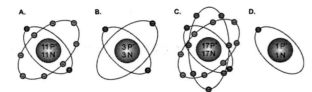

27 Noble gases are nonmetallic elements that do not readily react with other elements. What accounts for this non-reactivity?   SPS1a

A Noble gases have six valence electrons.

B Noble gases have eight valence electrons.

C Noble gases have ten valence electrons.

D Noble gases have two valence electrons.

28 Consider the pH scale shown right and the pH of the labeled items. Which answer choice lists household items in order from the most basic to the MOST acidic?   SPS6e

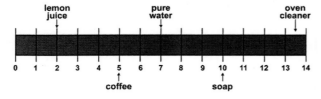

A oven cleaner, soap, coffee, lemon juice

B soap, oven cleaner, pure water, lemon juice

C lemon juice, coffee, soap, oven cleaner

D coffee, lemon juice, pure water, soap

29 Tammy's room contains a lamp, a hair dryer, a radio and a TV. She uses an ohmmeter to determine that the overall resistance of the circuit increases as she plugs each appliance in. What kind of wiring is the circuitry in Tammy's house?   SPS10b

A series

B parallel

C mixed

D direct

30 Sodium has a violent exothermic reaction with water, producing hydrogen gas and a clear, aqueous sodium hydroxide solution. What else is produced in this reaction?   SPS7b

A gamma rays

B heat

C ice

D electricity

31 Refer to the equation below. It is a/an _____ reaction.   SPS7b

$$P_4 + 5O_2 \longrightarrow P_4O_{10} + \text{heat}$$

A exothermic

B neutralization

C endothermic

D decomposition

Go On

32 An ionic bond results from _____ SPS1b
_____ electrons, while a cova-
lent bond is a result of _____ electrons.

  A   shared, transferred

  B   transferred, shared

  C   outer, inner

  D   inner, outer

33 Two electrons are located 10^{-10} SPS8b
meters apart (the diameter of a
typical atom). Identify the effect of the
electrostatic force between the two electrons and its magnitude (size) compared
to the gravitational force between the electrons.

  A   The electrostatic force is repulsive
and stronger.

  B   The electrostatic force is repulsive
and weaker.

  C   The electrostatic force is attractive
and stronger.

  D   The electrostatic force is attractive
and weaker.

34 You rubbed a balloon against SPS10a
your hair and touched it to a
wall. The balloon stuck to the wall.
Select the correct explanation of why
the balloon stuck to the wall.

  A   electrostatic forces between the
particles of the balloon

  B   magnetic forces between the particles
of the wall

  C   electrostatic forces between the particles of the balloon and the particles
of the wall

  D   magnetic forces between the particles
of the balloon and the particles of the
wall

35 A battery provides a total of SPS10b
2.0 volts to a video game controller. If the controller has an operating resistance of 4.0 ohms, the current
through the video game controller is

  A   2.0 amps.

  B   0.50 amps.

  C   8.0 amps.

  D   6.0 amps.

36 Which of the following cor- SPS7d
rectly places the phases of
water in order from the MOST dense to
the LEAST dense?

  A   solid, liquid, gas, plasma

  B   solid, gas, plasma, liquid

  C   liquid, solid, gas, plasma

  D   plasma, solid, liquid, gas

Go On

37 The diagram below shows two identical spheres, X and Y, separated by distance *r*. Each sphere has the same mass, but they have opposite charges.

SPS8b

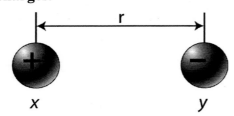

Which diagram below best represents the electrostatic force, F_e, and the gravitational force, F_g, acting on sphere X due to sphere Y?

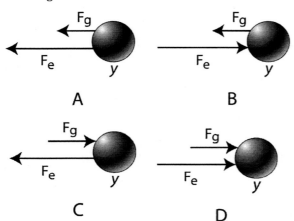

38 Which subatomic particle will be MOST electrostatically attracted to a negatively charged object?

SPS10c, 1a

A   proton

B   a nucleon

C   electron

D   a beta particle

39 Which two particles have approximately the same mass?

SPS1a

A   proton and electron

B   proton and neutron

C   electron and neutron

D   electron and alpha particle

40 When a potassium atom (K) forms a potassium ion (K^+), the atom

SPS1a

A   gains a proton.

B   gains an electron.

C   loses a proton.

D   loses an electron.

Section II

41 In the experiment shown in the diagram below, a student is to record how much time elapses from the time the Bunsen burner is lit until the wax on the end of each rod begins to melt. Which of the following would be the BEST title for a laboratory report describing this experiment?

SPS7c

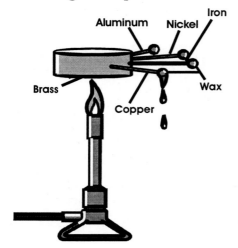

A Rate of Radiation of a Candle Flame

B Generation of Electric Currents in Various Metals

C Rate of Thermal Conduction in Various Metals

D Determining Specific Heat in Wax

42 A sample of helium at standard pressure has a volume of 150.0 mL at a temperature of 120 K. What is the new temperature of the gas if the volume of the sample is decreased to 50 mL and the pressure is kept constant?

SPS5b

A 40 K

B 4 K

C 360 K

D 3.6 K

43 The nucleus of an atom of gold-198 contains

SPS1a

A 79 protons and 119 neutrons.

B 79 protons and 118 neutrons.

C 197 protons and 197 neutrons.

D 198 protons and 198 neutrons.

44 Which substance represents a compound?

SPS2c

A C

B O_2

C CO_2

D Co

45 Atoms in the _____ phase have the MOST distance between them. Atoms in the _____ phase generally have LESS distance between them.

SPS5a

A solid; gaseous

B gaseous; plasma

C plasma; gaseous

D liquid; gaseous

Go On

46 In the following concept map, some items are missing. Which of the following is an item that could appear as a non-metal? SPS4a

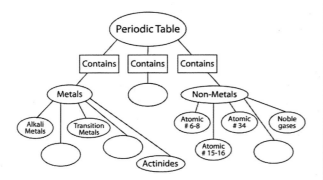

A alkali earth metals

B metalloids

C halogens

D lanthanides

47 Jill places a message in a bottle and drops it off the side of a mountain, into the ocean. When does the bottle have the greatest kinetic energy? SPS7a

A when Jill holds the bottle in her hand, just before dropping it

B just after Jill releases the bottle

C just before the bottle hits the surface of the water

D when it is floating on the surface of the calm water

48 A chemist has two magnesium (Mg) samples. One is a small, solid block. The other is a vial of powdered magnesium. He adds the small block of Mg to a water sample. Small bubbles slowly begin to form at the surface of the block. What will happen to the powdered Mg sample if the chemist adds it to a separate beaker of water? SPS6b

A The Mg sample will disappear.

B The Mg sample will change color.

C The Mg sample will bubble much more slowly than the solid sample did.

D The Mg sample will bubble much more quickly than the solid sample did.

49 The table below shows the values of the properties determined by analysis of substances 1, 2, 3 and 4. SPS1b

Substance	Melting Point (°C)	Boiling Point (°C)	Conductivity
1	-90	-10	none
2	25	200	none
3	350	790	as solid
4	850	1325	in solution

Which substance is MOST likely an ionic compound?

A 1

B 2

C 3

D 4

Go On

50 Which graph BEST represents the electric force between a proton and an electron as a function of their distance of separation? SPS8b

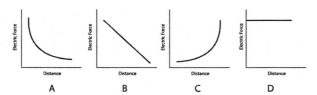

51 Which of the following scenarios would make the box easiest to move? SPS8e

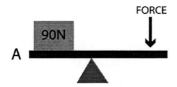

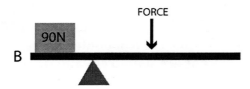

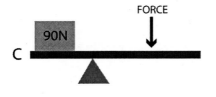

52 Four resistors are wired in series. R1=3 ohms, R2=4 ohms, R3=3 ohms and R4=1 ohm. What is the total equivalent resistance of this 12V circuit? SPS10b

A   23/12 Ω

B   23 Ω

C   11 Ω

D   132 Ω

53 Conductivity in a metal results from SPS4a

A   high electronegativity.

B   having a large atomic radius.

C   highly mobile protons in the valence shell.

D   highly mobile electrons in the valence shell.

Use the data table to answer question 54.

Element	Density (g/cm^3)
tungsten (W)	19.25
iron (Fe)	7.86
magnesium (Mg)	1.74
aluminum (Al)	2.7

54 Archie has a 4-gram sample of an unknown metal. His job in lab is to figure out which metal it is. Using water displacement, he determines that his sample has a volume of about 0.5 cm^3. Which metal is Archie's sample composed of? SPS2a

A   tungsten

B   iron

C   magnesium

D   aluminum

Go On

55 Which of the following internal parts of a light bulb conducts electricity? *SPS10a*

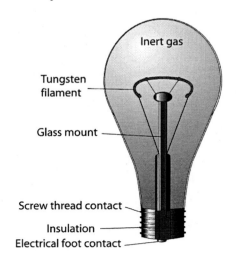

Inert gas

Tungsten filament

Glass mount

Screw thread contact

Insulation

Electrical foot contact

A inert gas

B tungsten filament

C glass mount

D insulation

56 A nuclear power plant uses the fission process to generate heat, which turns turbines, which in turn create electricity. A solar cell absorbs radiant solar energy and turns it directly into electricity. A hydroelectric power station uses the movement of water to turn turbines, which in turn create electricity. Electricity is generated from each of these energy sources. Which does NOT involve the use of mechanical energy? *SPS7a*

A nuclear power generation

B solar power generation

C hydroelectric power generation

D All of these methods involve the use of mechanical energy.

57 Lithium has an atomic number of 3. How many electrons are in its valence shell? *SPS4b*

A 1

B 2

C 3

D 8

58 Which of the following substances is acidic? *SPS6e*

A liquid soap

B vinegar

C baking soda

D flour

59 Consider a molecule of H_2 gas. Each hydrogen atom has one electron and needs two to complete its first energy level. Since both hydrogen atoms are identical, neither atom dominates in the control of the electrons. The electrons are shared equally. This makes H_2 a(n) *SPS1b*

A polar bonded molecule.

B non-polar covalent molecule.

C polar covalent compound.

D non-polar ionic compound.

Go On

Use the following information to answer questions 60 and 61.

Mark builds a simple electromagnet out of copper wire, an iron nail and a battery. The copper wire is wrapped around the nail 8 times. The battery is 1.5 volts.

60 **What powers this electro-** SPS10c, 10b
magnet?

   A   alternating current (AC)

   B   direct current (DC)

   C   resistance (R)

   D   iron (Fe)

61 **What two things will Mark** SPS10c, 10b
need to add to his design, in
order to convert his electromagnet to a
simple motor?

   A   a wheel and axle

   B   a permanent magnet and an axle

   C   another battery and a permanent magnet

   D   two more coils of copper wire around the nail.

62 **Select the type of matter that** SPS6a
includes solutions.

   A   ionic compounds

   B   molecular compounds

   C   heterogeneous mixtures

   D   homogeneous mixtures

63 **A standard transistor radio** SPS6b
battery is 9V. If the local store
was out of 9V batteries, how could you
construct an equivalent power source?

   A   Securely connect three 1.5V batteries in series.

   B   Securely connect six 1.5V batteries in series.

   C   Securely connect six 1.5V batteries in parallel.

   D   Securely connect nine 1.5V batteries in parallel.

64 **Identify the correct descrip-** SPS6c
tion of a saturated solution.

   A   a solution of an ionic solid in an ionic liquid

   B   a solution that is composed of multiple solutes and solvents

   C   a solid solution made by cooling a hot mixture of two liquid metals

   D   a solution in which no more solute can dissolve at the given temperature

65 **Latisha rubbed a balloon vigor-** SPS10a
ously on her shirtsleeve. She
then observed that small bits of paper
stuck to the balloon. Select the BEST
explanation of why the bits of paper
stuck to the balloon.

   A   The balloon was magnetized by friction.

   B   The balloon was magnetized by conduction.

   C   The balloon was electrically charged by friction.

   D   The balloon was electrically charged by induction.

Go On

66 Two objects attract each other electrically. Identify the statement that correctly describes the electrical charge of the two objects. SPS10b

 A The objects must be like charged.

 B The objects must be oppositely charged.

 C The objects are either like charged or electrically neutral.

 D The objects are either oppositely charged or one is charged and one is neutral.

67 Stella stands in an elevator on a scale. She presses the down button. The reading on the scale decreases for a moment. What is the BEST explanation? SPS8c, 8d

 A Stella's mass has decreased.

 B Stella's acceleration has changed.

 C The force of gravity has decreased.

 D The force of gravity has increased.

68 The radioactive isotope bismuth-212 decays in a couple of different ways. 64% of its decay occurs by beta (β) emission and 36% occurs by alpha (α) emission. Which of the following is a logical product of the β decay of ^{212}Bi? SPS3a, 3c

 A ^{212}Po

 B ^{208}Ti

 C ^{224}Ra

 D ^{212}C

69 A voltage (V) is applied to a circuit with resistance (R) produces a current (I). Identify the current when a voltage (V) is applied to a circuit of resistance 5R. SPS10b

 A 0.2 I

 B I

 C 5 I

 D 10 I

70 Heat will transfer from a high temperature area to a low temperature area by several different methods. The heat generated by a burning candle is an example of transfer by SPS7a, 7b

 A convection.

 B combustion.

 C radiation.

 D conduction.

71 In this diagram, a weight rests in the middle of a supported board. Gravitational force pushes the weight toward the floor. What opposing force pushes upward on the weight? SPS8b

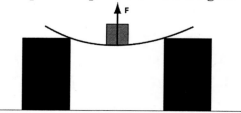

 A kinetic frictional force

 B rolling frictional force

 C inertial force

 D normal force

Go On

72 A wet cell battery is an example of stored potential energy. Once connected to a load, the stored energy is converted. Describe the conversion of energy in a battery powered clock that results in the motion of the hands of the clock. SPS7a, 9a

   A   chemical to electrical to mechanical

   B   chemical to thermal to electrical

   C   electrical to thermal to mechanical

   D   chemical to electrical to thermal

73 A given radionuclide R_A has a half life of 100 years. Another radionuclide R_B has a half life of 25 years. One thousand kilograms of each material are placed in a hazardous waste receptacle. How much of each will be around after 100 years? SPS3c

   A   500 kg R_A and 62.5 kg R_B

   B   500 kg R_A and 125 kg R_B

   C   250 kg R_A and 250 kg R_B

   D   250 kg R_A and 125 kg R_B

74 Which of the following common substances will have a pH that is closest to neutral? SPS6e

   A   lemonade

   B   blood

   C   baking soda

   D   soapy water

75 A 200 mL gas sample is maintained at constant temperature, and pressurized from 10 atm to 50 atm. What is its new volume? SPS5b

   A   40 mL

   B   2.5 mL

   C   0.4 mL

   D   1000 mL

76 A machine performs 60J of work but uses 100 J of energy. What is the machine's efficiency? SPS8e

   A   6000 J^2

   B   6%

   C   60%

   D   6

77 Salt is added to a beaker of boiling water until no more will dissolve. As the solution cools SPS6c

   A   the concentration of salt in the water will increase.

   B   the concentration of salt in the water will decrease until room temperature solubility is reached.

   C   the concentration of salt in the water will not change.

   D   the concentration will go to zero as all of the salt crystallizes.

Go On

78 Fission and fusion are two methods of producing nuclear energy. Which method is used in nuclear power reactors and why?   SPS3d

A   Fusion, because it creates less waste.

B   Fission, because it produces more energy per atom of fuel and fusion.

C   Fusion, because it produces more energy per atom of fuel that fission.

D   Fission, because fusion requires a large input of energy in order to occur.

79 What is the BEST way to heat a beaker of water on a Bunsen burner?   SCSh2a, b, c

A   Place the beaker on a covered tripod over the flame. Heat for 5 minutes, then add the water.

B   Add water and boiling stones to the beaker, place on the covered tripod stand and then heat until boiling.

C   Fill the beaker with water and boiling stones, then use metal tongs to hold it over the flame.

D   Fill the beaker with water and boiling stones, then hold it over the flame using your hand.

80 What element MUST be present for combustion to occur?   SPS2d

A   carbon

B   nitrogen

C   oxygen

D   iron

hypothesis, 22

I

Ideal Gas Equation, 125
incident ray, 197
inclined plane, 182
indicator (pH), 144
induced fission, 87
induction, 213
inert, 71
inertia, 158
inference, 30, 48
infrared waves, 205
instantaneous rate, 151
insulators, 211
interference, 200
    constructive, 200
    destructive, 200
internal energy, 127
International Union of Pure and Applied Chemistry
  (IUPAC), 98
intrinsic properties (of matter), 115
inverse square law, 165
ion, 78, 95
ionic bond, 78, 97
ionic compound, 78
ionization energy, 74
ionized gas, 116
ions, 74
isotopes, 83
IUPAC, 72, 98

J

joule, 172
journal, 24

K

Kelvin, 59
kilogram, 57
kinetic energy (KE), 171
kinetic friction, 159

L

laboratory equipment, 51
lanthanide, 72
law
    inverse square, 165
    of gravity, 165
    of motion, first, 157
    of motion, second, 159
    of motion, third, 161
    reflection, 197
    Snell's, 198
law of conservation of energy, 177
law of inertia, 158

length, 57
lever, 181, 183
line graph, 29
linear motion, 149
liquid, 116
litmus test, 144
lodestone, 223
logarithmic, 143
longitudinal wave, 193

M

machine, 181
magnet, 223
magnet, de-magnetize, 224
magnetic
    field, 223
magnetic force, 166
magnetite, 223
mass, 57, 166, 172
material safety data sheet (MSDS), 42
matter, 65
mechanical advantage, 182
mechanical pan balance, 51
mechanical waves, 192
mechanics
    classical, 157
    Newtonian, 157
    quatnum, 66, 164
    relativistic 164
medium, 192
Meitner, Lise, 85
melting point, 119
Mendeleev, Dmitri, 72
meniscus, 58
meson, 167
metalloids, 71
metals, 71
meteorology, 119
meter, 57
meter stick, 53, 57
metric unit conversion, 60
microwaves, 205
model, 31
molecule, 95
molecules, 71
motion, 149
motor, 228
multiple line graph, 29

N

natural phenomena, 22
net force, 161
neutralization reaction, 143
neutron, 65

Seaborg, Glenn, 72
semiconductors, 71, 212
senses, 23
    types of, 22
series circuit, 216
sharp Instrument safety, 40
SI unit, 55, 58, 172
simple machines, 182
    pulley, 181
Snell's law, 198
solid, 116
solubility, 136, 137
solute, 135, 137
solution, 135
solvent, 135
sound wave, 192, 202
specific heat, 127
speed, 151
speed of light, 204
spring scale, 53
stable (isotope), 88
standard SI measurement, 57
static electricity, 212
stator, 229
subatomic particles, 65
subjective, 27
sublimation, 119
subscript, 95
superconductors, 212
supercritical, 90

T

telescope, 53
temperature, 116, 127
    measurement of, 59
Temperature-Volume (T-V) Relationship, 123
test tube, 51
thermal conductors, 128
thermal energy, 127, 178
thermal insulators, 128, 134
thermal inversion, 198
thermometer, 51
Three Mile Island, 90
tongs, 53
transactinides, 72
transition metal, 71, 75
transmission, 196
transverse wave, 193
trends, 27
triple-bean balance, 53

U

U.S. Customary System, 55
ultraviolet waves, 205

un-ionized gas, 116
unstable (isotope), 88

V

vacuum, 192
valence electrons, 66, 78
valence shell, 66
vector quantity, 150
velocity, 150, 151, 153
visible light, 198
visible light waves, 205
volatile compunds, 123
voltage, 214, 218, 220
volts, 214
volume, 57

W

watch glass, 51
water displacement, 58
watt (W), 187
wave, 192
    behavior of, 196
    energy, 194
    types of, 193
wavelength, 193, 194, 199
wedge, 181
weight, 57, 165
wheel and axel, 181
work, 180

X

X-rays, 205

Y

Yucca Mountain, 91